Sensitometry for Photographers

Sensitometry for Photographers

Jack Eggleston

Focal Press
London & Boston

Focal Press
is an imprint of the Butterworth Group
which has principal offices in
London, Sydney, Toronto, Wellington, Durban and Boston

First published 1984

© Jack Eggleston, 1984

British Library Cataloguing in Publication Data
Eggleston, Jack
    Sensitometry for photographers.
    1. Photographic sensitometry—Handbooks,
    manuals, etc.
    I. Title
    661'.808   TR280

    ISBN 0-240-51144-1

Library of Congress Cataloging in Publication Data
Eggleston, Jack.
    Sensitometry for photographers.
    Bibliography: p.
    Includes index.
    I. Photographic sensitometry. I. Title.
    TR280.E4 1984   771'.53   83-25316
    ISBN 0-240-51144-1

Photoset by Butterworths Litho Preparation Department
Printed in England by Butler & Tanner, Frome, Somerset

Preface

With the superb cameras, materials and equipment available today, we can all produce photographs of good average quality. We may even achieve an optimum now and again, but only a competent photographer who understands and uses sensitometry can exploit high-quality equipment and materials to full advantage, and with minimum wastage, whether the lens is one millimetre away from the subject as in photomicrography, or ten thousand metres away as in aerial photography.

Sensitometry has been described as the study and measurement of the response of photographic materials to light and to processing conditions, so it deals with the relationship between exposure and the results achieved after processing. The word itself suggests that it is concerned only with the measurement of sensitivity, but in fact sensitometric methods are used to deal with all aspects of tone and colour reproduction in the photographic process, from exposure of the film right through to viewing the final image. Sensitometry is used both by the manufacturers of photographic materials, to obtain the best possible quality and uniformity in their products, and also by the photographer in order to obtain optimum results. It provides the universally accepted way of describing, linking together and controlling the events that occur in photography.

Most sensitometric information is shown in a simple graphical form; it is therefore easy to understand and can be put to practical use once a knowledge of what the graphs mean has been achieved. The photographer who can plan and carry out work by using sensitometric methods has a great advantage over those who work by purely automatic means, or those who rely solely on their experience.

In the simplest case the photographer reads the manufacturer's instructions on exposure and processing and carries them out. However, such instructions relate only to average situations. How much better to be able to interpret the manufacturer's published sensitometric information and graphs, or produce our own, so that we can relate them to our particular needs. If we think of top-quality results as being on the peak of a curve, even a slight move to the left or right will give less than top quality. Our aim is to hit the peak and to keep on hitting it, and this is where sensitometry will help.

This book is addressed to those who wish to use the technology of sensitometry in order to improve their standard of photography, whether as student, professional or amateur photographer or in association with another art, science or technology. It deals with the principles and applications of sensitometry, progressing gradually from the basic to the more advanced. A simple understanding will suffice for some readers, to enable them to think in sensitometric terms, to visualize the effects of exposure and processing in a graphical form, and to apply this to their work. The last chapter of the book describes the type of sensitometry that can be carried out without the use of any special exposure and measuring instruments.

Some parts of the book pay particular attention to aerial photography, which provides an impressive example of the need for correct exposure and correct processing which is present in all photographic tasks, and also of the relationship between these and other factors that affect quality.

Brief definitions of the main sensitometric terms and expressions are given as they occur in the text, and many of the sections also contain self-assessment exercises. If you wish to test your learning it is suggested that you should: (1) read through each chapter quickly to get the general idea; (2) read through again carefully, making sure that you understand each part of the text and diagrams; (3) read the self-assessment questions and write your answers in a notebook, leaving plenty of space for additional notes or corrections; (4) with the help of Appendix F, check your answers by reading the relevant text or re-measuring the data, and then do any necessary revision.

The book presents sufficient sensitometric theory

to enable the reader to relate it to practical situations. Items that would disrupt the flow of information, or do not fit easily into any particular section, are given in the form of appendices at the end of the book. Internationally agreed terms and standards are used throughout. Reference to particular equipment, materials and processes, other than those necessary as an illustration, has been avoided. Up-to-date information on the latest colour process, for example, can be obtained only from the manufacturer. If you wish to extend your knowledge or to examine a particular application of sensitometry you will find more information in the appropriate literature, some of which is listed in Appendix G.

I should like to express my appreciation of the help given by my colleagues Graham Saxby, who advised during the initial preparation, and Peter Davies, who has given me a great deal of help throughout, particularly with regard to colour photography. Their constructive comments and suggestions have greatly assisted the preparation of this book. In addition I should like to acknowledge the valuable contribution of Dr G. G. Attridge, who edited the manuscript and gave me a great deal of help and advice, particularly with regard to absolute sensitometry and the calibration of sensitometers, subjective tone reproduction, the sensitometry of colour exposures, colour masking and inter-image effects. Thanks are also due to Liz Downes, who did most of the typing. I should also like to acknowledge the help given by the British Standards Institution, and by the manufacturers of photographic materials and equipment, who provided illustrations and information on their products.

J.E.

Contents

1

Introduction

1.1 Photography is a means of visual communication in which information is collected, recorded and stored ready for use at any time. The information, which may be artistic, educational, entertaining, pictorial or technical, is collected and recorded on film when a photograph is taken, and made into a visible and permanent image by photographic processing. The communication is successful whenever a viewer looks at the final image and receives the information required. This information may be an overall visual sensation obtained by a casual glance, or it may only be found by a detailed examination of the image. However the photograph is used, the degree of success in the communication depends to a major extent on the skill and applied knowledge of the photographer and processor.

1.2 If it is to present the maximum amount of information in whatever form, the photograph must have a high standard of excellence. Such an achievement will, to a great extent, depend on the correct selection and use of photographic materials and processes, and can be obtained by using the technology of sensitometry. Sensitometry is the term used to describe the scientific method of evaluating the technical performance of photographic materials and processes in the recording of images. In the first place it provides the means by which the quality and characteristics of photo-

graphic materials are controlled by manufacturers. To obtain uniformity, the required standards have been established by international agreement. Thus photographers world-wide can obtain and use products which are of a high quality and alike in their response to exposure and processing. Having obtained reliable and high-quality materials, the photographer needs to use them to advantage. Sensitometry will help in this. It is the control tool of the photographer and the photographic technician, for without its application they are like a carpenter with good wood and a sharp saw, but without a measuring rule. By understanding and using sensitometry, we introduce a measure of precision into our work and do away with the guesswork that wastes our time and materials.

Sensitometry is mainly concerned with measuring the effects of exposure and processing on light-sensitive photographic materials, so it relates to the entire photographic system, from the original subject right through to viewing the final print. By using sensitometry, the effects and results of the photographic process can be shown in graphical form or in figures. Thus we can have an accurate indication of the capabilities of photographic materials and we can also control the photographic process in order to obtain the desired result. Now let us see how these measurements can be made and how we can get useful information from them.

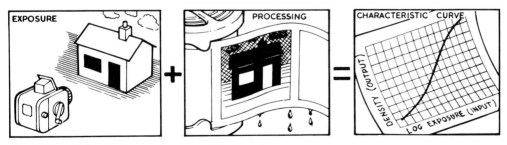

Fig. 1.1 The relationship between the range of light intensities received during exposure and the range of densities produced after processing can be shown as a curve on a graph.

A step wedge or grey scale can be used to represent the various tones of any photographic subject.

1.3 We can consider the photographic process simply as a transfer of visual information, from the input of a range of light intensities onto the film in a camera, through to the output of a range of optical densities on the negative or print. If the input and output are measured, a graphical representation of the relationship between them can be made in the form of a characteristic curve. This curve (Figure 1.1) will show the tonal response of the photographic material to the two main events in photography, exposure and processing, under one particular set of conditions.

Let us consider the above statement in more detail. The photographic process starts with 'exposure', meaning a range of different light intensities from the various tones of the subject, passing through the lens and falling onto the film in the camera whilst the shutter is open. The process ends with a range of different densities on the negative produced by the exposure and processing of the film. Exactly the same situation applies when a print is made from a negative. In printing the photographic process is simply repeated. It starts again with exposure, meaning that light passing through the negative falls onto the printing paper as a range of different light intensities, and it ends with a range of different densities on the print. Thus the photographic process starts with *a range of light intensities* and ends with *a range of densities*.

Now if we can measure each range we can make a graph of the relationship between the two, and this will show the tonal performance of the photographic material under the given conditions of exposure and processing. This is in effect what is done in sensitometry. However, in photographic practice it is difficult to measure the light intensities actually received on the film from the subjects photographed, as the intensity changes over each small area of the image. Furthermore, the majority of subjects photographed present only a narrow range of light intensities. In sensitometry we often want to show the full capabilities of a photographic material and thus need to expose it to a very wide range of light intensities which can be easily measured.

1.4   A suitable range of intensities, wide enough to embrace that given by any subject, can be produced by using a step wedge (often called a step tablet). This in its simplest form is a piece of film containing a series of densities with regular density increments. When held up to a light, these show as a wide range of light intensities (Figure 1.2). A step wedge can therefore be used to represent the various tones of any subject we wish to photograph.

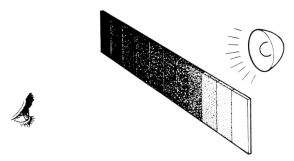

Fig. 1.2 A step wedge illuminated from behind will show a wide range of light intensities. If placed in contact with a piece of film it can be used to produce a wide range of well defined exposures.

The densities on a step wedge are well defined, progressing in a series of regular steps from a dense black to almost clear film, and the density value (light-stopping ability) of each step is known. A step wedge can therefore be used to produce a wide range of light intensities, increasing in steps which cover areas large enough for accurate measurement. We can make our own step wedges on film or obtain better quality wedges from photographic material manufacturers.

Basic sensitometric procedures

1.5   To show how a film responds to light we need to expose and process it, then we need to measure and describe the result. This basic sensitometric procedure is carried out as follows. A step wedge is placed in contact with a piece of unexposed film and a known amount of light is allowed to fall on it. Each step allows a certain amount of light to pass through to the film. The least dense step of the wedge passes the most light, and the denser steps progressively less light. The range of exposures received on the film is thus controlled by the densities of the step wedge. The density value of each step is known, so the difference in exposure through each successive step can be found. The instrument used to produce such a range of exposures is called a *sensitometer*.

The film is then processed under known conditions and the resultant densities caused by each different exposure and by development are measured. The instrument used to measure the densities is called a *densitometer*.

There will then be two sets of figures, one set giving the series of exposures given to the film and the other one, the series of densities after development. A graph showing the relationship between the two sets of figures is made, the figures for exposure being marked on the horizontal axis of the graph and the figures for density on the vertical axis of the graph. In order to obtain a characteristic curve with a shape which can be easily interpreted, both the exposure values and the densities are plotted using logarithmically numbered scales. The reasons for this are explained later in paragraphs 2.35 and 2.53. Figure 1.3 depicts the basic sensitometric procedure.

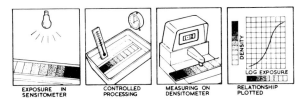

EXPOSURE IN SENSITOMETER   CONTROLLED PROCESSING   MEASURING ON DENSITOMETER   RELATIONSHIP PLOTTED

Fig. 1.3 The basic sensitometric procedure of controlled exposure, processing, measuring and plotting on a graph.

1.6   To construct the sensitometric graph each measured density is plotted against the logarithmic value of the exposure which produced it, and the plotting points are joined up. This produces a curved line which shows how a wide range of exposures and the subsequent development can affect the film and produce different amounts of blackness (density). This line is usually shaped as illustrated in Figure 1.4, and because it represents the characteristics of the film and of its tonal response to exposure and processing under one set of conditions, it is called a characteristic curve.

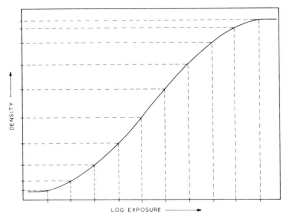

Fig. 1.4 A typical film characteristic curve made by plotting density produced, against the log of exposure given. The shape of the curve represents the tonal response of the film to a wide range of exposures and to one particular processing condition. As the slope of the curve decreases, the ability of the film to record the contrast between different exposures also decreases, and stops completely as the curve becomes horizontal.

A basic sensitometric test thus simulates what happens in an ordinary photographic procedure, but in addition it enables the exposures given and the densities obtained to be measured and the relationship between them to be evaluated.

1.7   The curve on the graph shows the tonal response of the film to a very wide range of exposures and to one particular processing condition. It is the result of a sensitometric test, and thus shows the full range capabilities of the film. However, in photography, relatively short ranges of exposure are usual, so in practice only part of the curve is used.

What the characteristic curve indicates

1.8   Looking at the curve and relating it to the exposures given and the densities produced, we can see that different parts will produce different results. The curve shows a gradual flattening at each end, rather than being a sloping straight line throughout. This indicates that there are limits beyond which exposure cannot be varied without

loss of density increase or contrast in the shadows (low exposures), or in the highlights (high exposures), when the film is used in practical photography. Notice, on this graph, that for equal increases in exposure we do not get equal increases in density; this fact is shown by the shape and slope of the curve. It is the shape, slope and position of the characteristic curve on the graph that we measure or compare with other curves, to obtain sensitometric information.

Different types of film, different developers and different development conditions will give variously shaped characteristic curves. The same system can also be used to find out how printing paper responds to exposure and development.

1.9   The normal way of presenting a characteristic curve is as shown in Figure 1.4, with the log exposure axis below the curve and the density axis on the left. This is the usual convention, but the log exposure axis can be placed above or below a curve, just as the density axis can be to the left or right. It makes no difference to the results shown by the curve.

1.10   By using sensitometric graphs, we can predict how the photographic process will proceed from exposure, as in a camera, right through to viewing the final print. We can also measure accurately and give numerical values to such variables as the relative speeds of films and printing papers, the range of tones, and the contrasts they can produce. Sensitometric graphs can also be used to compare the effects of different emulsions, developers and processing conditions and are applicable to all types and aspects of photography, both in black-and-white and in colour.

The sensitometry of a typical photographic process

1.11   We have been considering the testing of photographic materials and processes, but sensitometry is of course applicable also to normal photographic procedures. Sensitometric graphs and response curves are used to illustrate the effect of exposure and processing on the materials used, and the overall effect of the photography. A representation of a typical photographic procedure and its basic sensitometry is shown in Figure 1.5.

The inner part of Figure 1.5 is a block diagram of a normal photographic process, starting with the input to the camera and film of a range of light

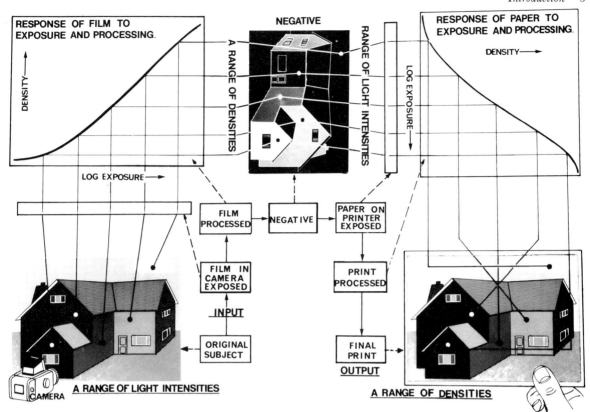

Fig. 1.5 A typical photographic process and its basic sensitometry. Starting from the bottom left, camera exposure is followed by processing to produce a negative image. The negative is then printed, to produce the final positive image for viewing. Read paragraph 1.11 before studying this diagram.

intensities from the original subject, through to the output to the viewer of a range of densities on the final print. The outer part is a graphical representation of the process and its basic sensitometry. Study Figure 1.5 starting at the bottom left, and relate the subject matter and the basic sensitometric curves to the block diagram. Refer to paragraphs 1.3 and 1.8 if you so wish.

1.12 The facilities for constructing sensitometric graphs may not be available, but this does not prevent us from using sensitometric methods in practical photography. With an understanding of sensitometry we can have a clear mental picture of the progress of any photographic task and can apply our knowledge to obtain the results we require. To do this we do not need instruments or curves on graph paper, but simply need to think in a logical sensitometric manner, to visualize the effects of exposure and processing on the chosen material, and to apply this thinking to the task. Of course, if the information is available, we can also interpret and use existing sensitometric data, or

instructions from manufacturers' literature. Figure 1.6 outlines the benefits we can gain by applying a knowledge of sensitometry to the photographic process.

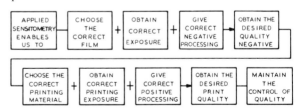

Fig. 1.6 The benefits obtained by applying sensitometry to a typical photographic process.

The use of sensitometric methods in the choosing of suitable photographic materials and in the control and manipulation of all photographic processes is of particular importance. It will promote the consistent production of optimum quality results without delay and without waste of materials. With a working knowledge of sensitometry we will also have a better appreciation and understanding of the whole photographic process.

1.13 *Origins of sensitometry.* The first significant scientific work on sensitometry was carried out in Britain in the 1890s by Ferdinand Hurter and Vero Charles Driffield, who were concerned with establishing a reliable method of expressing the sensitivity to light of photographic emulsions. They devised the present method of relating photographic densities to the exposure given, and the basic characteristic curve of an emulsion is still often called the 'H and D curve' in their honour. Strangely enough, the present standard symbol for exposure is H and the symbol for density is D.

Hurter and Driffield also applied sensitometry to the study of photographic 'tone reproduction'. Tone reproduction refers to the relationship between the various tones of the original subject or scene and those of its photographic reproduction. This is of course, fundamental to the photographic process and had been considered since the early days of photography, but Hurter and Driffield were able to use sensitometry to put the study of tone reproduction on a more scientific basis.

Light and colour

1.14 In sensitometry and photography we use light and colour both in exposure and in measuring or viewing the end product. Therefore, before considering sensitometry in more detail, we need to know something about light and how the colours of light are obtained and how they are specified and measured.

1.15 Light is that small part of the spectrum of electromagnetic radiation that we can see. The visible spectrum consists of a band of radiation covering wavelengths between approximately 400 and 700 nanometers. (The abbreviation is 'nm'; 1 nm is one-millionth of a millimetre.) If white light is dispersed into a visible spectrum by a glass prism as shown in Figure 1.7, we see a change in wavelength as a change in colour (or hue).

Many colours that gradually merge into one another can be distinguished in the visible spectrum, but for photographic purposes it is often convenient to divide it into three broad bands, namely blue from 400 to 500 nm, green from 500 to 600 nm and red from 600 to 700 nm. These are the three primary hues used in colour photography, and the visual sensation we call 'white light' can be produced by an appropriate mixture of all three. However, if some parts of the visible spectrum predominate over others, we see light as being coloured. Objects we look at appear coloured because they reflect or transmit different wavelengths to a different extent. Objects which look white, grey or blackish reflect all wavelengths in equal amounts. The visual sensations obtained when two of the three primary hues are mixed together are called 'secondary' or 'complimentary' colours (hues), and these are yellow, magenta and cyan. Figure 1.8 illustrates these effects. It shows the images from three projectors, fitted with blue, green and red filters, falling onto a white screen.

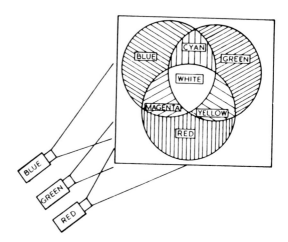

Fig. 1.8 The visual effect of separate and of mixed blue, green and red light. A correct mixture of all three produces white light. A mixture of two in proportion produces yellow, magenta or cyan. Unequal mixtures can produce an almost infinite variety of hues.

Photographic emulsions are sensitive to visible light and also to other invisible radiations with wavelengths much shorter than 400 nm, such as ultraviolet and X-rays. Emulsions can also be sensitized to infrared radiation, with wavelengths slightly longer than 700 nm.

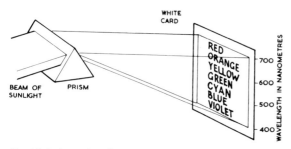

Fig. 1.7 A glass prism disperses a ray of white light into a visible spectrum of colours.

Light sources and colour quality

1.16 Most of the light we use in photography, such as sunlight and tungsten light, is produced by heat which causes the source to become incandescent (glow with heat) and emit light comprising all the visible wavelengths. Such sources are described as having a continuous spectrum and give what we loosely class as 'white light'. However, although all the wavelengths are there, the light produced is seldom equal in its blue, green and red content. Some sources have a higher red content and are slightly reddish or yellowish; some have a higher blue content and are slightly bluish. The predominant hue of the light depends on the physical temperature of the source and as temperature rises so the blue content increases and the red content decreases.

1.17 Our sense of vision can, to a large extent, adapt to differences in colour quality, and within a few minutes we accept quite large changes as still producing 'white light'. On the other hand, photographic materials – and colour materials in particular – are very sensitive to such changes. The colour quality of light is therefore important in photography, both in exposing the material and in viewing the finished photograph. In general black-and-white photography, varying the colour quality can vary the result obtained, but with most materials the effect is minimal and can often be ignored. However, in all aspects of sensitometry and in colour photography, the colour quality of light used in exposure and in measuring or viewing, is a very important factor.

Spectral energy distribution

1.18 The colour quality of a light source can be shown by a curve on a graph that is a plot of the relative amount of light energy emitted at each wavelength, against the wavelength itself. The curve is described as a 'spectral energy distribution curve' or 'spectral power distribution curve'. We can see in Figure 1.9 that some light sources, such as dawn sunlight, have a high red content compared with their green and blue content, and others have a higher blue content. Average 'standard' daylight is more or less equal in its blue, green and red content and is the light that is used in sensitometry for testing general purpose films. It is also the light to which 'daylight' colour films are balanced.

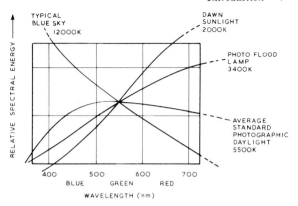

Fig. 1.9 Relative spectral energy distribution curves of typical photographic light sources. That the curves intersect near the centre of the graph is simply for convenience the curves being adjusted so that their relative energies are equal at 550 nanometers.

Spectral energy distribution curves provide a complete description of the quality of light from a light source, but for photography and sensitometry it is usually satisfactory and more convenient if a single figure can be quoted which adequately describes the colour quality of light.

Colour temperature and mired values

1.19 A concise and convenient way of specifying the colour quality of light is by reference to its correlated colour temperature. This means the temperature to which a full radiator (sometimes called a black-body radiator) must be heated in order to emit light that visually matches the colour of the light being considered. A 'full radiator' is a material that does not reflect any light when it is cold, but emits radiation due to heat applied to it. The filament of a tungsten lamp is not a precise full radiator, but for all practical purposes it can be considered as being one.

A simple way to understand colour temperature is to think of what happens in 'slow motion' when a tungsten lamp is switched on (Figure 1.10). At first the filament is relatively cold and emits no visible radiation, then as the filament temperature rises it emits a red glow, then it becomes a yellowish-red, getting increasingly brighter and whiter as the filament temperature increases. If we could raise the temperature further without melting the filament (by increasing the voltage applied to the lamp) the white light would be visually bluish. We can think of the light as a broad and predominant band of wavelengths with a peak that moves along the spectrum as the filament temperature increases, as shown in Figure 1.10.

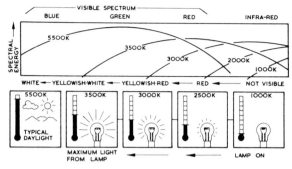

Fig. 1.10 A concept of colour temperature and colour quality. As the filament temperature of a lamp increases, so the band of wavelengths of emitted light moves along the spectrum towards blue.

The temperature of the light source is related to the colour produced; therefore the value of temperature can be used to describe the correlated colour quality of the light and is expressed as a 'colour temperature'.

1.20   Approximate colour temperature values can be measured by using a colour temperature meter. This in its simplest form is an instrument that compares the relative intensity of the red and blue content of the light source. The readings on the meter scale can be expressed in 'kelvins' or in 'mired' values. The kelvin (symbol K) is the standard SI unit of temperature, and the kelvin scale is equal to the Celsius (Centigrade) scale plus 273. The kelvin scale is based on the fact that the temperature of all material is due to molecular vibration, and the slower the vibration the lower the temperature. Therefore the lowest possible temperature, called absolute zero, is when all molecular vibration stops. This is zero on the kelvin scale and −273° on the Celsius scale.

Colour temperature in photography

1.21   Strictly, the term 'colour temperature' should only be applied to light emitted by a glowing body. These incandescent light sources emit light of all wavelengths and thus produce a continuous spectrum. For other light sources used in photography, such as electronic flash tubes and fluorescent lamps which do not produce light by incandescence, effective correlated or 'equivalent' colour temperature values are often quoted. Indirect sunlight from the sky ('skylight') can also be given a colour temperature value. Note, however, that although fluorescent lamps may have a similar visual value to an incandescent

source, their photographic effect may not be the same, particularly for colour photography.

1.22   For photography and sensitometry, the colour temperature of the light may not be suitable for the film being used. In this case the colour temperature can be adjusted by using suitably coloured filters over the light source or over the camera lens. A reddish filter will reduce the blue content and thus decrease the colour temperature, whilst a bluish filter will reduce the red content and thus increase the colour temperature. Such filters are said to produce a 'mired shift'.

Mired values

1.23   Unfortunately, when colour temperature is expressed on a kelvin scale the relative blue content of light does not increase evenly with an increase in colour temperature. The kelvin scale of colour temperature therefore has a non-linear relationship to both visual and photographic effect. This can be seen in Figure 1.11 as the crowding of the kelvin scale on the left, as the blue content of the light increases.

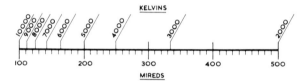

Fig. 1.11 A comparison of kelvin and mired scales of colour temperature. For photography, kelvin values are usually converted and expressed as mired values. This is because, on the mired scale, equal differences correspond to equal visible changes both in colour and in photographic effect. For example, a colour filter can be given a mired value that will have the same effect whatever the colour temperature of the original light source.

To overcome this difficulty a system of expressing the colour temperature on a mired (pronounced 'my-red') scale is also used in photography and particularly in colour photography, where corrections in colour quality are often needed. The mired scale (mired is short for *micro reciprocal degrees*) is found, as its name indicates, by dividing the colour temperature in kelvins into one million. The million has no particular significance; it is used only to obtain mired numbers of a convenient size.

$$\text{Mired value} = \frac{1\,000\,000}{\text{Colour temp in kelvins}} = \frac{1 \times 10^6}{K}$$

For example, 2000 K is 500 mireds and 5000 K is 200 mireds. Decamired figures are sometimes quoted (one decamired equals 10 mireds), as an accuracy of 10 mireds is sufficient for most practical work. The mired figure is a reciprocal, so the higher the colour temperature in kelvins, the lower the mired value and vice versa. Either value can be quickly and easily found from the other by using reciprocal tables.

The system gives us a scale of values that decrease evenly with each increase in the relative blue content of light, so equal intervals on the mired scale correspond to equal visible changes in colour. Mired values can be given for lights, filters and colour films, so they are convenient to use when working out the filters required for colour temperature changes in colour photography or sensitometry. A filter can be given a specific mired shift value that will be correct whatever the colour temperature of the original light source. Reddish filters which lower the colour temperature in kelvins will give a positive (+) mired shift, and bluish filters which raise the colour temperature in kelvins will give a negative (−) mired shift. We shall be considering filters and their effects in more detail later in Chapter 11.

Sensitometric and photometric terminology

1.24   The science of measuring the visual effect of light is called *photometry*. Sensitometry involves both the measuring of light and its effect on the photographic emulsion, so a basic knowledge of the meaning of the photometric terms and units that may be relevant to both sensitometry and photography will be of value. These are best explained in a diagram (Figure 1.12) and listed as a table (Table 1.1) that can be referred to as required. Purely sensitometric units and quantities will be explained as they are encountered in the text. As photographers dealing with sensitometry, all we need is an understanding of the basic concept of photometry and of the descriptive words used. We need not be particularly concerned with the relationship between the units of measurement.

From the diagram we can see that a light source has a luminous intensity (measured in candelas)

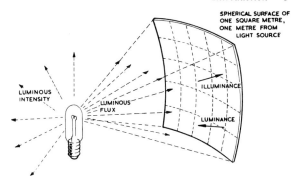

Fig. 1.12 The basic units and concept of light measurement. A surface of one square metre, one metre from a source of one candela receives an illuminance of one lux. If the surface is a perfect reflector it reflects a luminance of one candela.

Table 1.1 Photometric terms and units relevant to sensitometry and photography.

Quantity	Basic concept	Unit used
Luminous intensity	Total all-round output of light source.	Candela
Luminous flux	Amount of light flow, e.g. within a solid angle of one steradian (area one square metre, one metre from source).	Lumen
Illuminance	Incident light. Light falling on a surface.	Lux (lumens per square metre)
Luminance	Emitted or reflected light from a source or a surface.	Candelas per square metre

and the source radiates a luminous flux (measured in lumens). When the luminous flux falls on a surface, illuminance occurs (measured in lux) and when light is reflected from the surface, luminance occurs (measured in candelas). This of course, describes the conditions that exist when we look at a scene, or when a photograph is taken, or when we look at a photograph.

Because in photographic sensitometry we are concerned with measurement and standardization, the terminology used must be definite. Even such familiar photographic expressions as exposure and density need to have a precise meaning if they are to be measureable. We shall be dealing with these in the next chapter.

2

General sensitometry

2.1 Sensitometry can be described as 'the study and measurement of the response of photographic materials to light and to processing conditions'. In these early chapters of the book we are concerned mainly with the sensitometry of conventional black-and-white materials when exposed to daylight or visible light. However, the same principles and most aspects of sensitometry are equally applicable to other monochrome and colour materials, and to the use of other electromagnetic radiation to which photographic materials may respond, for example ultraviolet and infrared. The specific application of sensitometry to tone reproduction and colour photography is described later in the book.

Method used for tests

2.2 Sensitometric information is obtained by carrying out five progressive steps:

(a) Exposing the photographic material under controlled and measurable conditions.
(b) Processing the material, using known and controlled conditions.
(c) Measuring the densities produced, using standard and controlled conditions.
(d) Plotting the results as a graph.
(e) Interpreting the graph.

The photographic material to be tested sensitometrically is exposed to a standard and repro-

Plotting the characteristic curve of a film after using a sensitometer, processing, and then measuring the results on a densitometer.

ducible light source and given a series of successively spaced exposures which increase in a constant ratio (for example, 1, 2, 4, 8, 16, 32, etc.). The series of exposures is obtained by varying either the level of illuminance falling on the material, or the duration (time) of the exposure, in a sensitometer. The exposed photographic material is then processed under known and controlled conditions of:

(a) Developer composition (mixing and dilution).
(b) Developer temperature.
(c) Development duration.
(d) Developer agitation.
(e) Fixing, washing and drying.

The result of the processing is a step wedge negative (called a 'sensitometric strip') containing a series of progressively darker steps, from almost clear emulsion to a fairly dense image.

The density of each step is then measured on a densitometer and the values related to the exposure and development that produced them. The results are presented graphically in the form of a curve which can be interpreted by the photographer. Thus, for example, a film may be exposed to a known light source, producing a range of known illuminances and processed under known conditions, so that its previously unknown response to light and processing can be found.

For sensitometric results to be of practical value, the conditions of exposure and processing must be similar to those that the material under test will receive in practice.

Now that we have a good idea of what sensitometry is all about, we can consider the factors involved in more detail; starting with exposure in the sensitometer.

Sensitometric exposure

2.3   Exposure in a sensitometer (or in a camera) is given by the product of the two variables involved: the illuminance falling on the photographic material and the duration of the exposure. So we can say that:

Exposure = Illuminance × Duration

Using the standard symbols, this is expressed by the equation:

$H = E \times t$

The unit of illuminance is the lux and the unit of duration is the second, so exposure to visible radiation can be expressed in 'lux seconds' (abbreviation lx s). Note that the equation is often traditionally given as $E = I \times t$ in many textbooks; however, by international agreement, the symbols now used should be H, E and t. Exposure is also, by tradition, still often expressed in metre-candle-seconds instead of its equivalent, lux seconds.

Sensitometers and wedges

2.4   A sensitometer is an instrument used for exposing photographic material to a wide range of controlled exposures. It simulates the effect of exposure in a camera, but whereas in a camera the different exposures over the film depend on the random illuminances from the scene, in a sensitometer they are a well defined range; after processing, the resultant steps along the sensitometric strip have a large enough area for accurate measurement.

2.5   There are two fundamental types of sensitometer:

(a) One in which the intensity of illuminance is fixed and the duration of exposure is varied. This is called a 'time scale' sensitometer.
(b) One in which the duration of exposure is fixed and the intensity of illuminance is varied, called an 'intensity scale' or 'illuminance scale' sensitometer.

Because of 'reciprocity failure' (which is explained later), these two different methods of producing a series of exposures may give different results. Therefore, a sensitometer using the exposing method that the photographic material will receive in practice should be used.

In most aspects of photography, the duration of an exposure is fixed by the camera shutter speed, and the illuminance is varied over the image by the different luminances of the scene, so a sensitometer that varies the illuminance falling onto the photographic material is used.

Sensitometer components and functions

2.6   The essential components and functions of a typical intensity (or illuminance) scale sensitometer are (see Figure 2.1):

(a) A reproducible light source of constant luminous intensity and colour temperature (colour quality) operated from a stable (direct current) power supply.
(b) A means of controlling the colour quality and the illuminance level of the exposing light so that it

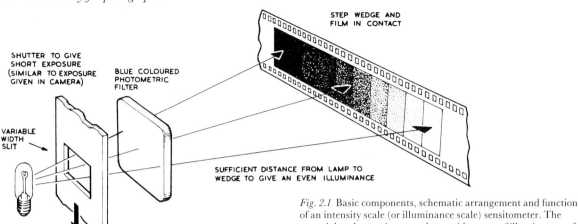

SHUTTER TO GIVE
SHORT EXPOSURE
(SIMILAR TO EXPOSURE
GIVEN IN CAMERA)

BLUE COLOURED
PHOTOMETRIC
FILTER

STEP WEDGE AND
FILM IN CONTACT

VARIABLE
WIDTH
SLIT

SUFFICIENT DISTANCE FROM LAMP TO
WEDGE TO GIVE AN EVEN ILLUMINANCE

Fig. 2.1 Basic components, schematic arrangement and function of an intensity scale (or illuminance scale) sensitometer. The material under test is exposed to a wide range of illuminances of known colour quality for a fixed exposure time. The conditions of exposure are similar to those the material will receive in practice.

is suitable for the different photographic materials that are to be tested.

(c) An accurate shutter or a device to control the duration of exposure and to ensure that the light source is exposed only when it has reached its correct colour temperature.

(d) A means of modulating (varying) the exposure reaching the photographic material by known amounts in order to produce a series of exposures.

(e) Sufficient distance between the light source and the photographic material to ensure uniform illuminance at the exposure plane; or some other means of ensuring an even illuminance, such as a light diffuser.

(f) A means of holding the photographic material under test in the correct position and also ensuring that it is exposed only to direct light from the shutter aperture.

Paragraph 13.20 gives suggestions for making a simple sensitometer.

2.7 The light source in a sensitometer is usually a specially selected high-intensity lamp, similar to those used in slide projectors. The lamps are pre-aged in order to obtain a standard and reproducible performance. In use they are suitably aligned in the instrument and under-run, to ensure stability in light output over a long period of time. Such lamps are supplied by the manufacturers of the sensitometer, and sometimes with calibration data that enables the colour temperature and luminous intensity to be determined for different values of applied voltage. The colour temperature, luminous intensity and operational life of a lamp

are, of course, affected by changes in applied voltage and also by the aging, during use, of the lamp filament and its envelope. Normally an increase in applied voltage gives an increase in colour temperature and luminous intensity, but shortens the operational life. A five per cent change in voltage will have a significant effect, hence the need for a stable power supply to the exposing lamp. The lamp envelope must also be kept clean and not touched with bare fingers. The calibration of sensitometer lamps is described in Appendix B.

2.8 The light used for sensitometric testing should be similar to that which the material is expected to receive in practice; for most camera films this is daylight, after it has passed through the camera lens. The colour temperature of natural daylight is of course variable, but a standard 'photographic daylight' value of 5500 K (kelvins) is usually adopted in sensitometry. As the filament of a lamp would melt before reaching this value, the lamp is operated at a fixed lower colour temperature (usually 2850 K). The light then passes through a blue photometric filter, which converts it to the required standard. Adopted standards of daylight and other illuminants are changed now and again as new techniques are introduced, but such changes are usually small and of no practical significance in photography.

   The illuminance level of the exposing light can be adjusted to suit photographic materials of different speeds, by fitting suitable optical quality neutral-density filters in the exposing beam. These are filters that do not cause scatter or change the colour temperature of the light (once again, see

Appendix B). Note that neutral-density filters made by light-fogging photographic film are not the best type to use in a sensitometer. They may not have a uniform density and also tend to scatter the exposing light. However, if optical quality filters are unavailable, more suitable photographic neutral-density filters can be made by the method described in paragraph 13.20.

2.9   The photometric filters used in a sensitometer may be of dyed acetate or gelatin foil, or dyed glass; for even more exacting work they may be liquid filters. These consist of coloured liquids held in special glass cells; their virtue is that they can be accurately controlled by adjusting the solution strengths. The Davis-Gibson liquid filter is specified for precise sensitometry by the International Standards Organization and most national standards institutions. When testing materials that are to be exposed to light other than standard daylight, the photometric filter may be removed, or other filters fitted to obtain the required colour temperature.

2.10   Some sensitometers use an electronic flash (a xenon flash) as a light source to give the very short durations necessary to test materials properly, particularly those intended for high-speed photography. No shutter is required as the output of the flash can be controlled electronically. The illuminance from a xenon flash approximates the colour quality of daylight.

2.11   To avoid the effects of reciprocity failure (explained later), the duration of exposure in a sensitometer should be similar to that which the material is likely to receive in practical use. Therefore the shutter action should be capable of providing accurate and repeatable exposure times over the expected range. Exposure must also be made in one operation and not as an intermittent series of shorter exposures. In a sensitometer using an electronic flash (xenon flash) as a light source, exposure is controlled by the duration of the flash, which may be as brief as one-millionth of a second.

For general-purpose black-and-white films, a duration of $1/30$ to $1/250$ second should be satisfactory for comparative sensitometry. For slow materials, such as printing paper, a longer exposure duration may be necessary (see also paragraph 5.2). The general effects of reciprocity failure are considered in Chapter 8 and, for colour materials, in paragraphs 11.31 and 11.119.

2.12   A series of exposures is obtained by using a step wedge, sometimes called a 'master' step wedge, in contact with the material being tested. The step wedge varies the illuminance, and the emulsion under each step receives a different exposure. The wedge must be neutral; in other words it must not alter the colour quality of the exposing light. A typical step wedge might have 21 steps, with each second step in the series giving an approximate doubling in exposure, i.e. a range of approximately 1000 to 1. More information on sensitometer wedges is given in paragraphs 2.20 to 2.26, and in Appendix B.

Density calibration and identification of sensitometer wedges

2.13   It is difficult to make step wedges with precise and equal increments between successive steps, nor is there any real need for such precision. Because of this, all step wedges need to be individually 'calibrated' before use so that the density values that produce the actual increments of exposure are known.

The list of densities, known as a 'calibration list', must be clearly identified with the particular wedge. If several wedges are to be used, they and their associated calibration lists should be numbered or lettered, for example wedge A, B, C, etc. (Figure 2.2). The wedge identification should be

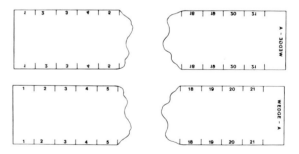

Fig. 2.2 Identification on master wedge (top) and result on sample (bottom). Identification is such that the numbers and letters are the right way round and therefore readable, when the resulting sample (the sensitometric strip) is in position for measuring. All identification marks are kept well away from the area to be exposed and measured.

positioned so that it is recorded on all the resultant samples when the sensitometer is used. In addition, to assist in identification when measuring results, the steps need to be numbered in such a manner that the numbers appear and are the right way round on the exposed and processed samples. Subsequent density reading will be simplified if opaque numbers are positioned along one edge of the wedge and clear numbers along the other edge. The division between steps can be indicated by short opaque lines between the less dense steps, and very thin clear lines between the denser steps. The lines should be fairly short and must not be drawn right across the wedge. Figure 2.2 illustrates this type of marking on a typical master wedge, and on the resultant sensitometric strip after exposure and processing. The calibration of sensitometer wedges is further considered in Appendix B.

Serviceability of wedges and sensitometers

2.14 Sensitometers and wedges must be kept optically clean and serviceable at all times and periodic tests must be made to check the instrument in accordance with the manufacturer's instructions. Depending on the function and versatility of the sensitometer, these may include checks on the stability and reproducibility of the exposing light in the film plane with regard to the effects of lamp ageing, filter fading, exposure duration variation, wedge variation and optical or mechanical changes (see also Appendix B). An essential test is to check the uniformity of illuminance over the exposing area. This is usually carried out by removing the step wedge and in its place exposing pieces of high-contrast film or printing paper, so that after full development a mid-range density is obtained. Densities are then measured at several points along the strips to establish whether or not illuminance is uniform.

Photographic tests carried out to check the stability of a sensitometer must of course be independent of variables in the result which may be caused by the processing and measuring of the test sample. The effect of these unwanted variables can be eliminated in the final result by making several well-separated exposures on one length or one piece of photographic material, the material being positioned on the sensitometer left to right and then right to left for each successive exposure. Processing is carried out in one operation (for example, development in a dish) to obtain uniform development and equal subsequent treatment. The results of each test strip are then all measured on the same densitometer several times; and averages of the readings taken (see also paragraphs 2.51, 6.3, 6.4 and 6.7 to 6.16).

Note that if the photographic material is processed to a higher or lower gamma than 1.0 (see paragraph 2.81), variation as measured will be

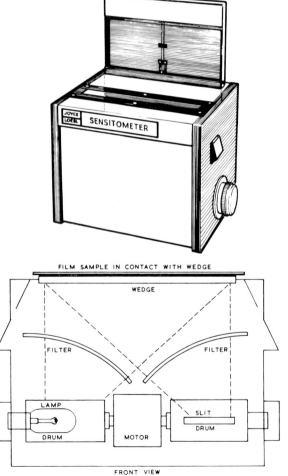

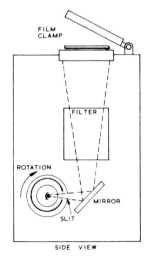

Fig. 2.3 General layout and arrangement of the Joyce Loebl Type 2L sensitometer.

either emphasized or minimized respectively. Emphasis will of course make small variations more evident. If necessary, the true variation can be found by plotting back through the characteristic curve of the material used, in a similar manner to that described in paragraph 13.10 and shown in Figure 13.3. Paragraph 6.4 also refers in particular to the care of sensitometers and wedges.

Commercial sensitometers

2.15 There are many different sensitometers, ranging from the precise instruments used in research work to the home-made sensitometer of the keen amateur photographer. The quality and versatility of a commercial sensitometer is in general related to its cost.

We can consider in outline two of the less complex instruments to see how the functions of a sensitometer are incorporated into a commercial instrument.

2.16 *Joyce Loebl Type 2L sensitometer.* A typical instrument, which will give reliable results on a comparative basis, is the Joyce Loebl Type 2L sensitometer (Figure 2.3). The instrument is operated from a mains supply and exposure is made by depressing a push button. It is compact, portable, and contains all the essentials of a sensitometer (see paragraph 2.6). Variations in exposure can be obtained by using either a step wedge or a continuous wedge. Two stabilized and matched exposing lamps are used and are precisely positioned so that:

(a) The illuminance incident on the wedge is even.
(b) A relatively high level of illuminance is obtained.
(c) The sensitometer is reasonably compact.

2.17 A fixed duration of exposure (usually $\frac{1}{50}$ second) is made by a slit in each of two drums that cover the lamps and are driven by a constant-speed motor. When the sensitometer is operated, the drums rotate and the slits allow the exposure to be made only when the lamps have reached peak intensity. After exposure, the supply to the lamps is reduced in order to increase lamp life.

The colour temperature of light from the exposing lamps is sufficiently high to give results suitable for comparative sensitometry without the use of colour conversion filters. However, filters may be fitted for tests in which the colour quality of the exposing light is of particular importance. A correct exposure level for photographic materials of different speeds is obtained by fitting suitable neutral-density filters in the path of light from each lamp.

2.18 *AGI-Milligan sensitometer.* The AGI-Milligan sensitometer (Figure 2.4) is a low-cost, portable, hand-held sensitometer which can be operated from its own internal rechargeable battery. The instrument is used by holding it with its exposing area in contact with the photographic material and exposure made by operating a button situated conveniently on the top. An audible signal

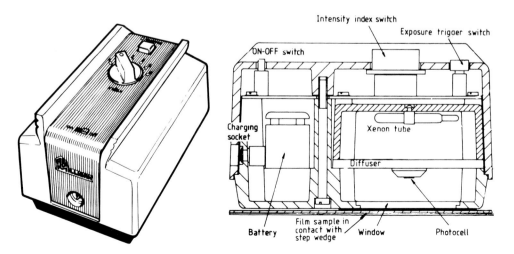

Fig. 2.4 General layout and arrangement of the AGI-Milligan sensitometer.

indicates when the sensitometer is ready to be operated. A series of exposures is obtained by using a step wedge which can be arranged on an exposing area approximately 55 mm square. The step wedge is fitted onto a transparent window which may also be used, as necessary, to position light filters.

2.19   The light source for exposure is a xenon flash tube, which has a nominal flash duration of $\frac{1}{500}$ second and a spectral distribution that closely simulates daylight. The exposure level for different types and speeds of photographic material can be switched in a series of exposure double-ups, over a 32 to 1 range. A photocell monitors the light intensity during exposure, and when the correct light output is reached the flash is quenched. Uniform illuminance is obtained by using a white-painted light tunnel and a perspex light diffuser on which the photocell is centrally mounted.

Types of sensitometer wedge

2.20   Sensitometer master wedges consist of lengths of glass or film holding a layer of black-dyed gelatin, a carbon black dye suspension, or a processed photographic silver emulsion. The basic elongated shape is such that they can fit along a length of 35 mm film. The transmission density of the wedge decreases from near opaque to almost clear along its length, and should ideally be neutral or non-selective in its effect. In other words, it should absorb all the wavelengths of light equally so that the colour quality of the exposing light is not changed as it passes through the wedge. There are two main types, the step wedge and the continuous wedge. Figure 2.5 shows a representation of part of each type. The neutrality and calibration of sensitometer wedges is considered in Appendix B.

2.21   On a step wedge the density decreases in substantially equal steps, usually by a factor of the square root of 2, or on some wedges, by the cube root of 2. This means that in the first case each second step of the wedge gives a nominal doubling of exposure, and in the second case each third step. For example, exposure will vary by a factor of two, through steps 1, 3, 5, 7, etc. or steps 1, 4, 7, 10, etc., respectively. So that the density value of the steps can be measured easily, each one should cover an area of about one square centimetre. The wedge steps are usually arranged along a narrow strip,

but for some applications it may be more suitable to arrange them in the form of a step tablet so that they produce a rectangular or square image. Also, by using such an arrangement, uniform illuminance of the wedge in the sensitometer may be more easily achieved.

2.22   On a continuous wedge the decrease in density is gradual and uniform, typically giving a doubling in exposure for each centimetre along its length. Thus, unlike a step wedge, there is no limit to the fineness of the log exposure increments that it can give. Sensitometric strips produced by using this type of wedge can only be properly measured on an automatic recording densitometer, such as is used in sensitometric testing laboratories. The strip is fed into the instrument for measuring, and a recording device produces a characteristic curve directly on to graph paper.

2.23   The exposure range given by a step or continuous wedge on a sensitometer should be greater than that required for adequately testing a typical film. By this means, films having somewhat different speeds can be tested or compared directly without adjusting the exposure given by the sensitometer. An exposure range of 1000 to 1 is sufficient for testing most photographic materials. It may not be large enough to cover the full exposure range of low-contrast films, which will produce a long characteristic curve. However, because the upper part of the curve of these and similar films is not used in practice, there is usually no need to measure and plot its effect. This is why many of the film characteristic curves published by photographic material manufacturers do not include the top part of the curve.

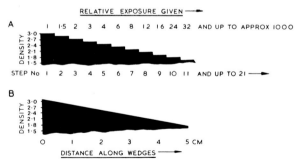

Fig. 2.5 A representation of part of a sensitometer wedge.
(A) Part of a typical step wedge where density decreases in steps. Each second step in the series gives a doubling in exposure.
(B) Part of a continuous wedge where density decreases gradually giving a steady increase in exposure along the length of the wedge.

2.24 Some wedges have small tricolour blue, green and red filters incorporated in the clear part of the wedge. The density produced behind each filter may be used to indicate the colour response (the general spectral sensitivity) of the film under test, or to compare its response with that of other films (see Chapter 10).

2.25 A grey (or gray) scale is another name for a step wedge. The term is most often used to describe a reflection step wedge on printing paper, with reflection density decreasing in substantially equal steps from black to white. A grey scale is often used in photography as a reference object that can be easily measured.

2.26 Step wedges, grey scales and neutral-density filters can be made by the photographer, but except for special purposes it is probably easier to buy what is required from photographic material manufacturers. Kodak and other manufacturers can provide many such items which are already nominally calibrated, as step tablets, grey scales and density guides, and these will probably have more uniform areas of density than home-made wedges. An advantage in using standardized calibrated items is that they provide an established density or series of densities which are then suitable for universal application. Manufacturers of densitometers also supply accurately calibrated wedges primarily intended for setting up and checking the instruments.

Processing sensitometric samples

2.27 After correct exposure in the sensitometer, the material is processed to produce a visible image that can be measured. Ideally, the effect of exposure and processing should be such that the lowest step density on the produced strip, is at the fog level (see paragraph 2.62(a) and (b)). The conditions of sensitometric processing must either be similar to, or correlate with, those that the material will receive in practical use. The processing conditions must also be controllable and repeatable. Of the steps used in sensitometric testing, processing is the one most difficult to control because it involves several factors that can cause significant variations in the results. The main factors are: developer compostition, development temperature, time, agitation and, to a lesser extent, fixation, washing and drying. We shall consider the main factors and their effect on the

characteristic curve in Chaper 3. Practical techniques for obtaining controlled and repeatable processing of photographic materials are described in Chapter 6.

Density and its derivation

2.28 The end product of exposing a film in a sensitometer and processing it is a series of steps, each with a different degree of blackness and thus a different light-stopping ability. This blackness is called 'density'. Density can be measured on a densitometer, and the value found will indicate the sensitivity to light of the photographic material under test. We can see that in sensitometry 'density' has a precise meaning; we can best understand this by considering the stages involved in deriving it numerically. In practical sensitometry we directly evaluate density and there is no need for us to calculate it. Nevertheless you should have an understanding of the meaning of density, why it is evaluated and how it is derived.

Figure 2.6 shows in diagrammatic form a step (called a 'sample') being measured on a densitometer and sets out also the numerical derivation of density as a value.

If the amount of light reaching the step (properly called the 'incident luminous flux') is measured and the amount of light that emerges from the step (the 'transmitted luminous flux') is also measured, then the light-passing ability, or transmittance, of the step can be obtained.

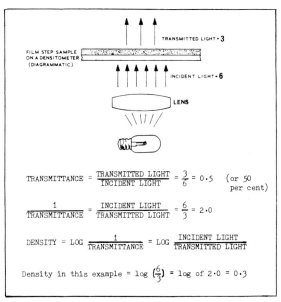

Fig. 2.6 Transmission density and its numerical derivation, as explained in the text.

2.29   *Transmittance* is the ratio of transmitted light to incident light, and is always less than unity. Transmittance is usually expressed either as a decimal fraction or as a percentage.

Because transmittance is always less than unity and decreases as blackness increases, it is not an appropriate unit of measurement to use in sensitometry. However, if its reciprocal is taken (by turning the fraction upside down), an expression of the light-stopping ability will result and the figure will always be greater than unity.

2.30   The reciprocal of transmittance (1 ÷ transmittance) is the ratio of incident light to transmitted light and is always greater than unity. This quantity was formerly known as 'opacity', but the term has now been deleted from standard terminology because strictly speaking there cannot be degrees of opacity (opaqueness). A material is either opaque or it is not.

The reciprocal of transmittance increases as blackness increases, so it is a more convenient way of expressing blackness than transmittance, but its numerical value can range from 1 to over 10 000. Such a large range of values would be difficult to plot on a graph, as the scale would be so compressed that the important small values could not be read accurately.

However, meaningful characteristic curves can be easily produced if equal increases in 'blackness' are shown as equal increases in distance along the axis of a graph. This is done by using the logarithm of the reciprocal of transmittance. This quantity, log (1/transmittance), is called 'transmission density'.

2.31   *Transmission density* (standard symbol D) is defined as 'the logarithm of the reciprocal of transmittance'. As mentioned previously, you should understand why density is used and how it is derived. However, in practice there is no need to obtain density values mathematically as densitometers are calibrated to give direct readings of density.

Density and visual response

2.32   One advantage of using density as a measurement is that an equal increase in density is shown by an equal increase in distance along the axis of a graph. This makes interpretation of the graph easier. Another important reason for using density as a measurement of blackness is that the response of our eyes to light variation (luminance differences), is approximately logarithmic. Photography is a visual communication system, so its effect depends on what is seen on the photograph. Therefore it is sensible to measure the effect by using logarithmic values. Thus density is directly related to the appearance of the photographic image. For example, when looking at a negative or a print, except in the very dark areas, our eyes see equal increases in density as equal increases in blackness.

2.33   The densities of images on non-transparent and reflective bases such as paper prints, which are viewed and therefore measured by reflected light, are referred to as *reflection densities*. (This is explained in Chapter 5).

2.34   It is useful to remember that, as density is a logarithmic function, density values are additive. For example, if a negative sample of density 1.2 is placed in contact with another sample of density 0.7, the combined density is $1.2 + 0.7 = 1.9$.

Logarithmic series and scales

2.35   Logarithmic series and scales of values are used in all aspects of photography with regard to exposure control and measuring or evaluating the events that occur. In fact, most of the things we use or can adjust, such as exposure meters, film speeds, camera shutter speeds and *f*-stops have scales that are logarithmically graduated (although the markings on them may not look like logarithmic figures). By being scaled in a logarithmic manner they can all be related to each other, and density, being a logarithmic function, can also be related to them.

In photography we often increase or decrease exposure by a factor of 2, by doubling or halving the exposure. Any series or scale that increases by a constant factor is a logarithmic series (also called a 'geometric series'). For example:

(a)   A series of printing exposures of 2, 4, 8 and 16 seconds is logarithmic.
(b)   A series of camera exposures of $\frac{1}{1000}$, $\frac{1}{500}$, $\frac{1}{250}$ and $\frac{1}{125}$ second is logarithmic.
(c)   A series of film speeds of ISO 100/21°, ISO 200/24° and ISO 400/27° is logarithmic.
(d)   A series of camera *f*-numbers of *f*/2, *f*/2.8, *f*/4, *f*/5.6 is a logarithmic series because the exposure they allow is changed each time by a factor of 2.

Common logarithms

2.36 A factor of 2 is of obvious importance, so when solving practical problems involving exposure and density it is useful to remember that the common logarithm of 2 is 0.3. Thus an increase in log value of 0.3 represents a doubling up. You should remember also the logarithms of 1, 10, 100, 1000 and of 0.1, 0.01, 0.001.

The important points to note from Table 2.1 are:

(a) Adding 0.3 to a logarithmic value means a doubling.
(b) Subtracting 0.3 from a logarithmic value means a halving,
(c) Adding 1 to a logarithmic value multiples the number by 10.
(d) Subtracting 1 from a logarithmic value divides the number by 10.

The two-figure logarithms in Table 2.1 are easy to remember and will suffice for many photographic and sensitometric derivations, but logarithm tables or a suitable electronic calculator can be used to find the logarithm of any other number as required. If you wish to refresh your memory on logarithms and logarithmic scales, refer to Appendix A.

Self-assessment questions

2.37 If you want to try a few examples, work out the missing values for the spaces in Table 2.2(b) in a similar manner to the examples in part (a) of the table. Use logarithm and reciprocal tables as required.

Table 2.1 Two-figure logarithms.

Logarithm	Number		Logarithm	Number
0.0	1		$\bar{3}$.0	0.001
0.3	2		$\bar{2}$.0	0.01
0.6	2		$\bar{1}$.0	0.1
0.9	8		0.0	1.0
1.2	16		1.0	10
1.5	32		2.0	100
1.8	64		3.0	1000

Table 2.2 Density and its related measurements.
(a)

Transmittance	1/transmittance	Density
0.50	2.0	0.3
0.25	4.0	0.6
0.125	8.0	0.9
0.062	16.0	1.2
0.031	32.0	1.5
0.016	64.0	1.8

(b)

Transmittance	1/transmittance	Density
	1.25	0.10
0.70	1.43	
0.31		0.51
0.11	9.0	
	17.0	1.23
0.03	33.0	
0.02		1.70
0.013	77.0	

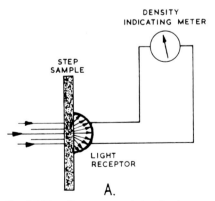

A.

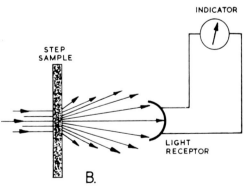

B.

Fig. 2.7 The effect on transmission density measurement of light scattered by the sample. (A) With the light receptor in contact, all the transmitted light is measured and a low value of density is indicated. This simulates a contact-printing condition.

(B) With the light receptor at a distance, some of the scattered light is missed and thus a higher value of density is indicated. This simulates a particular enlarging condition.

Effect of light scatter on density

2.38   The method by which the transmitted light is measured can affect the value of density obtained (Figure 2.7). When light is passed through a step (or through a negative) it is partially scattered away from its regular path (diffused) by the granular structure of the image. If the light receptor of the densitometer is in contact with the step, it receives all the transmitted light. If it is at a distance from the step, it receives for the most part the direct (parallel) light only and thus indicates a different value of transmission density.

The lowest numerical value of transmission density is obtained when the light receptor is in contact with the step. In this position all the transmitted light is received, therefore the lowest density is indicated. We can see that similar situations apply when a negative is either contact printed or enlarged. The effect is more evident with silver images, as monochrome and colour materials with dye images have a much lower light-scattering effect.

In some microfilm and other similar non-silver materials the image is composed of minute bubbles (vesicles) held in a rigid plastic binder. It is interesting to know that with such material the image is made visible almost entirely by the differential light-scattering effect of the vesicles. Therefore, for this type of material, density variation and effective image contrast are dependent on the optics of measurement or printing used.

2.39   When a conventional negative is being printed, the actual values of transmission density and the effect on the light receptor (photographic material) depend on the optical system of the printing equipment – for example, whether direct or diffuse light is being used. This effect of light scatter in printing is dealt with in more detail in Chapter 9.

Densitometers

2.40   A densitometer is an instrument used for measuring the density of exposed and processed photographic materials. An instrument designed to measure the density of films is called a 'transmission densitometer', and one designed to measure the density of prints on paper is called a 'reflection densitometer'. Older types of densitometer operated on a visual comparison basis. The user looked into an eyepiece and moved a calibrated neutral-density wedge until a particular density matched the sample being measured. They were tiring to use and their efficiency obviously depended on the operator. Nevertheless, visual densitometers may still have a place where only a few density measurements are required. They are relatively simple, and reasonably accurate when properly used. Most modern densitometers measure the density by means of a photoelectronic device and use electronic integrated circuitry to measure and display the density values directly. Some also have a computer capability, and may have an automatic system for plotting and displaying sensitometric graphs and data directly. Modern densitometers are therefore reliable, more suitable for measurements in quantity, and do not lead to fatigue.

There are two basic types of photoelectric densitometer, null-reading instruments and direct-reading instruments. Null-reading densitometers are more complex but usually similar in their basic operation to visual densitometers. A typical null-reading instrument operates by comparing and matching the light that has passed through the sample density with the light beam, from the same source, that has not passed through the sample. Density readings are made by moving a calibrated measuring wedge in the light beam, until the indicating meter shows no deflection from a null position.

Direct-reading densitometers are most commonly used, so we will consider the basic function and operation of this type of density-measuring instrument in more detail.

2.41   The essential components and functions of a direct-reading photoelectric or photoelectronic densitometer (Figure 2.8) are:

(a)   A light source with standard characteristics giving a controllable luminous intensity, and operating with the densitometer from a stable power supply.
(b)   A condenser lens to give a concentrated beam of light on the step or sample being measured.
(c)   A small aperture with an opaque surround, on which the sample is placed.
(d)   A photoelectric receptor or sensor (photocell, photomultiplier or photodiode) to receive and to measure the intensity of the light. The receptor is screened so that it only receives the light that has passed through the sample.
(e)   Not essential, but usual: an amplifier to amplify the current produced by the action of light on the photosensor.

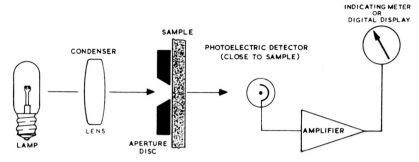

Fig. 2.8 The basic components and schematic arrangement of a direct-reading photoelectric, transmission densitometer. It operates by comparing the incident light with the transmitted light (see also Figure 2.6). The meter is set to zero density with no sample in place on the aperature disc. When the sample is positioned it absorbs some of the incident light and thus the ratio of incident to transmitted light is changed. The logarithm of this ratio is the density, and as the meter is calibrated in density units it indicates the value directly.

(f) An indicating meter calibrated directly in density units (many densitometers show the density value conveniently as a digital display).

2.42 Photoelectric densitometers operate basically by comparing the intensity of the incident light on the sample with the intensity of the transmitted light (or, for reflection densitometers, the reflected light). To ensure stability, some photoelectric densitometers may need to be switched on for a 'warm-up' period before use (five minutes or so is usual). The meter is set to read zero density and, when the sample is put in place, its density value is shown on the meter scale or digital display. The photoreceptor of a transmission densitometer may not be in actual contact with the sample, but most instruments are constructed so that they can measure all the transmitted light (see also paragraph 2.38). If a densitometer is to be used at frequent intervals, it is often convenient to leave it in an operating condition, but with the lamp switched off as this helps to keep the receptor and amplifier stabilized. However, in all cases the manufacturer's instructions for operation should be followed. The zero density setting should be re-checked before use and at regular intervals during use. To prevent the possibility of stray light entering the receptor, densitometers should be used in a situation away from strong light, such as direct sunlight.

Calibration and control of densitometers

2.43 All densitometers must be kept optically clean and serviceable, and periodic tests must be made to check the instrument in accordance with the manufacturer's instructions. Accuracy of reading is checked by using a standard reference step wedge containing known densities. Such calibration wedges (or reference plaques) are often supplied with the instrument; if not, a good-quality step wedge can be measured when the instrument is new and be kept as a calibration wedge. An accuracy of ± 0.01 is as high as can be expected of a typical instrument. Calibration wedges must be handled with care and stored in an envelope when not in use.

The calibration, correct operation and maintenance of the densitometer are particularly important. Because it is often the one step in a sensitometric procedure that is not being investigated, inaccurate density readings can easily be accepted, and misinterpreted as indicating the proper response of the material or process under test. A typical checking procedure might be:

(a) Set up and calibrate the instrument as recommended by the manufacturer.
(b) Each day, before use and also during use, measure and record the values of selected steps of the calibration wedge. These are usually a low, a medium and a high density – for example, 0.3, 1.0 and 3.0 for transmission densitometers (2.0 for reflection densitometers).
(c) Compare the readings with previous records to check for any variation from the normal. If found, establish the cause and correct it.
(d) For an initial period of a month or so, average all the readings of each selected step to obtain typical standard values for the instrument.
(e) Thereafter, use the established standard values to check the accuracy and correct operation of the instrument. See also paragraphs 2.51, 6.4, 6.19 and 11.37.

Practical response of a densitometer

2.44　A densitometer simply provides a means of measuring densities that will be of use on a comparative basis, or will be applicable when the material being measured is used in practice – for example, as viewed directly or being printed onto photographic paper. Ideally, when the material is to be printed, the spectral and optical characteristics of the combination of densitometer light and optical elements, and the spectral response of the receptor, should match those of the printer and the photographic material that will receive the printing light. This ideal situation is obviously not possible, as the characteristics of individual printing conditions will vary. Fortunately, with black-and-white materials the effect of differences in the spectral characteristics are usually not critical, but if necessary the response of the receptor can be corrected by using colour filters in the light path. However, when measuring the densities of photographic colour materials, such differences are important and the special densitometers and colour filters used conform to an established standard (see Chapter 11).

The spectral and optical characteristics of most modern densitometers are designed so that the density measurements obtained can correspond to the practical use of the material being measured (either viewed directly or printed), and to an agreed method of density measurement. This is considered later, in Chapters 9 and 11.

Measuring ability of eye and densitometer compared

2.45　It is interesting to compare the sensitivity and discriminating ability of the average human eye with that of a modern densitometer. When looking at a black-and-white negative or sensitometric strip, the unaided eye can see adjacent differences to a limit of about 0.03 transmission density units over a maximum density range of about 2.5 but is very poor at evaluating single density samples. On the other hand, a good general-service photoelectric densitometer can detect and indicate differences of 0.01 density units over a density range of 4.0 or more and does not require a comparison to be made at each measurement. A photoelectric densitometer can thus offer a higher precision than the human eye, and it is not subject to eye strain.

With regard to reflection densities, the human eye can discriminate between small density differ-ences in the highlight areas of a print, but cannot distinguish similar differences in the dark shadow areas which can be detected by a reflection densitometer (see paragraphs 5.7 and 5.8).

Reflection densitometers

2.46　Some commercial densitometers incorporate a device for measuring reflection densities. In a reflection densitometer the angle of the beam of light incident on the print sample must be such that no specularly reflected light enters the receptor. This is often done by arranging the lighting system so that the centre of the incident beam is at an angle of 45° to the surface of the sample and the reflected beam collected by the receptor is a narrow cone normal (i.e. perpendicular) to the sample surface (Figure 2.9). On some

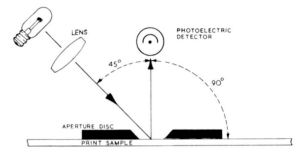

Fig. 2.9 Principle of a reflection densitometer, showing the path of incident and measured light. The print sample is illuminated from above and part of the reflected light is measured. Incident light is at 45° to the sample surface; to avoid the effect of specular reflections, only a narrow cone of perpendicularly reflected light is collected and measured.

reflection densitometers the roles are reversed, the incident light being directed normally to the surface of the sample and the reflected light collected at 45° to the sample. Most reflection densitometers have a movable measuring probe; some probes convey light by means of a fibre-optic light guide to the receptor, others incorporate a receptor in the probe head. This is particularly convenient when measuring large prints, as the measuring probe can be placed on the print sample instead of the sample being placed on the instrument.

Densitometry

2.47　The use of a densitometer to measure density and the study and evaluation of results is part of sensitometry as a whole, but is properly referred to as 'densitometry'.

Commercial densitometers

2.48 There are many different densitometers varying from elaborate automatic recording microdensitometers to the simple adaptation of an exposure meter, the quality and versatility of a commercial instrument being in general related directly to its cost. We can consider in outline two typical densitometers to see how the functions of a densitometer are incorporated into a commercial instrument.

2.49 *Melico Photolog TD2 transmission densitometer.* This is a typical instrument (Figure 2.10). It has the essentials and functions of a densitometer (see paragraph 2.41) plus extra facilities to help in its efficient operation, and it may be used for colour or black-and-white densitometry. A fibre-optic light

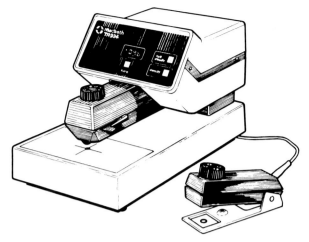

Fig. 2.11 The Macbeth TR 924 transmission–reflection densitometer.

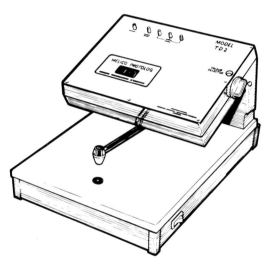

Fig. 2.10 The Melico Photolog TD2 transmission densitometer.

guide is used to convey light to a photomultiplier, from a probe head that can be lowered onto the sample aperture. A switching system enables a filter to be selected appropriate to the measurement desired. Density measurements are shown as a digital display which can be locked to retain the reading. Melico make several different densitometers, and also other light- and colour-measuring instruments for use in photography and the graphic arts.

2.50 *Macbeth TR 924 densitometer.* This is a twin, transmission–reflection densitometer (Figure 2.11). It has the essentials and functions of a densitometer as well as many extra features. It may

be used for colour or black-and-white densitometry by transmission or by reflection. Two photodiodes are used, one for the transmission and one for the reflection head. Each head is positioned with its probe over the measuring area and contains a series of interchangeable light filters which can be selected to suit the type of measurement to be made. Density measurements are shown on a digital display. Macbeth make a range of densitometers, and also associated light- and colour-measuring instruments for use in photography and the graphic arts.

Measuring and recording sensitometric results

2.51 After exposure and processing, the sample to be measured is placed in position on the densitometer with the emulsion facing the receptor, to ensure correct collection of transmitted light. This simulates contact printing, where the film emulsion faces the paper emulsion. The density of the central area of each step is then measured. The largest usable aperture of the densitometer should be used, to ensure that small local variations in density have the minimum effect. (Dust spots, marks and scratches obviously interfere with accurate density readings and must be avoided).

If steps or areas much larger than the aperture of the densitometer are to be measured, it will be necessary to take several (five or more) readings at different places (not close to the edges) and to average the results. The five readings should be in the same relative place on each step. If the several readings vary widely, investigation is necessary.

To avoid mistakes in plotting, the density measurements should be recorded in a notebook or on a prepared proforma, together with the step numbers and densities of the sensitometer master wedge (Table 2.3). All the relevant data on the test must also be noted (see paragraph 2.63). As the sample densities are read, each one is listed opposite the appropriate density and step number of the master wedge. The graph can then be prepared and the readings plotted.

Table 2.3 A typical proforma for recording density measurements.

Master wedge density	Step no.	Sample densities					
		A	B	C	D	E	F
—	D_{min}						
3.10	1						
2.96	2						
2.80	3						
2.63	4						
2.50	5						

Constructing a characteristic curve

2.52 Figure 2.12 shows a typical characteristic curve. Any type of squared graph paper can be used for plotting characteristic curves or any other sensitometric curves. The smallest practical size is standard A4 (210×297 mm) as this is convenient for filing with other A4 size documents. However, for accuracy and ease of plotting, a somewhat larger size of graph paper such as A3 (420×297 mm) is more suitable. Probably the most useful is 1 cm squared graph paper with the squares subdivided into 5 or 10 divisions. Each centimetre can then be used to equal 0.1 scale units and subdivisions can be plotted to an accuracy of

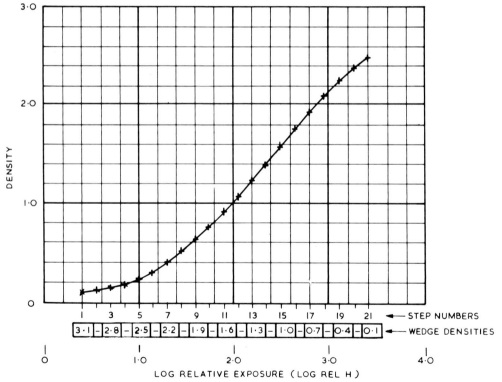

Fig. 2.12 Plotting a characteristic curve. Suitable scales of density and log exposure are constructed on the graph paper. Marks indicating the log relative exposure values are made by plotting the densities of the sensitometer step wedge in reverse order, starting from an arbitrary point on the exposure axis. The measured density values of a processed sensitometric strip are then plotted against the log relative values of exposure that produced them, and the plotting points joined with a smooth curve. To avoid confusion, in this diagram only the alternate step numbers are shown.

0.01. This degree of accuracy matches that of the densitometer readings.

The squared area of the graph paper should be large enough to accommodate logarithmic scales of, say, 3.0 by 4.0 for film curves or 2.0 by 3.0 for paper curves. When a particular format and layout is found to be satisfactory, it can be standardized to enable easy comparison between subsequent tests.

The grid lines can be grey or any colour preferred, but if the result is to be copied or reproduced photographically, graph paper with pale blue lines on a white background is most suitable. The scales and curves can be drawn in black ink and the blue lines eliminated by copying or by contact printing on a blue-sensitive photographic material. This is often convenient, because the lines may not reproduce too well and may also be confusing when curves are viewed. Sensitometric diagrams in manufacturers' literature and in textbooks are often presented in this way so that the general effect of the curve can be more clearly seen.

Having decided on the size of the graph paper, the next thing is to estimate how many squares will be needed for each axis and whether the paper will need to be horizontal or vertical with regard to its longer side. The scales can then be constructed in pencil and when satisfactory they can be inked in. Numbering and lettering can be added neatly by using stencils or ready-made stick-down transfers. The vertical axis of the graph is marked with a convenient scale of density (and so annotated), and the horizontal axis with a scale of the logarithm of relative exposure. This latter scale should strictly be shown as 'log relative exposure' or 'log rel H', but is often shown as rel log H (formerly rel log E). The expression log $(I \times t)$ is also sometimes used (see paragraph 2.3). It is usually desirable to use the same scale of units for both axes of the graph. This is so that the slope of a curve can be measured easily and also compared directly with the slope of other characteristic curves.

If similar graphs are to be made frequently, it may be convenient to draw the axes on strong translucent material as a master template. The plotting of curves can then be carried out on a viewing light box. Alternatively, the master may be covered with a transparent plastic sheet. Characteristic curves can then be drawn by using a suitable felt-tip pen.

Note that, when referring to graphs, the horizontal axis or scale is sometimes called 'the abscissa' or 'x-axis', while the vertical axis or scale is called 'the ordinate' or 'y-axis'.

2.53 A logarithmic scale of exposure is used on the horizontal axis of a graph, and the density values plotted against it are themselves log functions. The advantages of using a log scale of exposure (instead of an arithmetic scale) are:

(a) A logarithmically numbered scale of exposures shows equal ratios of exposure as equal distances along the horizontal axis.
(b) The lower part of the characteristic curve, representing the significant low values of exposure, is by this means given prominence over the upper part.
(c) With a logarithmic scale of exposures, the characteristic curve has an almost straight line representing its most useful portion, so simplifying measurement and interpretation.
(d) The density range of a negative can be transferred easily to the log exposure axis of the print curve.
(e) Both the functions used in constructing characteristic curves are logarithmic. Therefore the relationship between the variables involved can be easily measured all the way through the photographic process, from the original subject to the final print.
(f) The characteristic curve produced is closely related to the visual appearance of the print, the negative, and the subject itself. This is because the response of the human eye to varying densities is approximately logarithmic.

See also paragraphs 2.32 and 2.35, and Appendix A paragraph 6.

Relative values of log exposure

2.54 Absolute (actual) values of exposure in lux seconds are not always easy to obtain. However, for most purposes relative values of exposure are sufficient, and are therefore widely used in practice. When relative values of exposure are used, the scale remains the same, and the differences between the successive values remain the same as if the absolute values had been used. An example of this relationship is shown in Figure 2.13.

2.55 A scale showing the log of relative exposure can be constructed by plotting and then marking in the density values of the sensitometer master step wedge so that they increase from right to left along the log exposure axis of the graph (Figure 2.12). The plot marks made will thus indicate log relative exposure increasing from left to right. This is

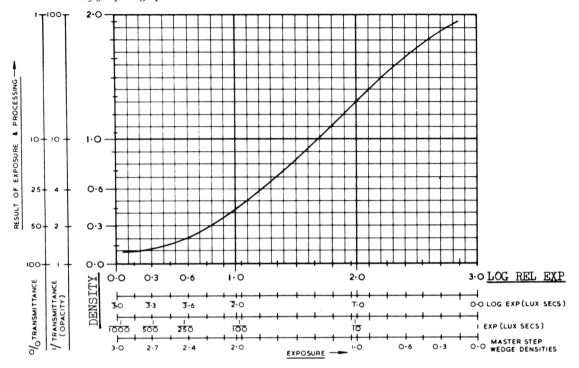

Fig. 2.13 A typical film characteristic curve and comparative scales showing some different ways of measuring and expressing exposure, and the results of exposure and processing. The scales almost invariably used in practice are density and log exposure.

because the least exposure is obtained through the densest step of the sensitometer wedge, and vice versa. It is usual to start marking the scale from an arbitrary point, say 0.2 to 0.5 units greater than the density range of the master wedge, and to enter the wedge step numbers in pencil under each mark. Note that to avoid a confusion of numbers in Figure 2.12, only the alternate steps are shown. Once the scale is constructed, the same scale can of course be used for plotting any further samples exposed using the same master step wedge. To assist in this, a template of the scale can be made on a strip of clear film.

An alternative method, which gives the same result, is to list the densities of the steps on the sensitometer step wedge, then subtract each one from some higher arbitrary value, say 3.50 or 4.0. You may like to work out for yourself why these two methods give the same result.

Plotting the characteristic curve

2.56 When the graph axes have been drawn, the densities of the sample are plotted in pencil against the logarithm of the relative exposure that produced them. In fact, they are plotted against the densities of the sensitometer master wedge, which amounts to the same thing. For accuracy, a pencil with a sharp point should be used. The plotting points may be indicated with small crosses. The 'best' curve is then drawn in pencil using freehand. This is the curve that most nearly fits all the plotted points. The aim is to draw a smooth curve that gives the best average between all the points. Check the smoothness of a curve by looking along it edge on. Any irregularities will then be obvious. When the curve is satisfactory, it can be inked in using freehand with the assistance of a 'flexicurve' rule or 'French curves'. The characteristic curve may in fact pass through all the plotted points, indicating that all the previous operations have been accomplished without error. If it does not, drawing a 'best' curve is not cheating as there are many, often unavoidable, irregularities than can creep in to affect the readings. This is particularly noticeable when dealing with short development times, which tend to cause uneven development.

When plotting, any odd 'rogue' readings that are a long way out should be circled to show that they are suspect and then investigated. It may be that one of the wedge steps has been missed when measuring on the densitometer. For inking in, any suitable drawing ink, ballpoint or felt-tip pen may be used. The aim is to produce a durable curve that is thin yet decisive. Precise measurements cannot be obtained from thick curves. Paragraph 2.59 is an exercise in constructing a characteristic curve, which you can carry out later.

In some circumstances it may be convenient to use tracing paper or clear film on which to plot curves. The results can then be used as an overlay on other curves, for direct comparison. When such a material is used, it is necessary to include also the horizontal and vertical axes so that the relationship of the curve to both its axes is established.

Density plotted against log exposure

2.57   On a characteristic curve graph the vertical axis is always scaled as a range of densities. Transmission density, as we know, is defined as the logarithm of the reciprocal of transmittance, log (1/transmittance), so either of these two factors, transmittance or its reciprocal, could be used on the vertical axis instead of density. The horizontal axis is mostly scaled as a range of the logarithms of exposure, which may be relative or absolute (actual). However, the horizontal axis could be scaled as 'subject densities' (for example, the densities of a sensitometer step wedge) or even as a scale of exposures in lux seconds or fractions of lux seconds. It may help understanding if all these factors, which relate to each other and to the presentation of a characteristic curve, are brought together and shown alongside the curve. Figure 2.13 shows a typical film characteristic curve and comparative scales for some of the different ways of measuring and expressing exposure and the results on the film. To avoid a confusion of figures, only parts of the scales are shown. It is again emphasized that, almost without exception, the scales used on characteristic curve graphs are in density units for the vertical axis and in log exposure units for the horizontal axis.

Self-assessment questions

2.58   If you want to test your learning, write out answers to the following:

(a)   List the essential features of an intensity (illuminance) scale sensitometer.
(b)   If a step wedge in a sensitometer has 21 steps and each gives a 0.15 log increase in exposure, what will be the arithmetic range of exposure it will give?

(c)   What conditions apply to the exposing light used in a sensitometer?
(d)   What is the basic difference between the two fundamental types of sensitometer?
(e)   Which type of sensitometer is more applicable for testing films that are to be used for general-purpose photography, and why?
(f)   What would be the resultant density of two neutral-density filters placed together if each transmitted one-fifth of the incident light?
(g)   List the essential features of a photoelectric, transmission densitometer.
(h)   What is the basic comparison made when a direct-reading photoelectric densitometer is used to measure density?
(i)   Why must a sample measured on a densitometer have the emulsion facing the photosensor?
(j)   Describe the arrangement of the illumination system in a typical reflection densitometer.
(k)   Describe how the axes of a characteristic-curve graph are constructed.
(l)   List three reasons for using a logarithmic scale of exposure, when plotting characteristic curves.
(m)   Explain how you would find and plot a log rel *H* scale.

Exercise in constructing a characteristic curve

2.59   On a suitable piece of squared graph paper prepare graph axes as described in paragraph 2.52 similar to the ones shown in Figure 2.14. Next, cover up the centre column of Table 2.4 (you can refer to this later). Using the other information given in Table 2.4 construct a scale of log relative exposure in pencil, starting from the right-hand vertical axis (see also paragraph 2.55). As each log

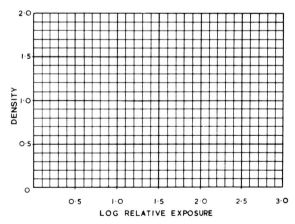

Fig. 2.14 Graph axes that can be used as an exercise in plotting a characteristic curve.

rel *H* point is marked in, enter the step number underneath it. Now check that your marks and step numbers agree with those in the centre of Table 2.4. Using the density information given in the table, construct a characteristic curve in pencil on your prepared graph lines as described in para-

Table 2.4 Measurements to be used in constructing a characteristic curve.

Step no.	Density of master wedge	log rel H (cover up this column)	Density of resultant strip
Fog	Maximum	Nil	0.12
1	2.86	0.14	0.12
2	2.54	0.46	0.16
3	2.20	0.80	0.26
4	1.88	1.12	0.52
5	1.54	1.46	0.84
6	1.16	1.84	1.14
7	0.86	2.14	1.46
8	0.54	2.46	1.70
9	0.22	2.78	1.85
10	0.02	2.98	1.92

graph 2.56. Vertical pencil lines can be drawn up from the log *H* positions to assist in locating the density plotting points. The aim is always to draw a smooth curve that gives the best average between all the plotted points.

Note that in Table 2.4 the values of log rel *H* have been found by subtracting the sensitometer master wedge densities from 3.0. However, the same curve would be obtained if the master wedge densities themselves were plotted to increase from right to left, starting from 3.0 on the scale. In most cases this latter method of constructing a scale saves time and effort, so it is suggested that you adopt it.

The characteristic curve

2.60 A sensitometric characteristic curve is often referred to as a *D* log *H* curve, a *D* log *E* curve, a response curve, or sometimes as an H and D curve, after Hurter and Driffield who originated the system. The curve indicates the way in which the photographic material responds to the two major events in photography, exposure and processing, under one particular set of conditions. The steepness of the curve slope shows the rate at which density increases as exposure increases.

2.61 If we plotted a curve for an objectively 'ideal' photographic emulsion, each log exposure

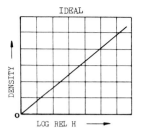 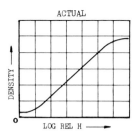

Fig. 2.15 Characteristic curves comparing the response of a theoretically ideal and of an actual photographic emulsion. An objectively ideal photographic emulsion and process would produce a linear response to any exposure increase. When an actual emulsion is processed, it produces a linear response for a limited range of exposure only, and its response declines when this range is exceeded. Nevertheless it is adequate for most photographic purposes when properly exposed and processed.

increase would give a proportional density increase, and the line joining any two points on the graph would be straight. This is called a linear response.

However, photographic emulsions are not ideal. The main differences between the response of an actual emulsion developed in an actual developer and that of a theoretical 'ideal' emulsion developed in an 'ideal' developer are as follows.

(a) Density is produced with no exposure.
(b) Very low exposure values do not produce a developable image.
(c) Log exposure increase gives a proportional density increase (a linear response) only where the line is straight.
(d) Very high exposure values do not increase density.

We shall consider the significance of these and other differences later. The main thing we can see in Figure 2.15 is that over the region where each curve is linear both photographic emulsions behave in a similar manner. This means that, provided we can control both exposure and processing, an actual emulsion can be made to give an almost ideal tonal response.

Parts of the characteristic curve and their function

2.62 We can now go on to name the distinctive features of a typical characteristic curve and consider the functions that they and other parts of the curve represent. Figure 2.16 shows a somewhat idealized curve for a film and illustrates its main features.

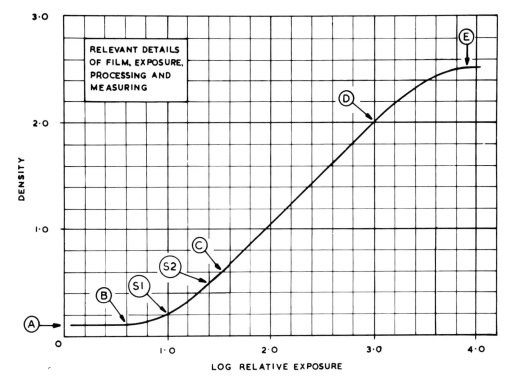

Fig. 2.16 Parts of the characteristic curve of a negative film. This curve has been idealized for the purpose of illustration. A: fog level or minimum density. A to B: inertia region. B: threshold points. B to C: toe or foot. C to D: straight-line region. D to E: shoulder. E: maximum density. S1 and S2: typical speed points.

(a) *Fog level (*D_{min}*).* This is the density obtained by processing an unexposed part of the film. If it includes the density of the film base it may be called 'base plus fog' or 'gross fog', and if not it is 'net fog'. In practice the term 'base plus fog' is often referred to as 'minimum density' or $D_{\min}$.

(b) *Inertia region* (Not strictly part of the characteristic curve). The low exposures corresponding to this region do not produce any measurable increase in density over the fog level, because exposure has not been sufficient to overcome the inertia (reluctance to change) of the light-sensitive emulsion.

(c) *Threshold point.* This is the point where exposure and processing start to visibly affect the emulsion and where the toe begins. It is the first perceptible density above fog.

(d) *Toe (or foot).* In this region the slope of the characteristic curve increases gradually, showing that equal increases in log exposure here produce progressively greater increases in density.

(e) *Straight-line region.* In the straight-line or linear region the slope of the curve remains fairly constant, showing that equal increases in log exposure here produce equal or proportional increases in density. Note that the straightness of the line shown in Figure 2.16 is not typical of many photographic emulsions; most have less well-defined 'straight-line' regions, which may be more like a gentle curve.

(f) *Shoulder.* In the shoulder region, the slope of the characteristic curve decreases gradually, showing that equal increases in log exposure here produce progressively smaller increases in density until there in no more increase.

(g) *Maximum density (*D_{max}*).* This is the maximum density obtained under the given conditions of exposure and processing. If exposure is continued far beyond this point the characteristic curve may turn downward. The effect is called 'solarization', and produces a reversal of tones in the image. To obtain this effect the exposure would need to be at least 1000 times that necessary to obtain D_{max} and may not be evident on many types of photographic material.

(h) *Typical speed points.* S1 is a point where the density is 0.1 above base-plus-fog level. It is used for determining the speed value of black-and-white films used in general-purpose photography. S2 is a point where the density is 0.4 above base-plus-fog level. It is used for determining the speed of films used specifically for aerial photography, as explained in Chapter 4. For other types of film and paper, different speed points may be used. The density level chosen as the speed point depends on the material and its intended use.

Additional information

2.63   A characteristic curve has no particular meaning unless the details of its production are given, so in practice all the relevant details of the photographic material, exposure method, developer and processing conditions must be recorded on the graph. Typical data might include some or all of that shown in Table 2.5.

Table 2.5 Typical data for inclusion on a sensitometric graph.

Prepared by	Date...................................
Film make and type	ILDAK XP6
Emulsion batch number	PRX 543
Date of maker's test	21 Apr 88
Sensitometer	2L N° 3
Exposure time	1/50 second
Filters	N/D 1.8
Developer	RIB NOX
Dilution	1 + 4
Temperature	20°C
Equipment or method	Tank
Agitation	Intermittent, 30-second intervals
Densitometer	Mac/T No. 3
Aperture	2 mm
Other data	
Development time	6 minutes (this is usually entered near the characteristic curve; see Fig. 3.1).
Comments	

The characteristic curve is only useful if we can obtain information from it regarding the performance of the material in practice, so the test conditions and the conditions under which the material is to be used must be similar.

2.64 The characteristic curve shows graphically what happens to a photographic material that has received a wide range of exposures and has been processed for one particular time, in one particular developer. If any of these factors is changed, a new curve can be plotted. Comparison of the two curves will then reveal the effect of the change.

2.65 Manufacturers publish characteristic curves for their photographic materials which have been exposed and processed under specified conditions. These give a good indication of the general performance of a material, and are of use in selecting a suitable material and processing for a particular task. However, they can only be used as a guide, as in practice the exposure and processing, and even the response of the material itself, will probably differ from that used for the published curves.

The characteristic curve in practical photography

2.66 The characteristic curve in figure 2.16 shows a response by the film over a log exposure range of approximately 3.3 (2000 to 1). The average log exposure range received on the film in a camera used to record a typical scene seldom exceeds 1.5 (which means an arithmetical range of approximately 30 to 1). In some situations the log exposure range may be somewhat longer (for example, if bright sky and white clouds are included in the scene), and in others much shorter. For example, in high-altitude aerial photography or landscape photography under hazy atmospheric conditions the log exposure range may be as short as 0.5 (3 to 1), so in the majority of cases only part of the characteristic curve is used.

2.67 In practice, we can choose which part of the characteristic curve to use to obtain optimum quality results. We must choose the part of the curve that suits the particular photographic task. We can then ensure that this part is used, by our control over the exposure and processing of the film. This is a practical application of sensitometry, and we shall be considering the factors involved throughout this book.

For the majority of photographic tasks the best part of the characteristic curve to use is the upper two-thirds of the toe and the lower part of the straight-line region. Figure 2.18 diagram 4 shows an example of this. When this 'correct exposure' region is used to record the exposure range of the subject photographed, we will obtain negatives that can then be printed to produce optimum results.

2.68 We need to remember that it is the final print that displays the quality of photography. Therefore a good negative can be defined as one that can be used to produce the best-quality print. To this we could add 'on a medium grade of printing paper'. The association of the negative with the print is one reason why we can use part of the toe of the negative characteristic curve. This is explained later, in paragraph 5.26

2.69 The upper part of the straight-line region is avoided as much as possible because of the undesirable increase in factors such as image spread and granularity, which occur as exposure and resultant density increase. This fact is sometimes not appreciated, because the effect is not evident on a characteristic curve. The lower toe is avoided because of the unwanted reduction in contrast that occurs as the curve flattens. Figure 2.17 shows these areas and effects in a simplified diagram.

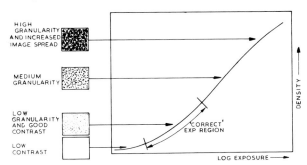

Fig. 2.17 A representation of the granular characteristics of a typical black-and-white (silver image) negative film. For general photography the best part of the characteristic curve, called the 'correct exposure region', is the upper two-thirds of the toe and the lower straight-line region. Below this region contrast is too low. Above it, increased granularity and image spread occurs.

2.70 *Effect of variation away from the correct exposure region.* Variation away from the correct exposure region of the characteristic curve may be caused by a wrong exposure in the camera, or by wrong development. The effect depends on the degree of variation, but in general the negative will have incorrect density and/or contrast. There will also be an associated loss of detail, partly caused by a loss of fine tonal differences, particularly in the extreme shadows or extreme highlights of the image.

2.71 *Effect of variation within the correct exposure region.* Provided that the exposure range of the subject photographed is kept within the correct exposure region, the effect on negative quality will be minimal. This means that in some camera work, for example where the exposure range of the subject is fairly short, there is some latitude or degree of tolerance in exposure level and development variation. Because of this, a good negative may still be obtained as long as neither exposure nor development is increased or decreased too much.

2.72 *Effects of variation in exposure and processing.* The diagrams in Figure 2.18 show examples of the effects of variation in exposure and processing. For ease of interpretation the same subject is used for each diagram, and so that the diagrams are not too large the characteristic curve has a fairly short range. The log exposure range from the image of

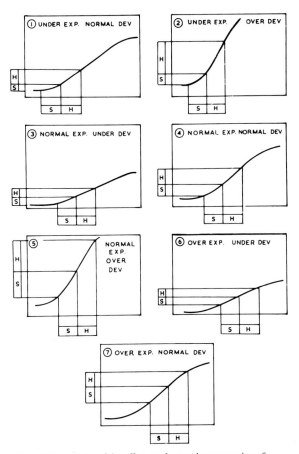

Fig. 2.18 Examples of the effect on the resultant negative of variation in exposure and processing. For each example the same subject is represented, S denoting the shadows and H the highlights.

the subject and the density range of the resultant negative are divided into two areas, shadows (S) and highlights (H). If you are not quite sure of what this means, read paragraphs 1.3 and 1.8 again.

Interpreting characteristic curves

2.73   The three main things we can see in Figure 2.18, other than the effect of normal exposure with normal development, are the effect on the resultant negatives of:

(a)   Varying the camera exposure only: diagrams 1 and 7.
(b)   Varying the development conditions only: diagrams 3 and 5.
(c)   Varying development in an attempt to minimize the effect of incorrect exposure: diagrams 2 and 6.

When interpreting the curves we need to bear in mind the position of the 'correct exposure region'. For general photography using conventional materials this should be such that the finished negative includes the upper two-thirds of the toe and the lower part of the straight-line region, as shown on diagram 4.

2.74   *Effect of varying camera exposure.*   The log exposure range, from the darkest shadow to the brightest highlight of the subject, is represented by the distance between the two outer marks on the exposure axis. Notice that an increase in exposure is shown by the whole log exposure range moving to the right (diagram 7) and a decrease in exposure by the whole range moving to the left (diagram 1). Varying the camera exposure thus moves the exposure range to different parts of the curve and therefore produces varying density and contrast on the resultant negatives. Incidentally, a move of 0.3 log exposure units represents a doubling or a halving of camera exposure equivalent to the effect of one *f*-stop.

2.75   *Effect of varying development conditions.*   The density range, from the lightest shadow to the darkest highlight of the negative, is represented by the distance between the two outer marks on the density axis. Notice that any change from the normal development (diagram 4) causes the characteristic curve to change its shape, its slope and its position on the graph (diagrams 3 and 5). Varying the development conditions thus causes the log exposure range already given to be placed

in a different position on curves that have different slopes. The effect produces varying density and contrast on the resultant negative and it also affects the fog level. As density increases so the granularity of the image also increases but this effect is of course not evident on the characteristic curve.

2.76   *Effect of varying development in an attempt to minimize the effect of incorrect exposure.*   The speed of a film is an expression of its response to both exposure and development. An increase in speed is shown on the characteristic curve as an increase in density for a particular exposure. Consequently, if development is varied the speed of the film is changed. For example, we can see in diagram 2 that increasing the development causes a small increase in speed, but that it also changes the contrast and density of the negative, particularly in the highlight areas. Because of this, the effect of varying exposure away from the correct exposure region cannot be fully corrected by varying the development conditions (diagrams 2 and 6). Nevertheless, provided the degree of exposure variation is not too great, the effect on the resultant negative can be minimized.

Interpretation exercise

2.77   Probably the best way to describe briefly the effect on the negative when exposure and development are varied is to tabulate the results. The differences can then be easily compared. It is suggested that you interpret the effects shown by the characteristic curves in Figure 2.18 with regard to shadow contrast S, highlight contrast H, average overall density, and fog level; and then refer the findings of your interpretation to Table 2.6.

It is interesting to notice that although the overall shadow contrast shown in diagram 2 is only a little less than that of the normal curve (diagram 4), the extreme shadows at the bottom of the toe will have a very low contrast. A similar effect is shown in diagram 1. In both cases the extreme shadows have only just been recorded on the film. Therefore, although the other parts may be printed, the contrast between the darker shadows of the original subject will probably not be visible on the print. We have not considered the combined effect of underexposure and underdevelopment, or of overexposure and overdevelopment. Later, as an interesting exercise, you may like to draw the appropriate curves for these situations on a piece of paper and work them out for yourself.

Table 2.6 The general effect on negatives of varying exposure and development of film.

Diagram No	Camera exposure	Development	Shadow contrast S	Highlight contrast H	Average density	Fog level density
1	under	normal	very low	normal	low	normal
2	under	over	fairly low	high	high	high
3	normal	under	low	low	low	low
4	**normal 'correct'**	**normal**	**normal**	**normal**	**normal**	**normal**
5	normal	over	high	high	high	high
6	over	under	low	low	low	low
7	over	normal	fairly high	normal	normal	normal

If you have successfully interpreted the effects shown by the characteristic curves in Figure 2.18, you are well on the way to using and appreciating sensitometry as a means of understanding and of showing what happens in the photographic process. You can visualize the practical effects of exposure and processing and of what happens if they are varied. Exposure and processing are the two main events that occur in photography: events that decide the quality of the results. With an application of sensitometric knowledge, they are both under your control.

Self-assessment questions

2.78 If you want to test your learning, study the characteristic curve in Figure 2.16 and answer the following. Imagine that you have used a film having the characteristics shown in the diagram, to take photographs of a subject giving a log exposure range of 1.0.

(a) Alongside the curve, or preferably on a copy of the curve, draw a faint pencil line to show where the density values of an underexposed negative with only the highlights showing will have been exposed.
(b) Again, indicate with a line where you think the density values of a correctly exposed negative might be placed.
(c) Indicate with a pencil line where the density values of an overexposed negative might be placed.
(d) On the density axis indicate where the fog level of each of the three negatives will be.

Still referring to Figure 2.16, write out answers to the following:

(e) What is the fog level density (D_{min}) of this film?
(f) Why is the logarithm of exposure used?
(g) What does 'log relative exposure' mean?

(h) Describe two methods of plotting a log rel H scale from the master wedge density measurements.
(i) What is the D_{max} of this film?
(j) What is the range of log exposure from point B to D_{max}?
(k) What is this range in arithmetical figures?
(l) If the density at point S1 was achieved on part of a negative after an exposure of $1/100$ second at $f/11$ in a camera, what exposure time would have been needed to make the same part of the negative reach point D, using the same f-number? (Ignore possible reciprocity failure effects.)
(m) What is the density range of the straight-line region?
(n) Starting from point A, describe the relationship between log exposure increase and density increase up to D_{max}.

Why are the lower and upper parts of a film characteristic curve usually avoided in practical photography?

Contrast

2.79 A characteristic curve is a graphical representation of the tonal performance of a photographic material under the conditions of test, but it is only of practical value if we can extract useful information from it. We can see the general shape, slope and position of a curve on a graph, and with an understanding of sensitometry we can compare it with other curves in order to form an opinion. However it is often more convenient if we can express some factors of the material's performance in a concise numerical manner. The main factors that are usually expressed in numerical terms are minimum density (fog level), which we have already considered, the degree of contrast produced by development, the relative speed or sensitivity to light and, in certain cases, the exposure latitude or useful exposure range of the photographic emulsion. We shall consider the meaning and interpretation of these factors and how they can be expressed as numerical data, but before this we need to have a clear idea of what 'contrast' means in photography and sensitometry.

2.80 In photography the word 'contrast' can have several different meanings. By common usage in sensitometry it describes what is really the contrast reproducing abilities of a photographic emulsion or a developer. For instance, we say that one film or one grade of printing paper has a higher (inherent) contrast than another. We also use the word when comparing or when describing the relationship between the tonal range of a subject and that of its photographic image. 'Contrast' is also used to describe the range of tones in a subject, image or reproduction. When used in sensitometric calculations in this context, the description should be expressed logarithmically so that all quantities can be related easily. It can be defined thus:

(a) *For a subject.* Log Subject Luminance Range (log SLR) is the difference between the logarithms of the maximum and minimum luminances, i.e. log SLR = log L_1 − log L_2.
(b) *For an optical image.* Log Image Illuminance Range (log IIR) is the difference between the logarithms of the maximum and minimum exposures, i.e. log IIR = log H_1 − log H_2. (Strictly, this should be the difference between the logarithms of the illuminances E_1 and E_2.)

(c) *For a negative or print.* Density Range is the difference between the maximum and minimum transmission (or reflection) densities, i.e. density range or $\Delta D = D_1 - D_2$.

The Greek letter Δ (delta), which is used as a symbol for an extent or difference, is often used to denote the range or the difference between two units. For example, ΔD 1.5 means a density range of 1.5; Δ log H 2.08 means a log exposure range of 2.08. When such a contrast is specified arithmetically, it is given as a ratio: for example, 20 to 1 or 30:1.

The definition of sensitometric contrast as given above is used also to describe the contrast between any two very small areas of the subject, image or photograph, and this is often called micro contrast. The expression can also be applied to individual parts, for example shadow contrast, middle-tone contrast and highlight contrast. When using these customary descriptive terms, it is often convenient to think of the range of tones in the subject, image or photograph as being divided into three particular regions on the sensitometric graph (Figures 2.21, 5.13 and 7.10 show examples).

We should bear in mind that, in black-and-white photography particularly, contrast is the factor that enables us to see the image of an object. It is only the contrast between an object and its surroundings that makes it visible. If there is no contrast or insufficient contrast, the object merges into its surroundings and is invisible.

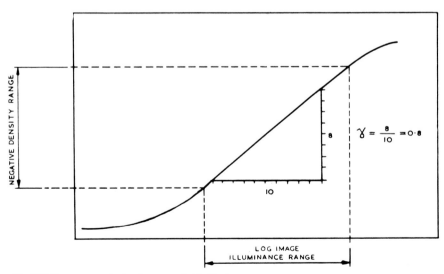

Fig. 2.19 Gamma equals density range divided by log exposure range (log image illuminance range) along the straight-line region of the characteristic curve.

Gamma and gradient

2.81 The contrast-reproducing abilities of a photographic material are indicated by the steepness of slope or gradient of its characteristic curve. The gradient of the straight-line region is given a numerical value by measuring the tangent of the angle that it makes with the log exposure axis (provided that both axes are equally scaled). In sensitometry, this gradient value is usually symbolized by the Greek letter γ (gamma), or the word may be spelt out in full. See Figure 2.19.

Gamma indicates how the tonal values of a negative on the straight-line region of the characteristic curve compare with the tonal values of the original subject image (the optical image) received on the film during exposure. Mathematically, it is given by the ratio

$$\text{Gamma} = \frac{\Delta D}{\Delta \log H}$$

and is simply calculated by measuring ΔD for a known $\Delta \log H$, along the straight-line region of the characteristic curve.

2.82 In order to obtain the value of gamma for a characteristic curve drawn on squared graph paper:

(a) Count *ten* units along from the bottom of the straight-line region parallel to the log H axis.
(b) From that point, count the number of units upwards to the straight line.
(c) Divide the number of units by *ten*; the result is the gamma. An accuracy to the nearest 0.02 is sufficient.

We can think of it as

$$\text{Gamma} = \frac{\text{Vertical distance}}{\text{Horizontal distance}}$$

For accurate results, select units that will cover most of the straight-line region (units of, say, 1, 2 or 3 squares on the graph paper should be suitable). We can use the same method to measure the gradient of any other small part of the curve by first drawing a straight line at a tangent to the part being considered.

2.83 If several characteristic curves have to be measured, an overlay on a sheet of clear film or a suitable scale on a piece of stout paper can be made to assist in measuring. Such a device is called a 'gammeter' (Figure 2.20). In use the gammeter is

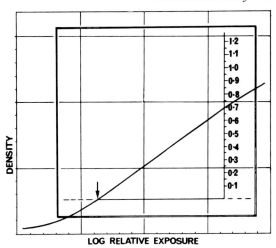

Fig. 2.20 A gammeter used for measuring the gamma value of a characteristic curve directly. The gammeter is placed over the curve with the arrow on the straight-line portion and the base line parallel to the graph. The gamma value (here 0.7) is shown on the vertical scale.

placed over the curve with the arrow at any convenient point on the straight-line region and with its base line parallel to the horizontal graph lines on the paper. The gamma value can then be read directly from the vertical scale where the straight-line portion of the curve (or an extension of it) crosses the scale.

For convenience, the vertical scale on the gammeter is often positioned 1.0 log exposure units to the right of the arrow. By this means, the scale of gamma values and the scale of the densities on the original graph are the same.

2.84 *Gamma and contrast.* Figure 2.21 shows some examples of gamma. At gamma = 1.0, the contrast (tonal range) of the negative equals that of the optical image of the subject in the camera. Below gamma = 1.0 the contrast of the negative is lower, and above gamma = 1.0 the contrast is higher than that of the original subject image.

2.85 *Contrast of materials with no straight-line characteristics.* Strictly, gamma applies only to the straight-line region of the characteristic curve. Many photographic materials produce little or no straight line, and exposures are placed on the curved part of the characteristic curve. In such conditions it is the average gradient over the part of the curve to be used that applies and that would be measured. This average gradient is often denoted by the symbol $\bar{G}$ (G bar), the bar above the G indicating 'average'. We shall consider average gradient in more detail later (paragraph 2.95).

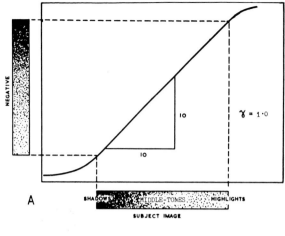

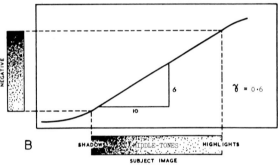

Fig. 2.21 Examples of gamma and contrast relationship. (A) On a negative of gamma 1.0 the contrast (tonal range) of the negative is equal to that of the subject's image. (B) On a negative of gamma 0.6 the contrast of the negative is less than that of the subject's image. If the contrast of the negative is greater than that of the subject's image, the value of gamma will be greater than 1.0.

2.86 *Effect on gamma and $\bar{G}$ of emulsion characteristics.* The value of gamma or $\bar{G}$ depends chiefly on the inherent contrast-producing characteristics of the photographic emulsion, which are incorporated during manufacture. For example, emulsions are made so that under their standard processing conditions they will produce a low, a medium or a high value of gamma or $\bar{G}$ contrast (see Figure 2.22).

2.87 *Effect on gamma and $\bar{G}$ of development variation.* Different developers and development times or conditions will vary the values within the range of inherent contrast. For any photographic emulsion the value of gamma and average gradient will increase up to a limiting value as development time increases, as shown in Figure 2.23. This subject is dealt with in more detail later.

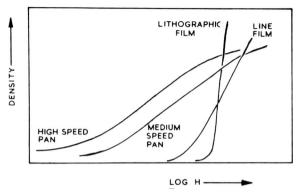

Fig. 2.22 The effect on gamma and $\bar{G}$ of the inherent characteristics of several typical film materials.

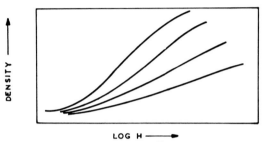

Fig. 2.23 The effect on gamma and $\bar{G}$ of different developers or development times.

2.88 *Effect on gamma and $\bar{G}$ of exposure conditions.* In practical photography the gamma and $\bar{G}$ of a negative may be affected by camera and lens flare (explained later) and by the exposure settings (lens aperture and shutter speed), which determine what part of the characteristic curve is used. Gamma and $\bar{G}$ contrast may also be affected slightly by the predominant colour of the light used in exposure. The effect depends on the emulsion type, but generally blue and ultraviolet radiations produce a lower value of gamma than white light, and red light produces a higher gamma. For

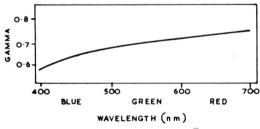

Fig. 2.24 The possible effect on gamma and $\bar{G}$ of the predominant colour of light used in the exposure of a typical panchromatic film, sometimes called the 'gamma/lambda effect'.

example, exposures made through coloured filters may process to a higher or lower gamma than expected. Terms often used to describe this are the 'gradient/wavelength effect' and the 'gamma/lambda effect'. Lambda is the Greek letter (λ) which is used as a symbol to denote the wavelength of light and other electromagnetic radiation. Although important in sensitometry, the variation within the visible spectrum is small and this effect can usually be ignored in general black-and-white photography. Figure 2.24 shows the general effect.

Gamma and Ḡ contrast are also affected by very short duration, high-illuminance exposures, and very long duration, low-illuminance exposures, due to reciprocity failure (explained in Chapter 8).

Derivative curves

2.89 In order that the contrast-reproducing properties of a photographic material at different exposure levels can be more clearly shown on a graph, the data on the characteristic curve may be used to obtain (derive) another curve, called a derivative curve (Figure 2.25). This shows the gradient at each part of the characteristic curve plotted against the log exposure values. The peak of the curve shows the gamma value obtained.

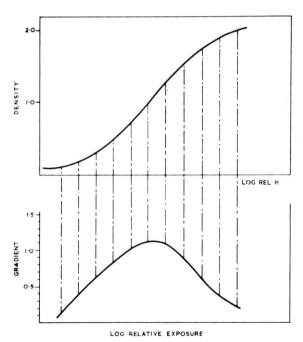

Fig. 2.25 A characteristic curve (above) and its derived curve (below), showing how gradient (and therefore the contrast produced) changes with log exposure. The peak of the derived curve shows the gamma value obtained.

Paragraph 2.82 describes a method of measuring gradient.

Similar derivative curves can be plotted, for example, for one type of film under different processing conditions or to compare the contrast-reproducing properties or the density differences of two different films.

Self-assessment questions

2.90 If you want to test your learning, write out answers to the following questions:

(a) Which part of the characteristic curve is used to measure gamma?
(b) Why can't the toe or shoulder be used to measure gamma?
(c) What is the 'contrast' of an image received on a film during exposure, and how is it found and expressed?
(d) What is the 'contrast' of a negative and how is it found and expressed?
(e) What does gamma indicate and how is it found and expressed?
(f) Explain how gamma is affected by progressive increases in development time.
(g) A negative is required to have a contrast and range of densities exactly equal to the contrast and range of log illuminance of the subject image. With reference to the characteristic curve of the film used, how will it be exposed and to what gamma will it be developed?
(h) What factors, other than development, can affect the gamma?
(i) What type of emulsion will give a high gamma and what type a low gamma?
(j) Draw several different characteristic curves on a piece of plain paper. Draw vertical lines from the ends of the straight-line region to the log exposure axis, and from the ends horizontally to the density axis. Work out the gamma by finding the slope, i.e. dividing negative density range by log exposure range.
(k) Using a scaled ruler, check your findings by the 'counting units' method (see paragraph 2.82).
(l) On a piece of graph paper, trace a copy of the curve shown in Figure 2.12, then produce a derivative curve showing gradient plotted against log rel *H*.

Useful log exposure range and resolving power

2.91 We know that only part of the film characteristic curve is of practical use in photography. In general terms this is the upper two-thirds of the toe and the lower part of the straight line, which we have considered previously as the 'correct exposure region'. (see Figures 2.17 and 2.18 diagram 4). The limits of this region are thus the lowest and highest useful points on the characteristic curve. The distance along the log exposure axis between these two points on the characteristic curve is known as the 'useful log exposure range'. However, such points cannot be defined precisely. The upper limit of the useful log exposure range may be governed by decreasing resolving power caused by increasing density, granularity, and the increase in image spread or scatter (often called 'irradiation') which usually occurs well before the shoulder is reached.

The lower limit of the useful log exposure range generally includes part of the toe, and the shape of the curve here is linked in practice with the shape of the characteristic curve of the paper on which the negative is printed (explained later). The lower limit is governed by decreasing resolving power caused by the lowering of contrast as the curve flattens. Figure 2.27 illustrates the general position of these limits.

The resolving power of an emulsion is important when considering the useful log exposure range, so we need to consider exactly what it means and how it can be determined.

2.92   Resolving power is an expression of the ability of a photographic material to record and reproduce very fine image detail. It is of particular importance, for example, in aerial photography, where very small images, often of low contrast, are to be recorded. Numerical values of resolving power, are usually obtained by recording a very small image of a test target on the film (often called a 'test chart' or 'test object'). a typical target consists of patterns of bars or lines and equal width spaces, sets of which get progressively smaller, as shown in Figure 2.26. After exposure and processing, the film is examined under magnification and the value of resolving power is given as the maximum number of lines and spaces (called 'line pairs' or 'cycles') that can just be distinguished per millimetre. The value is usually expressed as, for example, 50 lines/mm or 50 cycles/mm.

Resolving power depends chiefly on the thickness and light-scattering effect (turbidity) of the emulsion during exposure, the granular structure (granularity) of the image after processing, and in addition on:

(a)   The exposure level, as shown by the position of exposure on the characteristic curve.
(b)   The type and degree of development given.
(c)   The formation of and the contrast between the lines and spaces of the test target.

The measured value of resolving power depends to a great extent on the contrast of the test target used, being greater with high-contrast targets. Therefore values of resolving power for targets of differing contrast are often given. This enables the user to select a resolving-power value relative to the conditions expected in practical use.

Resolving power/log *H* curves, showing the values obtained at different levels of exposure, can

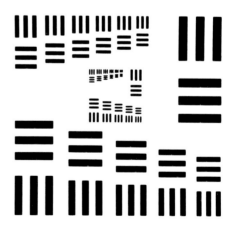

Fig. 2.26 The pattern of part of a typical high-contrast resolving power test target. Such targets usually consist of clear bars on a darker background in order to minimize light flare effects during exposure. The image of the target on the test film will be greatly reduced in size.

be produced for a particular set of conditions. Figure 2.28 shows an example of this.

Resolving power values describe only the limit of resolution, so when a study of the role of a film in a photographic system is being carried out, it is often preferable to specify the film resolution in terms of a 'modulation transfer function curve'. This is a curve that in effect indicates the contrast response of a film to different spacings of images, from the largest down to the smallest that can be resolved. This subject is considered in more detail in paragraphs 2.101 to 2.110, and also in Chapter 12.

2.93 *Useful log exposure range for general-purpose photography.* The exposure meters used in general-purpose photography are designed and calibrated so that, with correct use, the exposure range will be placed just above the lower limit of the useful log exposure range (Figure 2.27). The useful log exposure range can only be considered in general terms as it is dependent on:

(a) The type of emulsion.
(b) The type and degree of development.
(c) The sort of photography for which the film is to be used.

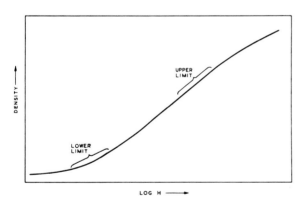

Fig. 2.27 Useful log exposure range for general photography. The limits of the useful exposure range cannot be defined precisely. In general, correct exposure and processing are obtained when the darkest shadow is $D\,0.1$ above fog $(D_{\min})$ and the lightest highlight on the lower straight-line region. The actual position of the highlights depends on the contrast of the subject and on the characteristics and processing of the film.

For example, because of increasing image spread and granularity, the upper limit may be lower for negatives that are to be enlarged than for negatives that are to be contact printed. In the majority of cases, the lower limit is taken to be the speed point $(D\,0.1$ above fog). Therefore, with correct exposure

and processing, the darkest shadow is positioned on or just above the speed point, on the toe of the characteristic curve. The middle tones and highlights are then positioned on the upper toe and lower straight-line region of the curve, depending on how far the exposure range of the subject image extends.

2.94 *Useful log exposure range for aerial photography.* In vertical aerial photography and for any long-range photography, particularly from high altitudes above the terrain, the earth's atmosphere has a considerable contrast-reducing effect. In these conditions the range of luminances presented to the camera is much less than in low-level aerial or general-purpose photography, and the ground detail is smaller. Under such conditions it is necessary to achieve both a high contrast and the best possible resolution from the film in order to record the fine detail. We can see from Figure 2.28 that the best resolution is obtained at the bottom of the straight-line region. This is the part where

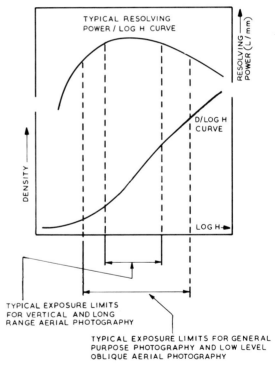

Fig. 2.28 Comparison of a typical useful log exposure range for general-purpose and for aerial photography. Because of the general low-contrast subject conditions in vertical or long-range aerial photography, and the need for high resolution in order to record detail, the useful log exposure range is less than in general-purpose photography. Exposure is limited to the lower straight-line region, and the negatives are usually processed to produce a higher contrast.

contrast is at a maximum at the same time as density is at a minimum. Therefore, camera exposure should be such that the log exposure range is placed on or near the bottom part of the straight-line region of the characteristic curve. Beyond this part, resolution falls off rapidly towards both ends of the characteristic curve. Below the region, reduction in resolution is shown by lowering of contrast as the curve flattens; above it, resolution is diminished by the increase in image spread and granularity as density increases. Thus in any aspect of photography where detail is required, and particularly in aerial photography, it is the resolving power of the film that controls the upper and lower limits of the useful log exposure range. From this we can deduce that the ability of a film to reproduce the image of very fine detail is, for the most part, governed by two factors: the contrast produced, and the granular structure of the exposed and processed emulsion.

Average gradient systems

2.95   As part of the toe of the characteristic curve is often used in practice, the term 'gamma' (which relates only to the straight-line region of the curve) cannot be properly used to describe the contrast produced (although it often is in photographic literature). Furthermore, there may be no truly straight line at all on many characteristic curves. To give an indication of the contrast-reproducing abilities of a photographic emulsion in such circumstances, a gamma value may be replaced by a $\bar{G}$ (G bar) value. For example, the $\bar{G}$ of general-purpose black-and-white negative films is defined as the slope of a line joining points on the characteristic curve at a density of 0.1 above D_{min} (base plus fog) and at a point 1.5 log units in the direction of greater exposure (see Figure 4.1). The numerical value of the $\bar{G}$ of a film is always less than that of gamma, and like gamma it is usually assessed to an accuracy of about 0.02. Sometimes $\bar{G}$ is described as beta, or the beta value, this being the German equivalent.

A related measure, but less restrictively defined, is the average gradient. This is the slope of a line joining two points on the characteristic curve representing the extremes of the density scale of the processed material (Figure 2.29). An average gradient value can be used to describe the average contrast produced in a particular negative or in a sensitometric strip. In sensitometry and photographic literature the symbol $\bar{G}$ is often used to indicate average gradient.

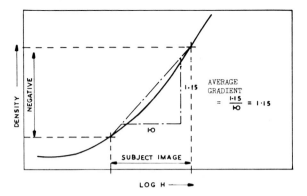

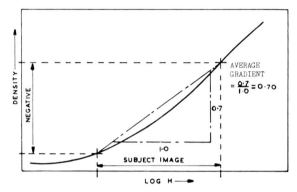

Fig. 2.29 Examples of average gradient, which is a measure of the slope of a line between two points on the characteristic curve. For any one negative, the line is from the lowest to the highest image density. The numerical value of average gradient can be obtained by the method described in paragraph 2.82, or by dividing the density range of the negative by the log exposure range of the subject image.

2.96   *$\bar{G}$ of the useful log exposure range.* $\bar{G}$ is used to describe the contrast-reproducing potential of unexposed films. It is expressed as the slope value of a line joining specified high and low points of a specified 'average' useful log exposure range for films. In this context, $\bar{G}$ contrast is linked with the speed determination of the film and is thus an indication to the photographer of the contrast that may be obtained when the film is used. This relationship is explained in more detail in Chapter 4.

If many characteristic curves have to be measured to find specific $\bar{G}$ values, a device similar to the gammeter described in paragraph 2.83 can be constructed. If it is made with a base line equal to the specified average log exposure range, $\bar{G}$ can be measured directly from the curve. For general-purpose films this average log exposure range is usually 1.5.

2.97 *Contrast Index (CI).* An alternative system that may be used is that of 'contrast index', which is a specific method of expressing average gradient for general-purpose films and is particularly applicable to high-contrast materials. The system involves the use of a special transparent overlay in the form of a protractor which, when placed in a prescribed position, describes two arcs on the characteristic curve, separated by a distance equal

to 2.0 log H (or density) units (Figure 2.30). The contrast index is then the slope value of a line joining the two points cut by the arcs. Like $\bar{G}$ it can be used to indicate the contrast capabilities of unexposed films.

A 'contrast index meter' which enables a quick assessment of film contrast to be made is available from Kodak. However, for most purposes sufficiently accurate CI values can be determined from characteristic curves of relatively low slope, by drawing an arc 2.0 log H units long, from the speed point (D 0.1 above fog) to cut the curve. The slope value of the line joining the two points is the contrast index. This is shown in Figure 2.31.

2.98 *Average gradient in sensitometric testing.* $\bar{G}$ contrast and contrast index produce similar but not identical values of slope. To avoid possible confusion, it is suggested that in sensitometry average gradient or $\bar{G}$ be used, either as related to a particular situation or as specified for the film or material under test (described in Chapter 4).

Exposure latitude

2.99 The term 'exposure latitude' means any tolerance that exists in choosing an exposure level that will satisfactorily record the subject luminance range. Strictly, if a print with the very best quality of detail is required from a negative, there will be

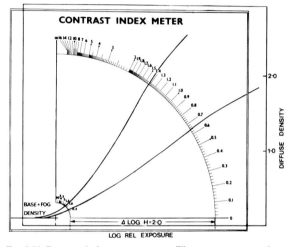

Fig. 2.30 Contrast index measurement. The transparent overlay is placed on the characteristic curve with its base-plus-fog line on the base-plus-fog level of the curve. It is then moved to the left or right until each arc intersects the curve at the same value. This value is the contrast index.

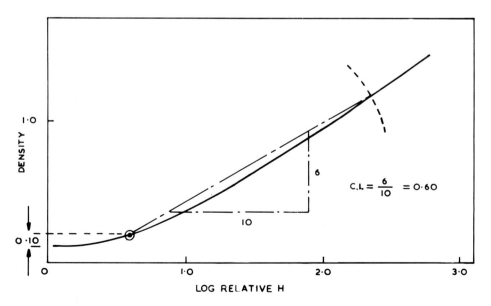

Fig. 2.31 An example of the method of measuring an approximate contrast index.

no latitude in the exposure of the negative. It can be seen from the resolving power curve in Figure 2.28 that the highest quality result can only be obtained by using the small area under the peak of the curve. A change in camera exposure will shift the whole log exposure range to the left or right and cause either shadows or highlights to lose resolution. Nevertheless, in most general photography this lower quality is acceptable, provided that the final print definition is satisfactory. Therefore in general-purpose photography exposure latitude can be expressed as: 'the number of times by which the minimum camera exposure needed to give a negative with adequate shadow detail can be multiplied, and still give a negative with satisfactory highlight detail'. For this purpose, latitude is usually rated in camera lens *f*-stops. Latitude can also be expressed in logarithmic terms as 'the difference between the useful log exposure range of the film and the log illuminance range of the subject image'. For example, consider Figure 2.32.

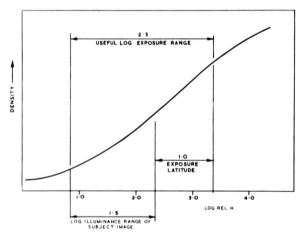

Fig. 2.32 Exposure latitude in general-purpose photography. Exposure latitude indicates the tolerance in the exposure that may be given without degrading the resultant image. The extent of the latitude depends on the luminance range of the subject photographed and the useful exposure range of the film. It can be described in 'lens stops' or in logarithmic terms.

The useful log exposure range is 2.5, the log illuminance range of the subject image is 1.5, giving an exposure latitude of $2.5 - 1.5 = 1.0$ log (10 times, or just over 3 lens stops). From this example we can see that exposure latitude depends mainly on the log illuminance range of the subject image. If this is equal to the useful log exposure range, there is no exposure latitude.

Exposure latitude depends also on the gradient of the characteristic curve, as shown in Figure 2.33,

which depicts in general terms the exposure latitude of different types of film. If the gradient is low or can be lowered, the exposure latitude is increased.

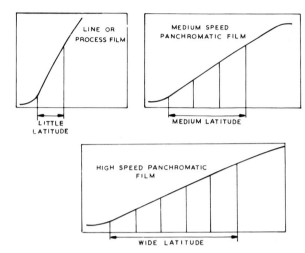

Fig. 2.33 The general exposure latitude of representative films. The lower the gradient, the greater the latitude.

The facility of a low-gradient characteristic curve is utilized in the mass photography market where correct exposure is often a hit-or-miss affair. Black-and-white and colour negative films are designed so that they can be machine processed to produce negatives having characteristic curves of fairly low gradient. This action elongates the useful log exposure range and thus extends the exposure latitude of the films. Lowering the curve gradient also minimizes the difference between negatives that have received widely different levels of exposure. This enables them to be successfully printed in automatic printing machines. The results may not be of optimum quality but they are considered to be satisfactory for the mass market.

2.100 *Exposure latitude in aerial photography.* In aerial photography the exposure latitude of the film is restricted by the need to resolve very fine image detail. The resolving power curve of the film emulsion passes through a maximum (see Figure 2.28) and indicates that, even with the low contrast of subjects met in long-range aerial photography, there is little latitude in exposure. Quite a small variation from the optimum will give a loss of resolution, so correct exposure is of paramount importance in aerial photography and in any photography that involves the reproduction of fine detail. The exposure latitude of a film depends on:

(a) The log illuminance range of the subject image.

(b) The average gradient ($\bar{G}$) of the characteristic curve (which may present a long or a short useful log exposure range).

(c) The resolving power characteristics of the emulsion.

Reproduction of fine detail

2.101   In practice, the image of fine detail may be distorted slightly before it reaches the film, owing to the inability of the camera lens to form a perfect image and (particularly in aerial photography) to atmospheric conditions and possible camera or aircraft movements during exposure. There is also a lower limit to the size of image that the film itself can adequately record; as images get smaller, the quality and accuracy of reproduction decreases. Degradation of the image received by the film is caused by three main factors:

(a) The turbidity (light-scattering property) of the emulsion during exposure, causing the image to be scattered and spread out as it enters the emulsion (Figure 2.34). This effect is often called 'irradiation'.

(b) The uneven distribution of fresh developer within the emulsion, causing irregular development of detail and 'adjacency effects' (Figure 2.35). These effects are minimized, but not normally avoided by using a correct level of agitation and an energetic developer. Further degradation or distortion of the image structure can be caused by incorrect processing techniques, including washing and drying, which may cause an actual shift in the position of the grains forming the image of fine detail See paragraphs 6.7 to 6.14.

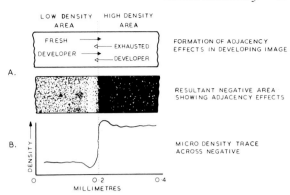

Fig. 2.35 (A) The formation and result of adjacency effects between low- and high-density areas during development of a negative. (B) Representation of a microdensitometer trace made across the same area of the negative. A low level of agitation allows cross-diffusion between exhausted and fresh developer in adjacent areas of low- and high-density. The contrast between the edges of these areas is thus emphasized.

(c)   The granular structure of the processed film, which tends to break up the visible image.

We can consider these three factors and their effects in a little more detail.

2.102   *Light scatter during exposure.* In general, exposure from the highlights of a subject penetrates and spreads into the emulsion more than exposure from the shadows (Figure 2.34). Penetration and spreading are also greater with a thicker emulsion (a typical emulsion is about $\frac{1}{100}$ mm thick). On larger, evenly exposed areas of the material the spreading and scattering of light during exposure is of little consequence. With correct development, the resultant density is still fairly uniform and only the edges of the areas show spread into the surrounding parts, but close-spaced, small-detailed

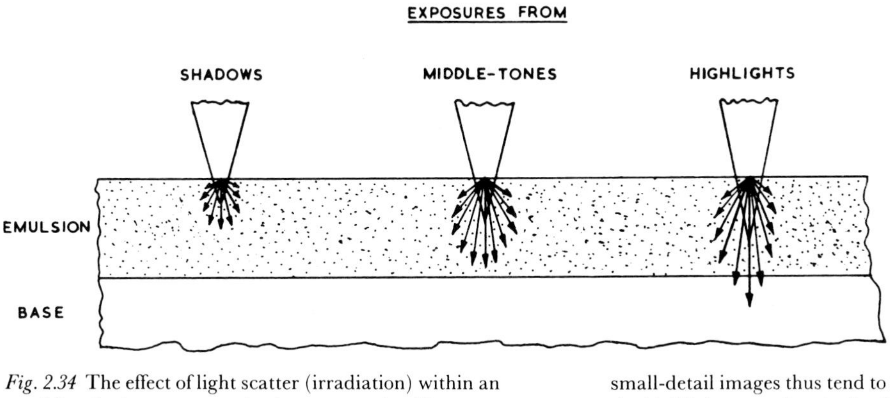

EXPOSURES FROM

Fig. 2.34 The effect of light scatter (irradiation) within an emulsion during exposure. As the exposure level increases, so penetration and scatter in the emulsion increases. Close-spaced,

small-detail images thus tend to spread into each other more in the highlight areas than in the shadows. This further reduces the contrast between them.

images spread into each other, and thus the contrast between an image and its surrounds is reduced.

This reduction in contrast worsens as image size decreases, so the contrast of very fine detail on a negative will be less than that indicated by the gradient of the characteristic curve (see Figure 2.36). This is found providing that development adjacency effects are not evident. Such effects may in fact cause a slight increase in the contrast of some of the fine detail.

2.103 *Adjacency and other effects in development.* Adjacency effects (or neighbourhood effects) are emphasized by low levels of agitation, which in turn cause uneven development. In these conditions, exhausted (inhibited) developer from a high-density area diffuses into an adjacent low-density area and retards its development. At the same time, fresh developer from the low-density area diffuses into the high-density area and increases its development. Thus the resulting contrast between adjacent areas is greater than it would otherwise be, particularly on the boundaries between the areas. Figure 2.35 illustrates this effect schematically, and shows the result of a micro-densitometer trace made across the boundary between adjacent areas. (A microdensitometer is explained in paragraph 12.4).

When adjacency effects are formed at the edges of large areas, the resulting light and dark lines are called 'Mackie lines'. When adjacency effects are applied to small, equally-exposed but different-sized and isolated images, the densities will vary; the smaller images having the higher general density. This is called the 'Eberhard effect'.

Adjacency effects may also cause a reduction in size and an increase in the separation of very small adjacent images, owing to a reduction in developer activity in the area between them. This can produce errors when precise measurements are made on a photograph, and is called the 'Kostinsky effect'.

Adjacency effects can be of value, and are often utilized when processing in high-definition or 'acutance' developers. Because of the emphasis on the density differences at edges, adjacency effects improve the apparent sharpness or the acutance of the image. The terms 'sharpness' and 'acutance' are explained in paragraph 2.107. As mentioned previously, adjacency effects may be present, but are minimized when adequate development and fairly vigorous agitation is given. They are also minimized by using an energetic phenidone–

hydroquinone (PQ) developer, because phenidone is an excellent developing agent for maintaining a constant rate of development, even when partly exhausted.

Similarly acting effects can be used to advantage with colour films and with chromogenically developed black-and-white films. Special development-inhibitor-releasing (DIR) couplers, which are incorporated in the film emulsion, react with the developer. One effect of this reaction is to improve the granularity and acutance of the resultant dye images. See paragraphs 4.18, 11.10 and 11.79, and Appendix D.

2.104 *Effect of a granular image structure.* The processed images of a conventional black-and-white negative are made up of irregularly shaped clumps of metallic silver grains (a non-homogeneous structure). In normal viewing this is not apparent, but under magnification the granular structure becomes visible. An evenly exposed and processed small area of the negative can be seen as an area of varying density, and the visual effect of this variation is called 'graininess'. The terms used, graininess and granularity, have different meanings so they should not be confused. Graininess is subjective, as it relates to the visual appearance of the granular structure in the image. Graininess increases with density from zero up to a maximum at D 0.3 or so and then beyond this region it decreases. Granularity is an objective quantity obtained by measuring (with a micro-densitometer) the fluctuations in density over a small evenly exposed area, caused by the granular structure of the image. Granularity increases with density from zero through the applicable density range.

It is the irregular granular structure that tends to break up the image of small objects, and as images on the negative decrease in size, so their definition deteriorates until they are no longer discernible (resolved). We should be aware that it is not so much the size of the grains that influence the quality of detail, but how the granular structure is formed in the negative. It is one of the emulsion maker's aims (with both black-and-white and colour films) to initiate a granular structure that will cause the minimum amount of light scatter and thus have a minimum effect on the resolution of fine detail. A method of comparing the effect of the granular structure of processed films is described in paragraph 2.122.

2.105 *Reproduction of detail in colour films.* The structure of images in colour film, and in black-and-white chromogenically developed film, is such that the granular structure is different from that of a black-and-white silver film. This is because the original clumps of opaque silver grains are replaced by larger or smaller, partially transparent, colour-dye grains or 'clouds', which are also less sharp-edged than those of silver. Nevertheless, colour and black-and-white chromogenically developed films still have a granular structure which gives them a grainy appearance under magnification. Because of their emulsion construction and the colour processing techniques used, such films tend to show a decrease in granularity as exposure is increased (over a limited range), the converse of that which would be obtained with silver images. All the other factors with regard to the reproduction of fine detail on black-and-white films, such as irradiation, adjacency effects and granular structure, also apply to colour films.

2.106 *The characteristic curve as an indicator of fine-detail contrast.* The characteristic curve of a photographic emulsion is obtained from exposure to the large uniform-density areas of the sensitometer step wedge, and density readings are made of wide areas of each step. The gradient of the characteristic curve therefore indicates the contrast of, or between, large areas (often called 'macro contrast'). The contrast of very fine detail (often called 'micro contrast') is usually lower. This is mainly due to light scatter in the emulsion during exposure (see paragraph 2.102). Micro contrast can be considered as being that within areas less

than about 0.5 mm in diameter. However, this does not reduce the importance of the characteristic curve as an indicator of fine-detail contrast. The contrast of fine detail is generally lower than that shown; but increases or decreases in the gradient of the characteristic curve produce similar increases or decreases in the contrast of very fine detail. Figure 2.36 shows a representation of the contrast of very small fine-detail images.

Sharpness and acutance

2.107 The visual appearance of the edges of detail in a photographic image can be described by their degree of sharpness. For example, when images are visually compared, one may be seen to be sharper than another. Because sharpness depends on visual observation and is not an actual measurement, the assessment is said to be subjective. There is sometimes a need to measure and express the ability of a processed emulsion to produce a sharp image, and this objective measure of sharpness is called 'acutance'.

2.108 Acutance for different exposure (or density) levels can be determined by contact printing an opaque knife-edge onto the photographic emulsion, using a direct (parallel) light beam and controlled exposure, so that any spread of the exposing light is caused only by the turbidity of the emulsion itself (Figure 2.37). The spread of the

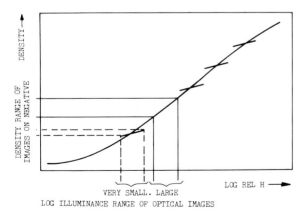

Fig. 2.36 A representation, superimposed on a normal film characteristic curve, of the effect on negative contrast of typical very small fine-detail images. The effective gradient or gamma of very fine detail is lower than that of larger images, owing to the small images spreading into each other, particularly during exposure.

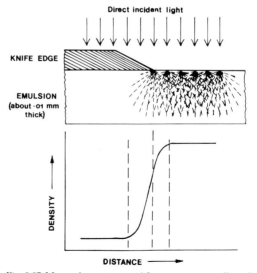

Fig. 2.37 Measuring acutance. After exposure to a direct light beam and development, the image is scanned on a microdensitometer. The slope characteristics of the resulting density/distance curve are used to determine the acutance for a particular density level.

exposing light in the emulsion causes the image of the knife-edge to be spread out, thus producing a measurable density change over a short distance. This is measured by using an automatic recording microdensitometer (see paragraph 12.4), which scans slowly across the border and records the density changes as a density/distance curve on a graph. A large density change over a short distance indicates a high acutance, and vice versa. Notice in Figure 2.37 that density starts to decrease before the knife-edge position is reached. This is because, over most parts of the exposed portion, density is caused by direct incident light plus the light scattered in the emulsion from either side; but near the edge there is little or no light scattered from the unexposed side. A numerical value for acutance can be obtained by measuring the gradient of several equal sections of the curve, squaring these values and finding the average of the squares. This figure is then divided by the density change $(D_{max} - D_{min})$ to obtain the acutance value. Gradient measurements are made at intervals between the two points (D_{max} and D_{min}) where the slope of the curve equals 0.005 when the distance is measured in micrometres (i.e. where it is just perceptible).

2.109   *Photographic definition.*   In a photographic system the acutance and resolving power of the photographic material, together with the quality of the image-forming optical system, affect what is called the 'definition' of a photographic image. Definition indicates the fineness and clarity of detail as seen by the viewer.

2.110   *The modulation transfer function.*   The combined effect on detail reproduction of the emulsion characteristics and the response to exposure can best be investigated and shown as a 'modulation transfer function curve', as mentioned previously in paragraph 2.92. This curve indicates the change that occurs in the quality and definition of detail reproduction as images become smaller. The combined effect can be shown also in a general manner on a gradient/log exposure curve (Figure 2.25) as an additional curve or curves for micro contrast. The concept of modulation transfer is considered in more detail in Chapter 12.

Comparative sensitometry

2.111   'Absolute sensitometry' (Appendix B) describes the sort of sensitometry that is used in film manufacturers' and other laboratories, for exam-

ple, to determine the precise speed of a film. It requires a knowledge of the definite colour quality of the light and the exact exposure in lux seconds that has been given in the sensitometer. However, for the majority of sensitometric requirements, we do not need to know the precise exposure conditions. As long as the exposures relate to practical conditions and are constant from test to test, comparing the results produced by different films, developers, development times etc. will give the information we need. This is known as 'comparative sensitometry', and we can consider some examples now.

Speed comparison

2.112   Photographic emulsions differ in their sensitivity to light. If two different films are exposed so that they produce identical negatives after identical processing, the one that requires less exposure is said to have a higher speed. There are several methods of finding and expressing the speed of a film, each depending on how the film is to be used; but with all speed systems an increase in speed shows as a shift of the characteristic curve towards the left along the log exposure axis. It is suggested that you should work out the logic of this yourself. Some of the speed-indicating methods used for films are described in Chapter 4.

2.113   The difference between the relative speeds of two or more films can be found easily by comparative sensitometry. Furthermore, if the

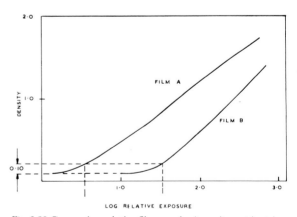

Fig. 2.38 Comparing relative film speeds. A sensitometric strip is produced under identical conditions of exposure and processing for each film, and characteristic curves are constructed. The distance along the log exposure axis between the two speed points indicates the difference in speed. If the speed value of one film is already known, the speed of the other can be found.

speed value or exposure index of one of the films is known, the difference found can be used to assess the speed value of the other film. The relative speeds of two hypothetical films are compared in figure 2.38, using the speed point for general-purpose black-and-white films (D 0.1 above fog level) as a point of comparison. To find the difference in speed between two (or more) films, carry out the following procedure:

(a)   Produce a sensitometric strip on each film, using identical conditions of exposure and processing.
(b)   Construct characteristic curves and mark in the speed points.
(c)   Draw a vertical line from each speed point to the log relative exposure axis.
(d)   The distance between the two marked points in log exposure units indicates the difference in speeds, and the antilog of this is the speed difference in arithmetic units.

2.114   *Other sensitometric comparisons.* A similar method can be used to compare other factors such as contrast reproduction, the effect of different developers, changes in agitation, and after-treatments such as reduction and intensification. We shall consider some of these later under their relevant headings.

Filter factor determination

2.115   If a subject with neutral grey tones is photographed on the same type of film, first with a filter and then without a filter, there will be a difference in densities of the two negatives. The difference in density will indicate the exposure effect of the filter. The same effect can be obtained by making exposures using a sensitometer with and without a filter in position and giving the samples identical processing.

2.116   The procedure for determining a filter exposure factor is similar to that for comparing film speeds, except that a different point of comparison is used. Characteristic curves are plotted for both cases (Figure 2.39), and the filter exposure factor for the type of film used is found by measuring the distance along the log relative exposure axis between the curves at some average value of density (typically 1.0). This method is valid, even though the slope of the 'filtered' curve may be slightly different from that of the 'unfiltered' curve (see paragraph 2.88).

2.117   *Using a camera to find filter factors.* A practical method of determining a filter exposure factor, where a filter may have to be used under specific conditions, is to expose two pieces of film in a camera focused on a 'grey scale'. One exposure is made with and the other without the filter in position. The image of each step of the scale must, of course, be big enough to be easily measured on the densitometer. The reflection densities of the grey scale are plotted as a log relative exposure scale, and short curves can then be plotted from readings of the processed negatives. An average density point comparison can then be made to determine the filter exposure factor.

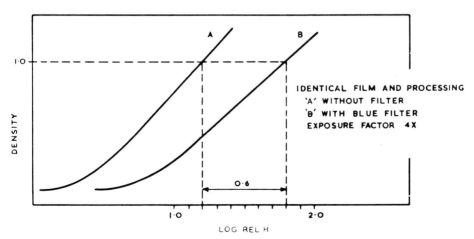

Fig. 2.39 Finding a filter exposure factor. A sensitometric strip is produced for each film using identical conditions of exposure and processing, except that one film is exposed through a filter. Characteristic curves are then drawn and the distance along the log *H* axis between the same average density (typically 1.0) on each curve is measured. The antilog of this value is the filter exposure factor. Notice that the curve slopes differ slightly.

Care must be taken to ensure that for each exposure the grey scale receives the same uniform illuminance and that camera lens flare is minimized by using a dark background and a lens hood.

Lens flare has a degrading effect on the image formed on the film in a camera and will modify the shape of the characteristic curve, particularly in the shadow regions. This effect is considered in more detail in paragraphs 7.5 to 7.7.

Shutter speed comparison

2.118 We can use a similar method to test the relationship between two or more shutter speeds. For example, changing the shutter speed from ¹⁄₆₀ second to ¹⁄₃₀ second should cause the characteristic curve to shift 0.3 units to the left along the log exposure axis. In practice several exposures should be made at each shutter speed to ensure the reliability of the test.

Using a transparent overlay

2.119 In comparative sensitometry we often need to compare a previously unknown factor with an already known and standard result. If this is to be done frequently, it may be convenient to plot the 'unknown' on a piece of tracing paper, using the same scales of D and log H. It can then be used, with the scales in register, as an overlay on the standard characteristic curve. The alternative is of course to have the standard itself as a transparency and to lay it over the plotted 'unknown' result. As both are to the same scale, differences can be easily seen, and measured if necessary.

Comparative sensitometry in process control

2.120 Comparative sensitometry is used as a routine procedure for checking the activity of processing solutions and conditions. For example, when processing quantities of film over a period of time it is necessary to have regular checks on the activity of the developer and the consistency of processing. We know that changes in development will affect the density and average gradient characteristics of a negative or sensitometric strip. Therefore, if identically exposed strips of the same type of film are processed at intervals, any differences in the results produced will indicate a change in processing conditions. These checks are carried out by processing standard pre-exposed sensitometric strips, called 'process control strips', at regular intervals either before or together with

the normal films. The densities on the processed control strips are then measured and compared with the densities of a known standard control strip (called a 'reference strip') which has been correctly processed.

2.121 In process control the information is usually wanted fairly quickly so that any necessary remedial action can be taken without delay. Therefore, instead of constructing a characteristic curve for each strip a simplified comparison is made. For example, only two densities need be measured and compared, one a little above the speed point and the other a higher density near the upper limit of the average gradient. Any difference between the density values of the control strip and those of the known standard reference strip, will indicate a change in processing conditions. Changes in the speed produced can be assessed from differences in the lower density, and changes in contrast will be indicated by differences in the range between the two densities. This method of quick comparison is used in most process control systems and may be obtained automatically by using a computer-controlled densitometer. Figure 2.40 represents the comparison of a processed control strip with a standard reference strip where both speed and contrast are a little below that of the standard aimed for.

In routine processes the differences in the density values between the measured control strip and the known standard reference strip are plotted in terms of plus or minus on a progressive chart. The procedure only takes a few seconds and thus

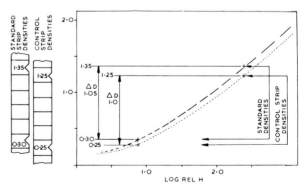

Fig. 2.40 A representation of the comparative sensitometry used in process control monitoring. For the quick acquisition of information, only two densities, a high and a low, need be measured and compared with an already known standard reference. Changes in speed can be assessed from differences in the low density, and changes in contrast from differences in the range between the high and low. The dotted and dashed lines indicate the probable positions of the full characteristic curves.

provides a quick, reliable and standard check on the state of processing. If more precise information is needed, a full characteristic curve can be constructed. Process quality control monitoring is described in more detail in Chapter 6.

Comparing the effect of the granular structure

2.122 The effect in printing of the granular structure of processed films, or of the same film at different densities, can be compared by making negatives on the material and viewing a series of enlargements made from them. However, with this type of examination the detail of the photographic image can confuse the comparison of graininess. A more satisfactory practical procedure to compare the effect of film granularity on the print can be carried out as follows:

(a) Expose the film samples to the same type of uniform and unfocused light, e.g. light from an enlarger. The exposure will need to be adjusted so that the required densities are obtained after processing. Four densities covering the region 0.3 to 1.0 should suffice for an overall comparison.
(b) Process the films together, using the same conditions for all.
(c) From the dry film, cut out small areas of each density, mark them for identification and mount them edge-to-edge (butt-joined) on a piece of glass so that they are held flat in the same plane. Mask any clear parts.
(d) Enlarge the assembly to, say, 20 times linear or more, onto a piece of hard-grade printing paper. Expose to obtain an image of each patch at a low middle density of, say, 0.6 after processing (or expose to give several steps of varying middle density).
(e) Compare the results under a good viewing light. The grainy appearance of the enlarged print is a negative image of the structure of the original sample. During viewing, any distractions such as the white borders of the print may need to be masked off so that they do not influence the eye.

The comparison can be helped if the viewing distance is varied, as at a certain distance the graininess may just be perceptible on one sample but not on the other. The minimum distance at which graininess is not visible is called the 'blending distance'.

2.123 It is of course essential in comparative sensitometry that any differences found in the results are caused only by the factor being investigated. All the other factors that can affect the results must be kept identical for each sample.

Self-assessment questions

2.124 If you want to test your learning, write out answers to the following questions:

(a) What factors decide the upper and lower limits of the useful log exposure range of a film used for general-purpose photography?
(b) What are the two main factors that decide the upper and lower limits of the useful log exposure range when a film is used for high-altitude aerial photography?
(c) How is $\bar{G}$ contrast defined and why is it generally used instead of gamma?
(d) The ability of a film emulsion to record properly the images of objects decreases as the images get smaller. Why is this so?
(e) List the essential steps you would take when carrying out a test to compare the speeds of two unknown panchromatic films.
(f) List at least three other comparisons you could make by using a procedure similar to that of question (e).
(g) Referring to Figure 2.38, why is a density of 0.1 used as a speed comparison point?
(h) In Figure 2.38, which is the faster film, and how many times faster is it?
(i) Describe how you would find the exposure factor of a yellow filter, using a camera.
(j) Referring to Figure 2.39, what factor may have caused the 'filtered' curve to have a different slope from the 'unfiltered' curve?
(k) If Figure 2.39 represented a comparison test of camera shutter speeds and curve A was produced by a duration of $1/15$ second, what was the shutter speed for B?

3

Effect of processing variations

3.1   So far we have considered the information we can get from single characteristic curves of films that have been processed under one particular development condition. Now we need to consider the effect on the curves of varying the processing conditions, so that we can obtain further useful information on the behaviour of photographic material. The main variable factors that influence the effect of a developer are development time, temperature and agitation. The state of the developer, whether it is fresh or partly exhausted, will of course also affect the result. Another variation involves modifying the photographic process so that, instead of obtaining a negative image, a positive image is produced directly. We should understand these effects and procedures, and their basic sensitometry. We can also consider how the effects of incorrect exposure and processing may be remedied, and how these remedies can change and improve the characteristics of photographic materials.

We can start by considering in turn the effect on

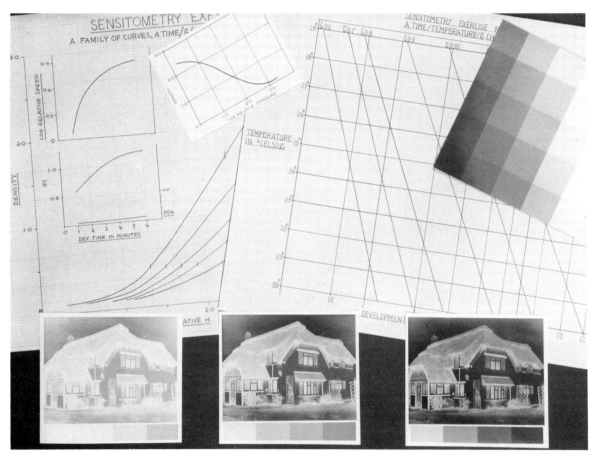

As development progresses, so density, contrast, emulsion speed and fog increase up to a limit.

characteristic curves of varying the time, temperature, and agitation of development. In black-and-white processing the usual situation is that the solution temperature and agitation are kept constant, while the development time is varied to obtain the desired result.

Variation in development time

3.2 As development progresses, the values of gamma, $\overline{G}$ contrast and speed increase until a maximum is reached, after which their values may begin to decrease. The slope and position of the characteristic curve is thus dependent upon the time of development. This relationship can be shown by constructing a family of characteristic curves.

3.3 To construct a family of characteristic curves, a number of pieces of the film under test are given an identical range of exposures through a step wedge. The sensitometric strips are then developed for varying times (see paragraph 6.10) using standard processing conditions; after measurement, the characteristic curves are plotted on one piece of graph paper. The family of characteristic curves thus obtained gives a better representation of the photographic process and more information than a single curve. To enable the $\overline{G}$ values to be

found when a specific useful log exposure range is being used or considered, the lower limit and the upper limit may be marked with short vertical bars as shown in Figures 3.1 and 3.2. The lower limit is also the speed point.

To prevent mistakes in plotting when constructing a family of curves, it may help if vertical pencil lines are drawn up from the exposure positions on the log exposure axis. Each line should be numbered with the step number of the sensitometer wedge; these can be erased afterwards. To prevent mistakes, it is advisable to use different symbols for each set of points and to draw in each curve as soon as the plotting points have been marked. Figures 3.1 and 3.2 are examples of families of characteristic curves for different types of film.

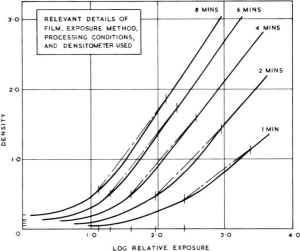

Fig. 3.2 A family of *D* log *H* curves for a typical aerial film. The caption of Figure 3.1 applies also to these curves.

To complete the graph, all the relevant details of the film, exposure method, developer and processing conditions, and the densitometer used must be recorded. See paragraph 2.63 and Table 2.5.

A family of characteristic curves can be used to give a quantitative measurable indication of the change in the photographic image as development proceeds. The parts of the curves that are of main interest are those on or near the useful log exposure range, which in general terms is between the speed point and the upper limit point. This is the area that is most often used in practice. By comparing the curves of Figure 3.1 or Figure 3.2 we find that with these films the factors and changes that are of chief importance are as follows:

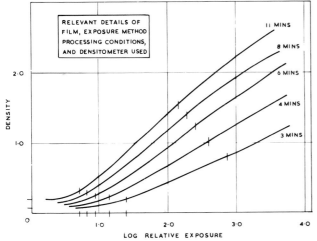

Fig. 3.1 A family of *D* log *H* curves for a typical general-purpose film. Five pieces of the same film are given an identical range of exposures through a step wedge. They are then processed in the same developer but for different development times. Characteristic curves are constructed, speed and $\overline{G}$ points marked in, and exposure and processing details entered. The change in contrast, fog, speed and possible exposure latitude caused by development time changes can be seen and measured by comparison of the curves.

(a) *Gamma and $\bar{G}$ contrast.* Gamma and $\bar{G}$ both increase as development time progresses. They increase quickly at first, then more slowly until they reach a maximum, after which no further increase occurs. The significance of this is that the contrast of the negative can be controlled within limits by varying the development time.

(b) *Fog level (D_{min}).* Fog increases very slowly at first, then more rapidly.

(c) *Speed.* Emulsion speed increases with development time, rapidly at first then more slowly.

(d) *Exposure latitude.* In general terms, exposure latitude should decrease as development progresses, owing to enhanced granularity as density increases.

For most applications of photography, $\bar{G}$ contrast is appropriate, rather than gamma. Gamma does sometimes apply, however, particularly in film duplicating and in copying processes where the photographic material used has a substantially straight characteristic curve.

Variation of gamma, $\bar{G}$ contrast, fog and speed, with development time

3.4   We can see in Figures 3.1 and 3.2 that the main factors given in the previous paragraph increase with increasing development time. However, their rates of increase and the relationships between the factors are not easily seen on the family of curves. To overcome this the data can be shown as a graph, which will give more easily interpretable results. This graph is constructed as follows.

The main data shown in a family of curves is the change in slope of the characteristic curve for differing development times. If these development times are plotted as the horizontal scale of a graph, the gamma, $\bar{G}$ contrast, fog and log relative emulsion speed can be plotted on the vertical scale. With this type of graph, the rate of change and the relationship between the factors will be clear. The curves for each factor are drawn so that they most nearly fit all the plotted points, and the aim is to produce a smooth curve which gives the best average between the points. The graphs produced (Figure 3.3 is an example) present a much clearer picture of the rates of increase or decrease than a family of curves. The speed increase can be plotted directly from the log exposure axis of the parent family of curves, using 0.3 log distance as indicating a doubling in speed.

Development times may be plotted on either an arithmetic or a logarithmic scale, and as long as the curves are not too steep or too shallow for proper use, the development time scale can be made to any length. When a log scale is used, the scale is gradually compressed as development time increases. (Figures 3.6 and 3.7 show this effect.) This causes the curves to be presented in a more nearly linear manner on the graph and may make it more convenient and easier to use.

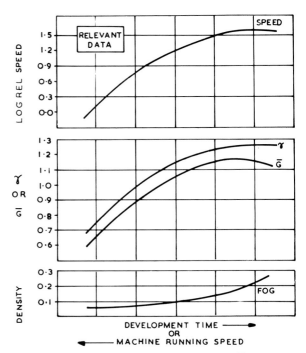

Fig. 3.3 Representative speed/time, gamma/time, $\bar{G}$/time, and fog/time curves for a typical film, derived from a family of D log H curves. The rate of change caused by development time increase, and in particular the relationship between one factor and others, is not easily seen on a family of curves. By plotting the change in value of contrast, fog and speed, against development time, separate curves can be produced for each factor. These show both the rate of change and the relationship between the factors in an easily interpretable manner. For continuous processing machines it is usual to plot the machine running speed instead of development time. Details of processing, as for the parent family of curves, must also be indicated. The graphs may be presented in any position relative to each other. For example, the speed/time curve may be positioned above or below the other curves.

In practice the factors described, when plotted against development time, are often presented together on the same graph. This is satisfactory as long as there is no confusion between the different vertical scales. For example, the vertical scales for gamma and $\bar{G}$ contrast are pure numbers, whereas the scale for fog is a density, and the scale for film speed is a logarithmic number. In Figure 3.3 the three graphs are shown separately for clarity.

3.5 A study of the curves in Figure 3.3 shows that the changes described in paragraph 3.3 (a), (b) and (c) are clearly visible. It also shows that:

(a) The effect of factors influenced by development time can be related to one another.
(b) Gamma and $\bar{G}$ contrast reach a maximum (γ or $\bar{G}_{max}$) and then start to decrease in value. This is because of the increase in fog level, which has a greater effect on the lower densities in the toe region of the characteristic curve.
(c) Maximum film speed is associated with high contrast ($\bar{G}$).
(d) $\bar{G}$ contrast cannot be varied by changing the development time unless a variation in film speed is also accepted. However, if a different $\bar{G}$ contrast is required, any exposure correction necessary can be estimated from the film speed/time curve.

The relationship between the curves shows the importance of not prolonging the development time beyond that necessary to give maximum gamma or $\bar{G}$ contrast, in a mistaken attempt to gain more speed or greater contrast.

To complete the graph, all the relevant details must be shown as for the parent family of curves, and the standard on which contrast and speed are based must also be stated. (Specified standards are given in Chapter 4.)

3.6 *Application to continuous processing machines.* When films are processed in a continuous processing machine, development time is determined by the running speed of the machine. As the running speed is inversely proportional to the development time, the horizontal axis of the graph is plotted as 'machine running speed'. The gamma, or $\bar{G}$/ running speed curve, can then be used as a basis for finding the running speed necessary to obtain the required results.

3.7 *Using the development time graph.* The curves on the graph are used to obtain the optimum development time for any specific conditions of contrast required. For example:

(a) In general-purpose photography it may be necessary to know the development time corresponding to a given gamma (or $\bar{G}$ contrast) higher or lower than that usually obtained. The γ or $\bar{G}$ curve shows this time, and the speed/time curve indicates any associated change in emulsion speed.

For example, referring to Figure 3.3, a lowering of $\bar{G}$ from 1.15 to 1.05 will result in a loss in emulsion speed of 0.3 log, necessitating one *f*-stop more exposure.
(b) In high-altitude aerial photography both a high contrast and the maximum emulsion speed are usually required, while for photography at low altitudes a lower contrast is often necessary. The curves indicate the optimum development time or machine running speed for such conditions and any associated exposure correction factor.
(c) In duplicating and copying tasks, and when preparing unsharp masks, it is usually necessary to produce results having a prescribed contrast (density range). The development time necessary to obtain the required gammas for the material can be found from a gamma/time curve. (This subject is dealt with in more detail in Chapter 7.) Gamma and not $\bar{G}$ is used for this type of work because the images need to be contained on the straight-line region of the film characteristic curve in order to avoid distortion of the tone scale.

3.8 *Contrast/time curve comparison.* Gamma or $\bar{G}$/ time curves are often produced for one type of film processed in two or more developers of differing activity or dilution as shown in Figure 3.4. Such

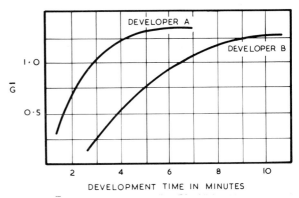

Fig. 3.4 $\bar{G}$/time curves for the same type of film and processing procedure. Comparison of the curves enables a choice to be made of the developer most suitable for obtaining the required G. For example, for a G of 1.0($\pm$0.02), developer A will allow a tolerance in development time of only 10 seconds, while developer B will allow 20 seconds. Processing in developer B is thus more likely to produce the required G.

curves can be used in choosing a developer that will be suitable for obtaining the required gamma or $\bar{G}$, bearing in mind that the steep part of a curve where contrast is changing rapidly should be avoided. By using the less steep parts of the curve, the effect of slight variations in development time will be minimal. For such a comparison, the relevant conditions of processing must of course be the same for each developer.

3.9 *Published development time curves.* The manufacturers of photographic materials publish technical data sheets which include gamma, or $\overline{G}$ contrast, or contrast index/development time curves for their films. The data will have been determined for films exposed and processed under specific conditions, often in a selection of different developers. These curves can give a good indication of the general performance of a film and developer combination, and are of use in selecting material and processing conditions for a particular task. However, they can only be used as a guide, because in practice, the exposure and processing and even the response of the film, will probably differ slightly from that used for the published curves.

Variation in developer temperature

3.10 Up to now we have assumed that practical processing is to be carried out at the same temperature as that used for the sensitometric tests. This was probably the film manufacturer's recommended processing temperature. There are sound reasons for using this recommended temperature, but in practice it is not always possible to do so. Operating conditions often demand that processing must be carried out at higher or lower temperatures. There are of course limits to the increase or decrease in temperature that can be used. The upper limit is governed by the swelling and softening that occurs as temperature is increased, thus making the emulsion more susceptible to damage. It also requires shorter development times, which may produce uneven development. The lower limit is governed by the adverse effect that lower temperatures have on some of the developing agents, and on the inconvenience of long development times. As with many other chemical processes, an increase in solution temperature increases the rate of development, the effects being similar to those produced by increasing development time. Thus in order to obtain a particular gamma or $\overline{G}$ contrast we need a graph or chart to show the development time appropriate to the temperature actually in use. Film manufacturers may provide such charts or guides showing the development time necessary for different solution temperatures. Nevertheless, these are only appropriate for particular developers and average processing conditions. Therefore it is often useful if we can produce a chart related to our own processing conditions.

Time/temperature/gamma (or $\overline{G}$) chart

3.11 To construct the chart, a family of $D \log H$ curves is first made for the highest and lowest temperature required, and gamma/time curves or $\overline{G}$/time curves made from them. It helps if a $D \log$

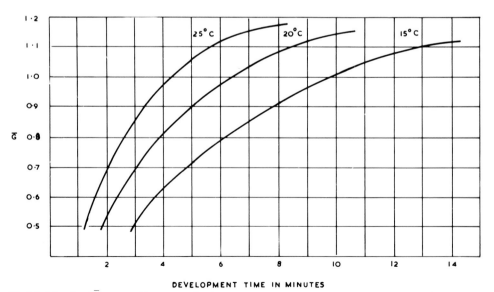

Fig. 3.5 A family of $\overline{G}$ contrast/time curves for the same type of film processed at three different developer temperatures. Such curves are used as the basis for constructiong a development time/temperature/$\overline{G}$ contrast chart.

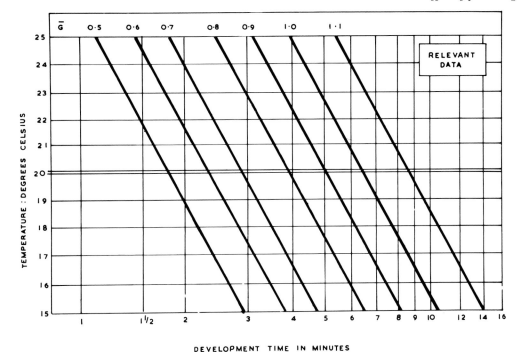

Fig. 3.6 A typical time/temperature/$\bar{G}$ contrast chart. Development temperature is plotted against time for a given $\bar{G}$ contrast. Development time is on a logarithmic scale so that straight lines showing the relationship are produced.

H family is made for a mid-temperature also, and a family of gamma or $\bar{G}$/time curves made from the three (Figure 3.5).

The time/temperature/contrast chart (Figure 3.6) is then made with temperature as a linear scale on the vertical axis, and development time as a logarithmic scale on the horizontal axis.

The values of development time for a selected number of values of gamma (or $\bar{G}$) are plotted along the line indicating the highest temperature. This procedure is then repeated for the line indicating the lowest temperature, and the respective plotting points joined with a straight line. (It has been found experimentally that, for a constant gamma or $\bar{G}$, developer temperature has a linear relationship with the logarithm of the development time.) The mid-temperature findings will help to identify the lines. If development time is not plotted on a logarithmic scale the lines will become curves, necessitating the plotting of points for several intermediate temperatures.

To complete the chart, the relevant details of the film and the processing conditions must be shown. As with the previous graphs, 'machine running speed' can be substituted for development time when this is applicable.

A time/temperature/gamma (or $\bar{G}$) chart is not an infallible aid; it is a guide to correct development time, and if precise results are required, a full sensitometric check must be made under actual working conditions.

3.12   To use the chart:

(a)   Find the required $\bar{G}$ value.
(b)   Follow the corresponding diagonal line down until it is opposite the temperature of the processing solution.
(c)   The point on the development time axis vertically below indicates the correct development time to achieve the desired $\bar{G}$.

Fig. 3.7 Constructing a logarithmic scale. The logarithms of a series of numbers (such as those of development time in minutes) are found, and then plotted as distances on the horizontal axis. (See also Appendix A, Figure A.1.)

3.13 *Constructing a logarithmic scale.* A convenient type of graph paper for constructing a time/temperature/Ḡ chart is 'two-cycle log–linear'. If this cannot be obtained, or if a different size of chart is wanted, a logarithmic scale may be easily constructed. To do this, find the logarithms of the development time numbers (to two decimal places) and mark these in as distances (using any suitable units) along the development time axis as shown in Figure 3.7. Enter the development time in minutes under each mark.

Agitation

3.14 Development time and temperature are fairly precise factors and can be easily controlled, but solution agitation is not precise and therefore cannot be easily controlled. Proper agitation is important throughout the photographic process, but is of particular importance during the development stage. Agitation should be such that a continuous supply of fresh developer is evenly distributed over and into the emulsion, while exhausted developer is removed. A proper degree of agitation thus has the effect of producing uniform development. The effect of a low level of agitation on the reproduction of fine detail is considered in paragraph 2.103.

3.15 The effect of insufficient agitation is a reduction in developer activity and thus in contrast (gamma and Ḡ), together with possible adjacency effects, but of more concern is the lack of uniform development. Insufficient agitation causes development to be slowed down owing to developer exhaustion, which is greater in the highlights (darker areas) of the negative than in the shadows. Thus the general overall contrast of the result is diminished and the development effect is uneven.

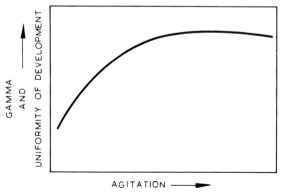

Fig. 3.8 The general effect of agitation during development.

A curve can be used to illustrate the general effect of changes in agitation on gamma and uniformity of development (Figure 3.8).

The figure shows that, up to a certain level, increasing agitation produces an increase in gamma and also a more uniform development. As agitation increases, so variation in these effects becomes smaller. Therefore, if a fairly high level of proper agitation is used, any small variations in agitation have no significant effect. However, if agitation is too vigorous a regular flow pattern of developer may be set up instead of a random flow, and this also causes uneven development. For example, a common occurrence is for a regular flow pattern to build up through film sprocket holes or in film-holding devices, causing development streaks.

The aim in photographic and sensitometric processing is to have the minimum amount of variation in agitation once a proper level has been established. Agitation techniques for both black-and-white and colour materials are considered in paragraph 6.9.

Reversal processing

3.16 We have considered the effects of varying the conditions of development. Now we can consider how the photographic process can be modified to produce a positive image instead of a negative. The normal black-and-white photographic process consists of producing a film negative and then making one or more positive prints from the negative. It can thus be described as a two-step method. If, however, only a single positive image is required, as when producing positive transparencies for projection, it is possible to process a camera film to produce the desired result directly, by using a modified processing procedure. This is called 'reversal processing', and the procedure is similar to that used for producing colour reversal transparencies.

3.17 After exposure in the camera to varying illuminances, the film is developed in the normal way to produce a negative image. The various deposits of silver in the negative are then dissolved and removed by using bleach and then clearing solutions. This leaves varying amounts of undeveloped silver halide in the form of a potential positive image. The film is then uniformly fogged, followed by development and fixation in the normal way to form the final positive image.

Thus the negative image is the result of variation in exposure of a uniform layer of emulsion, and the positive image is the result of uniform exposure of a variable layer of emulsion. Figure 3.9 shows the basic principle and procedures of the reversal process in diagrammatic form.

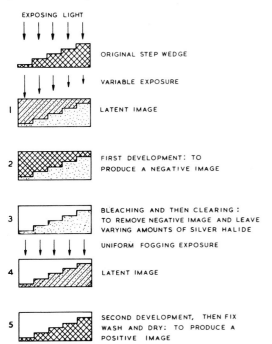

Fig. 3.9 The five main stages of a black-and-white reversal process. For convenience of presentation the reproduction of a step wedge is shown, but the same effect occurs when a camera-exposed film is reversal processed, Also, of course, the image is not normally formed literally as stepped layers in the emulsion.

3.18 *Exposure and processing.* Some manufacturers' films are especially designed to be suitable for the reversal process, and special 'direct-reversal' materials are available. Many conventional films can also be reversal processed, but with these success is more likely when slow or medium-speed film of medium to high contrast is used. Because it is a one-step method of photography, the control of final contrast and density depends for the most part on control of the subject contrast and on the camera exposure level. Thus for reversal films camera exposure is much more critical than it is for the normal negative–positive process. Reversal processing consists of first development, bleaching, clearing, re-exposure, second development (with interposing rinses), fixing, washing and drying. The recommended processing formulae and method vary somewhat for different types and makes of film. To obtain optimum results the manufacturers' instructions should be followed.

A satisfactory black-and-white positive transparency has almost clear extreme highlights, and a density range suitable for direct viewing or projection. After correct exposure this is obtained by using an energetic first developer together with a proportional amount of silver halide solvent (such as sodium thiosulphate). The silver halide solvent acts to dissolve some of the small and relatively insensitive silver halide crystals that have not been affected by the first developer. These crystals would otherwise remain to be developed in the second developer and thus veil the highlight areas of the positive. After the negative image has been bleached and cleared the remaining silver halide is fogged and then developed. The second developer may be of any conventional type, or the first developer with or without the halide solvent may be used. The second development is followed by normal fixing (to remove any residue of silver halide), washing and drying. As an alternative to the second exposure and development, some methods of reversal processing use a chemical fogging treatment. This procedure is useful if it is inconvenient to remove a film from a reel or spiral for re-exposure.

Figure 3.10 shows the characteristic curves of a black-and-white film and the general effect of exposure and the reversal process. Because it has been reversal processed, the characteristic curve of

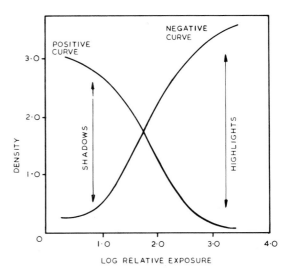

Fig. 3.10 Representative characteristic curves of a black-and-white film showing the typical placing of shadows and highlights and the general effect of the reversal process. The addition of a silver halide solvent to the first developer reduces the density range of the positive image and also helps to produce sufficiently clear highlights. This provides a transparency that is suitable for direct viewing or projection.

the reversed film slopes in a direction opposite to that of the original negative image. With reversal films, the end products of the original low-exposure values are high densities, and of the high-exposure values, low densities. The slope of the curves is in general greater than that of a typical negative. This is because a negative is only a means to an end, in that it has to be printed, and the printing paper characteristics will produce an appropriate higher contrast on the final positive. On the other hand, the processed reversal film is itself an end product, ready for viewing.

3.19   *Advantages of the reversal process.* Reversal processing provides some advantages compared with the conventional negative–positive method, the obvious one being the saving of time and printing costs. Another benefit is that, by the nature of the process, the final image produced by reversal consists of the finest grains in the processed emulsion, the negative having utilized most of the larger grains. The granular structure of the reversal positive is thus finer than that which would show on a positive obtained by normal negative processing and printing.

The reversal process can also be used for making direct negatives from negatives, or direct positives from positive transparencies.

Reduction and intensification

3.20   We have considered the effects of varying the conditions of exposure and processing, and how they can influence the characteristics of photographic material. In practice the ideal situation is when exposure and processing produce an optimum-quality result. However, if a mistake is made and the finished negative is unsuitable for printing, either the task will have to be repeated or, if this is not possible, some remedial action must be attempted. This may take the form of chemical reduction or intensification of the image, and we can now consider the effect and the basic sensitometry of these processes.

3.21   Negatives that have been wrongly exposed or processed, so that they are unsuitable for printing, may be improved by various 'after-treatments', in particular by chemical reduction or intensification. 'Reduction' refers to lowering the density and/or contrast, and 'intensification' to increasing the density and/or contrast, of the processed image. In general photography such treatments are for the most part used only when the photograph cannot be repeated. They are of value in obtaining a printable negative but are unable to fully rectify the effect of the original faults, and are therefore no substitute for correct exposure and processing in the first instance.

In the type of photography where the resolution of fine detail is of particular importance, both reduction and intensification may have a detrimental effect, as both treatments reduce the level of resolution already obtained. Chemical reduction not only reduces density and/or contrast, it may also remove some of the very fine detail. Chemical intensification increases density and/or contrast but it may also increase the size of the granular image structure. Reduction and intensification are applicable mostly to black-and-white films, although reduction can be used on prints when necessary. Colour prints and colour transparencies may have their densities modified by dye retouching or bleaching, which may be applied locally, selectively, or overall.

3.22   The effect of reduction and intensification can be measured using comparative sensitometry. A sensitometric strip is exposed in the usual manner, and the film processed to produce an image suitable for the particular test. The film may be developed as usual or it may be developed to produce a higher or a lower contrast than normal, depending on the reason for the test. For example, if the effect of a contrast-lowering reducer is being tested, the film may be given more development than usual.

For a test of reduction or intensification, the sensitometric strip is first processed using the normal developer. It is measured and the results are plotted to produce a characteristic curve on a graph. After this the strip is processed in the particular reducer or intensifier, the results are measured, and then plotted as a second curve on the same graph. The characteristics of the process can then be interpreted by comparison. If a visual comparison of the effect is needed, for example to investigate any change in resolution or image colour, two strips are exposed, one being treated and the other not.

Reducers

3.23   The three main types of reducer are named by the effect they each have on the photographic image: subtractive, proportional, and superproportional. Figure 3.11 shows the characteristic

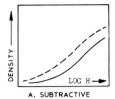 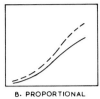 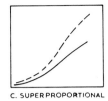

Fig. 3.11 The general effect on a negative image of the three main types of chemical reducer. The dashed lines represent the densities before reduction.

curves of sensitometric strips before and after treatment in the various types of reducer. The curves are somewhat idealized for the purpose of illustration.

3.24   A study of Figure 3.11 shows that:

(a)   A subtractive reducer gives equal all-over reduction of density with little change in contrast. It is therefore particularly suitable for the treatment of overexposed negatives and for the 'cutting' or clearing of fog from materials such as line negatives.
(b)   A proportional reducer lowers every density in approximately the same ratio. Therefore it acts proportionally on the densities, and contrast is lowered. The effect is as though an original negative had been given less development. It is therefore particularly useful for the treatment of overdeveloped negatives.
(c)   A superproportional reducer acts in a similar manner to a proportional reducer but lowers density much more in the darker areas than in the lighter. It is therefore particularly suitable for the treatment of slightly underexposed but overdeveloped negatives.

Intensifiers

3.25   There are several types of chemical intensifier. Like reducers they have been named according to the effect they are intended to have on the photographic image: subproportional, proportional, and superproportional. However, in practice, intensifiers do not conform to theory as well as reducers, and vary considerably in their effects on different types of emulsion. Most intensifiers have a general proportional effect opposite to that of a proportional reducer. They add more density to the darker areas and less to the lighter. Chemical

intensifiers differ mostly in that some produce a greater contrast increase than others.

Figure 3.12 shows the characteristic curve of a sensitometric strip before and after treatment in a typical intensification process. The curves are somewhat idealized for the purpose of illustration. It is worth remembering that an intensifier can be used to improve a weak photographic image, but in the areas where no image is present in the first place intensification cannot improve matters.

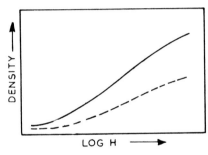

Fig. 3.12 The general effect on a negative image of a typical chemical intensifier. The dashed line represents the densities before intensification. The general effect is proportional, as though an original negative had been given more development.

Checking the effects of reduction and intensification

3.26   The effect of reduction and intensification on a negative can be investigated by direct comparative sensitometry as described in paragraph 3.22. The practical printing effect of the two after-treatments, and particularly that of intensification, is found by printing the samples. This is done either by making a print before and then after treatment, or by printing one treated and one untreated sample side-by-side on the same printing material. This procedure is often necessary because the treatment may produce a slight staining or a change in the colour of the image. The practical effect of these colour changes may not be evident by visual inspection or by measuring on a densitometer, but it could affect the response of the printing material. For example, a slight yellow stain will increase effective density when a negative is printed on a blue-sensitive paper or film emulsion.

When this sort of test is made, the printing material is in effect being used as a comparative measuring device. The result on the printing material of both the treated and untreated sample can be seen, and may also be measured and plotted

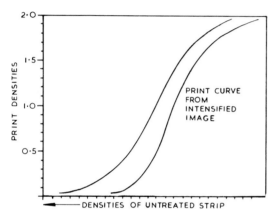

Fig. 3.13 The printing effect of chemical intensification of a negative image. Two identical sensitometric strips are made and one is intensified. Both are then printed together on the same material and the resultant characteristic curves plotted. The practical printing effect of intensification is found by comparing the two curves.

as comparative characteristic curves. The curves are also relevant to the particular printing conditions. Figure 3.13 shows this type of comparison as the effect on the printing material of an intensified and an untreated sensitometric strip image. The curves on the graph are constructed by plotting the reflection densities of the prints against the densities of the untreated sensitometric strip.

Self-assessment questions

3.27   If you want to test your learning, write out answers to the following questions:

(a)   Describe how $\bar{G}$ contrast changes with increasing development time.

(b)   Explain how emulsion speed changes with increasing development time.

(c)   Describe how a $\bar{G}$/time curve is constructed.

(d)   What advantage in use has a $\bar{G}$/time curve over a family of curves?

(e)   Under what conditions is 'running speed' applicable to the horizontal axis of a $\bar{G}$/time graph, and how would it be indicated on the axis?

(f)   How could changes in film speed be plotted on the same graph?

(g)   What is a logarithmic exposure change of 0.3, in terms of lens aperture stops?

(h)   What happens to the value of $\bar{G}$ after maximum $\bar{G}$ has been reached, and why?

(i)   Why is it important not to develop beyond maximum $\bar{G}$?

(j)   What data must be included with a $\bar{G}$/time graph to enable the graph to be used in practice?

(k)   Describe how you would construct a time/temperature/$\bar{G}$ chart.

(l)   Why is a logarithmic scale of development times used on a time/temperature/$\bar{G}$ chart?

(m)   Using a 30 mm distance as indicating a development time increase from 1 to 2 minutes, construct a logarithmic scale for development times of 1, 2, 3, 5, 7, 9, 11 and 15 minutes.

(n)   List the possible effects of no agitation, proper agitation and too vigorous agitation.

(o)   Describe the basic principle of the reversal processing of a black-and-white film.

(p)   What is the function of the silver halide solvent used in the first developer of a black-and-white reversal process?

(q)   Draw two characteristic curves to show the effects, on a typical negative, of each of the three main types of chemical reducer.

(r)   Describe how you would carry out a test to show the effect in printing, of chemically intensifying a low-contrast negative.

4

Film speeds and related factors

4.1   In this chapter we are concerned mainly with the speed of black-and-white films and factors related to speed, but the basic principles and most aspects of speed determination are equally applicable to other materials such as printing paper and those materials used in colour photography.

Speed, as applied to photographic materials, is a numerical value indicating the sensitivity of the emulsion to light or other radiant energy. The higher the speed number, the more sensitive the emulsion. The speed number is related to the exposure required to obtain a particular density on the characteristic curve when the film is given

normal (or standard) development. This density is called the 'speed point'. The actual density chosen as the speed point will differ according to the purpose for which the film is intended. For some applications of photography a speed point low down on the curve is used, for others a mid-curve point is more appropriate. At present, because we have previously compared them together, we can consider film speed as it relates to general-purpose films and to films intended for aerial photography. We shall consider speed with regard to printing paper and colour materials later.

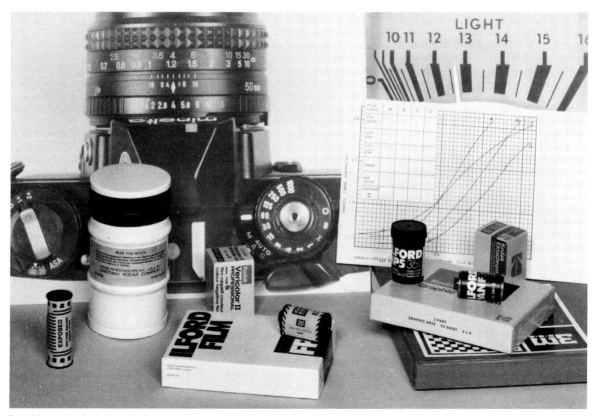

Speed is a numerical value that indicates the response of photographic material to exposure and processing. It is derived from the characteristic curve of the material.

Manufacturer's tests

4.2 Numbers indicating the speed of unexposed films appear on their containers, so that the speed number or exposure index can be used in exposure calculations. Speeds and other sensitometric characteristics are initially determined by the film manufacturer. However, because changes take place in the emulsion soon after its formation, photographic materials may be stored under normal conditions for three months or so to allow the emulsion to stabilize before tests (including the determination of speed) are carried out.

Tests and characteristic curves are made under standardized and precise conditions of exposure, processing and measuring; thus any variations in the result are due to changes in the photographic material only and not to any other factor. (Paragraphs 6.4, 6.38 and 6.39 refer in more detail to precision in sensitometric testing.)

The roll of film to be tested may be a metre or so wide and several hundred metres long. Therefore, to ensure that results are representative of the whole batch or type of film, several samples from different parts of the film roll are tested. Any slight differences found can then be averaged to give a representative result. With fresh film, the tolerance permitted between the nominal speed marked on the container and the actual speed of the film at the time of test is usually one-third of a stop (0.1 log exposure units).

4.3 *Using the exposure index.* The manufacturer's exposure index for a fresh film applies to the average conditions under which it is intended to be used, so it is only a guide to correct exposure. The speed of an emulsion is not fixed, but depends to some extent on the subject matter, and particularly on the processing conditions and how the film is to be used. The main factors influencing effective emulsion speed are:

(a) The contrast (luminance range) of the subject photographed, which may necessitate giving more or less development than usual.
(b) The colour of the exposing light.
(c) The duration and intensity of exposure.
(d) The type and composition of the developer.
(e) The degree of development.

The manufacturer's exposure index as marked on the film container should therefore be used as a guide only, and the factors that can influence the speed of the film must be considered when deciding an exposure. Film manufacturers often include instructions with their films regarding the exposure index or 'meter setting' recommended for use when the film is to be processed in different developers. If the emulsion is not truly panchromatic, recommendation may also be given regarding exposure to light of a different colour quality such as daylight or tungsten light.

General-purpose films

4.4 Standards of speed for general-purpose films are agreed by the International Standards Organization (ISO), and the ISO speed standard is now in all practical respects the same as the national ASA/BS and DIN speed standards. The abreviations refer to:

(a) ASA: originally American Standards Association, now ANSI, American National Standards Institute.
(b) BS: British Standard, issued by the British Standards Institution.
(c) DIN: Deutsche Industrie Normen, the German industrial standard.

Although all the national standards agree with the ISO standard, it is probable that the abbreviations ASA and DIN will still be in use for some time. This is because existing cameras and exposure meters may be numbered for either of the systems.

4.5 For practical convenience, the speed of most photographic materials is marked on the film container in the form of an 'exposure index' or 'meter setting' related to exposing the film in daylight. This is the number that should be set on the camera or exposure meter.

ASA exposure indices are 'arithmetic'. This means, for example, that a film rated at 400 ASA has twice the speed of one rated at 200 ASA. The DIN exposure indices are logarithmic. On the DIN scale, an increase of 3 means a doubling of film speed. Strictly, it should be 0.3 (0.3 being the logarithm of 2), but the indices are multiplied by ten to make them whole numbers. Thus a speed of 23 DIN represents a film having twice the speed of one rated at 20 DIN. A comparison of the most useful parts of the film-speed scales is shown in Table 4.1.

For convenience in use, ISO speeds can be expressed in either arithmetic or logarithmic terms and the tendency worldwide is for film manufacturers to adopt the ISO designation for film speeds in place of the ASA and DIN ratings. For example, a film previously rated as ASA 125/22 DIN may now be designated as ISO 125/22°. The degree sign (°) is included only to prevent the logarithmic index being mistaken for an arithmetic number. By

Table 4.1 Comparison and conversion between ISO arithmetic and logarithmic speed scales.

ISO and ASA speed (arithmetic)	ISO and DIN speed (logarithmic)	Relative speed
25	15	1
32	16	
40	17	
50	18	2
64	19	
80	20	
100	21	4
125	22	
160	23	
200	24	8
250	25	
320	26	
400	27	16
500	28	
650	29	
800	30	32
1000	31	
1250	32	
1600	33	64
2000	34	
2500	35	
3200	36	128

tracing the scales shown in Table 4.1 backwards, we can deduce that ASA 1 = DIN 1.

From Table 4.1 we can see that the logarithmic numbering system is probably simpler to use in practice than the arithmetic system. It has a limit of two digits, while the arithmetic scale can go up to four or more digits. A logarithmic index number is thus easier to use and in particular easier to read with other small figures on camera speed-setting dials. Furthermore, with a logarithmic series of exposure indices, for example 20, 21, 22, 23 etc., each successive number indicates a useful one-third *f*-stop increase. With an arithmetic series the numbers representing one-third *f*-stop are more difficult to find or to work out in practice.

In the USSR and some eastern European countries, GOST speeds are used. They are similar but may not be identical to ISO/ASA arithmetic speeds. However, for all but precise work, a GOST exposure index can be considered to be the same as ISO/ASA arithmetic. The USSR is a member of the International Standards Organization and has approved most of the ISO speed standards.

4.6 The method used for deriving ISO (ASA and DIN) speeds for general-purpose black-and-white films is based on the characteristic curve produced by conditions of exposure and processing found under average conditions in general-purpose

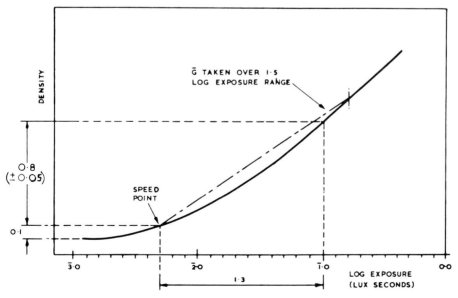

Fig. 4.1 Black-and-white general-purpose film, speed and typical Ḡ contrast criteria. Speed values are derived from a characteristic curve exposed and processed so that a density range of 0.8 ± 0.05, starting from 0.1 above fog, is obtained over

a log exposure range of 1.3. Contrast may be measured over a 1.5 log exposure range. This represents the average conditions relevant to general-purpose photography.

photography. Characteristic curves are made under known and controlled conditions to the specifications shown in Figure 4.1, so that a density range of 0.8 ± 0.05 is obtained over a log *H* range of 1.3. Note that for calculating speed numbers it is necessary to use the logarithms of absolute (actual) exposures and not a relative scale. It is helpful to understand how film speeds are derived, but the actual determination of film speed, for example in ISO units, is more the concern of the film manufacturer. For many practical purposes a simple comparison of an unknown film with a known one will suffice (see paragraph 2.113).

A point on the curve where the density is 0.1 above base-plus-fog density is taken as the speed point. It corresponds to the lowest point that should be used when making a negative in general-purpose photography.

The actual values of the ISO, ASA and DIN speed indices are obtained as follows:

(a)   The ISO (arithmetic) and ASA speed index is the reciprocal of the exposure in lux seconds at the speed point, multiplied by a constant (0.8). The speed index figure is rounded off to the nearest one-third *f*-stop, thus giving a suitable number for use with a similarly scaled exposure meter.

$$\text{ISO (arithmetic) speed} = \frac{0.8}{\text{Exposure at speed point}}$$

In Figure 4.1,

$$\text{ISO (arith) speed} = \frac{0.8}{\text{antilog } \overline{3}.7} = \frac{0.8}{0.005} = 160$$

The constant 0.8 used in the formula simply makes the resulting value suitable for use on a camera or exposure-meter dial. It has no other significance.

(b)   The ISO (logarithmic) and DIN speed index is the logarithm of the reciprocal of the exposure in lux seconds at the speed point, multiplied by 10. The speed index figure is rounded off to the nearest one-third *f*-stop, thus giving a suitable number for use with a similarly scaled exposure meter.

$$\text{ISO (logarithmic) speed}$$
$$= 10 \times \log \frac{1}{\text{Exposure at speed point}}$$

In Figure 4.1,

$$\text{ISO (logarithmic) speed} = 10 \times \log \frac{1}{\text{antilog } \overline{3}.7}$$
$$= 10 \times \log 200 = 23°$$

The reciprocal of the exposure is used so that the exposure index is greater for a faster film. A simple method of finding the log of the reciprocal of exposure is given later, in paragraph 4.15.

4.7   *Specified average gradient for general-purpose films.* The slope of a line joining the speed point to a point that has received an exposure corresponding to 1.5 units further along the log-exposure axis is called the G bar ($\overline{G}$). This is the part of the curve most likely to be used in general-purpose photography under average conditions. It is often described as '$\overline{G}$ contrast'. (See also paragraphs 2.95 and 2.96.)

4.8   *Other speed values.* The speed system for general-purpose black-and-white films is not really suitable for use with materials and applications in which a speed point of *D* 0.1 above fog is relatively unimportant – for example, in high-contrast copying work, when using radiographic materials, making paper prints, colour photography and in aerial photography. For such applications different criteria, usually based on a more suitable speed point, are used, and we shall consider some of these later. For the present we shall consider one typical application of a different speed point and criteria, namely that used for black-and-white films in aerial photography.

Aerial films

4.9   The film speed of unexposed aerial films usually appears as part of the information printed on their containers. The film speed is reckoned on the basis of the average conditions of exposure and processing used in aerial photography. At present there is no internationally agreed standard speed system for aerial films, but an ISO standard for black-and-white aerial films is under consideration. However, the systems used at present are very similar in their application, and it is probable that the future ISO standard will be based on these.

4.10   Because the range of subject luminance is generally much less than in general-purpose photography, aerial films are usually formulated, exposed and processed to produce a higher contrast than general purpose films in order to obtain a good separation of tones. Therefore different criteria are used to determine film speed, and the speed point is moved higher up the toe of the curve. The lowering of the rated film speed caused by moving the speed point is of course partly offset by a different emulsion formulation (when compared with conventional films) and also by the increase in speed obtained by development to obtain a higher contrast. (See Figures 3.1 and 3.2).

The method used for calculating aerial film speed is based on the characteristic curve produced by the conditions of exposure and processing found under average conditions in aerial photography. Characteristic curves are made under known and controlled conditions similar to the specification shown in Figure 4.2. The absolute (actual) log exposure scale is used rather than a relative scale.

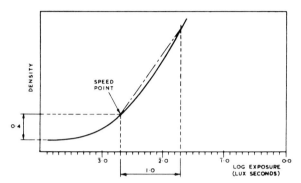

Fig. 4.2 A typical black-and-white aerial film characteristic curve, used to derive speed and contrast values. The film is exposed and processed under specific conditions relative to the average conditions found in aerial photography. Contrast may be measured over a 1.0 log exposure range.

For black-and-white aerial film the speed point is usually taken as the point on the characteristic curve where the density is 0.4 above base-plus-fog density. The American standard is at present $D\,0.3$ above fog. These densities correspond approximately to the lower acceptable limit of resolving power. (See Figure 2.28 and accompanying paragraphs.)

4.11 *Aerial film speed index.* The aerial film speed index is the logarithm of the reciprocal of the exposure in lux seconds at the speed point, multiplied by 10.

Aerial film speed index

$$= 10 \times \log \frac{1}{\text{Exposure at speed point}}$$

In Figure 4.2,

$$\text{Aerial film speed index} = 10 \times \log \frac{1}{\text{antilog } \overline{3}.3}$$

$$= 10 \times \log 500 = 27$$

The figure obtained is rounded off to give a suitable whole number to an accuracy of one-third *f*-stop. Note that this is the same method as that used for ISO logarithmic and DIN speeds with general-purpose films, except that a different speed point is used.

4.12 The exposure to be set on the camera is decided by relating the index figure to exposure tables or a calculator that takes into account the other factors affecting exposure. For some aerial photography tasks an exposure meter may be used as in general-purpose photography, or in the form of an automatic exposure control fitted inside the camera, and for this the film speed may be suitably expressed in ISO, ASA or DIN.

4.13 *Specified average gradient for aerial films.* The slope of a line joining the speed point to a point that has received an exposure corresponding to 1.0 units further along the log exposure axis, is the specified average gradient (often called the G bar, $\overline{G}$). This is the part of the curve most likely to be used in the majority of aerial photography tasks under average conditions; it is sometimes described simply as 'contrast'. (See paragraphs 2.95 and 2.96.)

4.14 *ANSI aerial film speed (ANSI standard PH 2.34).* A slightly different film-speed system, which produces similar results in practice, is that of 'aerial film speed' (or 'effective aerial film speed'). In this system a similar method is used to produce the characteristic curve, but the speed point is taken as a point on the curve where the density is 0.3 above base-plus-fog density instead of 0.4. The aerial film speed is expressed in arithmetic form and is given as:

$$\text{Aerial film speed} = \frac{3}{2 \times \text{exposure at speed point}}$$

The figure obtained is rounded off to give a suitable whole number to an accuracy of one-third *f*-stop, and the exposure to be set on the camera may be decided by the use of a special dial-type calculator that can be obtained from Kodak. The calculator takes into account the other factors affecting exposure.

Speed-related sensitometric information

4.15 *Finding the log reciprocal exposure value.* A simple way of finding the logarithm of the reciprocal of exposure is to count backwards from 0.0 on the log exposure axis up to the speed point, or alternatively to subtract the log exposure value at the speed point from 0.0, as shown in Figure 4.3. Using the reciprocal of exposure simply gives an exposure index that is greater for a faster film. If you wish to refresh your memory on logarithms, refer to Appendix A.

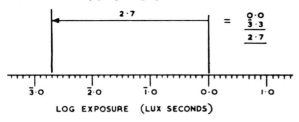

Fig. 4.3 The log reciprocal exposure value is easily found by counting backwards from 0.0 on the log exposure axis along to the speed point.

4.16   *Information on materials and emulsion characteristics.*   Containers of unexposed photographic material usually incorporate a label or information sheet listing the relevant speed, exposure index or meter setting to be used for average (or standard) exposure and development conditions. This information is often given together with other characteristics of the emulsion, many of which are of sensitometric importance. Depending on the type and intended use of the material these may include:

(a)   The batch number of the emulsion.
(b)   The size, type and thickness of base on which the emulsion is coated.
(c)   The date of test, being the date on which the film was tested by the manufacturer; or
(d)   The 'expiry date', considered by the manufacturer to be a guide to its useful working life under normal storage conditions.
(e)   A statement or indication of spectral sensitivity, often with reference to the use of filters.
(f)   Recommended exposure-meter settings relative to different exposure conditions.
(g)   Recommended exposure-meter settings relative to different development conditions.
(h)   Recommended processing conditions for optimum quality.
(i)   A statement or indication of the contrast that should be achieved with normal standard processing.
(j)   An indication of the granular structure of the exposed and processed material.
(k)   Storage, handling and safelight recommendations.
(l)   For black-and-white printing papers, the type, grade, weight, surface and base characteristics.
(m)   In addition, for colour printing paper, the filter and exposure adjustments needed when changing from one batch of paper to another.

During manufacture a particular batch of emulsion is coated onto rolls of film, which may be 1000 metres long and up to 130 cm wide. The large

rolls are then slit into strips and cut to the size required. Because of this it is impossible to manufacture films (even within the same batch of emulsion) having identical characteristics. The values of speed and other factors that may be given are averages, derived from several tests of a batch. Thus they may not define precisely the characteristics of individual films. However, the tolerances allowed in manufacture are stringent, such that, with fresh film, any slight differences will have an insignificant effect.

4.17   *Changes in sensitometric specification.*   Due to advances in technology and the need to apply photography to different situations, the criteria used to specify some sensitometric characteristics may be changed over the years. However, manufacturers of photographic materials publish up-to-date sensitometric information on their products and this can be referred to when necessary. Specific information on new methods of speed determination can be obtained from the relevant standards leaflets, which are generally in full agreement and go into detail defining all the factors involved. Currently the standards for black-and-white negative materials are ISO 6, BSI 1380 Part 1 and ANSI PH 2.5. An ISO standard for black-and-white aerial film is at present under consideration.

Variable-speed, chromogenically developed black-and-white films

4.18   As we know, the speed of a photographic material is not a fixed factor but depends on the nature of the material itself and how it can be used. An impressive example of the variable aspect of film speed is provided by chromogenically developed black-and-white films. These films are made to be processed in a similar manner to colour films, hence the expression 'chromogenically developed'. A typical film of this type can be used to obtain good-quality negatives when rated at any speed from about ISO 125/22° to ISO 800/30° or more.

This exceptional exposure latitude is obtained because with these films the useful part of the characteristic curve is relatively greater than that of conventional general-purpose film, and therefore exposures do not have to be so confined in order to obtain high-quality results. Furthermore, because of their construction and the processing techniques used, they present the advantage that as exposure is increased (over a certain range) there is a

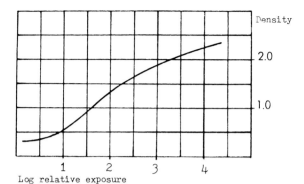

Density

2.0

1.0

1   2   3   4
Log relative exposure

Fig. 4.4 The characteristic curve of Ilford XP1-400, black-and-white, chromogenically developed film (courtesy Ilford Ltd). The curve was plotted from readings obtained using a tricolour blue filter to obtain the printing densities.

tendency to a reduction in granularity instead of an increase, as would be obtained with a conventional black-and-white film. Figure 4.4 shows the characteristic curve of Ilford XP1-400 black-and-white, chromogenically developed film. Agfa-Gevaert Ltd produce a similar film, designated Agfapan Vario-XL.

When this type of film is processed, a black-and-white silver image and an associated fine-grain dye image are produced. The silver image is then removed in a bleach-fix bath, leaving a fine-grain, silverless, brownish-black negative dye image. The improved performance characteristics of the film are made possible by applying colour-film technology to the production and processing of black-and-white film. Because the image-improving techniques used for colour photography can also be applied to these films, the negative image produced is better defined than it is when corresponding conventional films and processing techniques are used. In other respects chromogenically developed black-and-white films are similar to conventional films, and they are used in the same way with regard to their panchromatic qualities, using camera filters, consideration of reciprocity failure effects, etc.

The main advantages and the present disadvantages of the film, when compared with conventional black-and-white films, can be listed as follows.

Advantages

(a) Variable film speed, without necessarily changing the time of processing, and a consequential increase in exposure latitude.
(b) Exposure increase, within certain limits, produces an increase in density but with an associated reduction in granularity.

(c) High speed, together with the sort of fine grain structure that with conventional film is the attribute of slower films.
(d) Subjects of either high or low contrast can be accommodated correctly; and although development time is normally stabilized, some adjustment may be made to suit the contrast of different subjects.
(e) The silverless dye image causes less light scatter in printing. Prints can therefore be made using most types of enlarger without greatly affecting the contrast of the image or emphasizing any diffusion of image detail.
(f) All the silver is removed during processing and can be recovered from the bleach-fix bath.

Present disadvantages

(a) Initial costs are higher.
(b) Processing is more complicated and is carried out at a higher temperature.
(c) The dye images produced may not be as stable as silver images over a long period of time.

Self-assessment questions

4.19 If you want to test your learning write out answers to the following:

(a) List and explain the main factors that can influence the effective speed of a conventional black-and-white film.
(b) What difference in exposure will a film rated at ISO 200/24° need, to give a result similar to one rated at ISO 800/30°?
(c) Describe the criteria used for finding the ISO speed point of a general-purpose film.
(d) Why are these particular criteria of log exposure range, density range and speed point used?
(e) Describe the method used for finding the speed index of a general-purpose film.
(f) What is 'average gradient' $(\bar{G})$ and why is it generally used rather than gamma?
(g) On a piece of graph paper draw density and log H axes similar to those of Figure 4.1. Then draw a typical characteristic curve for an imaginary general-purpose film and calculate the arithmetic and logarithmic speed of the film using ISO formulae (see paragraph 4.6).
(h) Why are the method and criteria for finding the speed of an aerial film different from those used for a general-purpose film?
(i) What is the specified $\bar{G}$ of the film illustrated in Figure 4.1?

5

The sensitometry of photographic printing

5.1 The aim in printing is to transfer to the positive material all the relevant information contained in the negative image, without loss or degradation. An application of sensitometric knowledge will help us to achieve this aim without wasting our time and materials.

The sensitometry of photographic printing in many respects resembles that of film. In printing, the negative with its range of densities becomes the subject, and the printing paper or film is the material that is exposed and processed. When considering printing materials we need to differentiate between positives made on film that are to be viewed by transmitted light and prints on paper that are to be viewed by reflected light. The sensitometry of positive films is essentially the same as that for negative films, as the only differences between them are that films used for making positives are usually lower in speed and of higher contrast, and may be different in their spectral sensitivity. However, the characteristics of printing papers used in black-and-white printing are sufficiently different from those of negative materials to warrant consideration.

Printing paper and printing film characteristic curves in general have a steeper gradient than negative film curves. This is to compensate for the low characteristic curve gradient of most negative films. As we know, general-purpose films have a low gradient in order to give a satisfactory exposure range and some latitude in exposure, and this results in a lowering of image contrast in the negative. To obtain an acceptable print the contrast has to be increased, hence the steeper gradient of printing materials. This reasoning applies to both black-and-white and colour printing material. The specific application of sensitometry to colour printing paper is described in Chapter 11.

5.2 In practice, compared with negative films, printing materials are usually exposed to different illumination for a longer exposure time; therefore similar conditions should be used in sensitometric testing. Furthermore, because positive materials usually produce a higher contrast, a master step wedge with steps of, say, 0.1 density increment (instead of 0.15) should be used. This provides more plotting points for the steeper characteristic curves and thus leads to greater accuracy. The result produced, after exposure and processing of a print sample, is a sensitometric strip on paper.

If a suitable sensitometer is not available, a printing frame or a contact printer having a reasonably uniform illuminance over the exposing plane may be used instead. A calibrated step wedge can be positioned and suitably masked to exclude extraneous light. The evenness of illuminance can be checked before fitting the wedge, by exposing and processing a piece of extra-hard grade printing paper. The paper exposure should produce a mid-range density (about 1.0) after full development with good agitation (see paragraph 6.9). Evenness of illuminance can then be checked by using a reflection densitometer and measuring the density at several places along the strip (see also paragraph 2.14).

Reflection density

5.3 The characteristic curve of a printing paper is plotted in exactly the same way as that for a film, density being plotted against the logarithm of exposure. However, a print on paper is always viewed by reflected light, so its density values are obtained by measuring the light reflected from the image instead of the light transmitted through the image, as is the case with film. Printing paper density is thus a reflection density, and is defined as 'the logarithm of the reciprocal of the reflectance'.

$$\text{Reflection density} = \log \frac{1}{\text{reflectance}}$$

$$= \log \frac{\text{incident light}}{\text{reflected light}}$$

5.4 In practice, reflection densitometers (paragraph 2.46) are calibrated to give direct readings of reflection density after the instrument has been set to give a specific 'zero' density which simulates 100 per cent reflectance. Zero values for general and local comparisons in sensitometry are often obtained either from the unexposed area in the margin of the print being measured or from a piece of unexposed, undeveloped, but fixed printing paper. Such values may be similar but are generally not identical.

To obtain a more standardized zero, some reflection densitometers are supplied with a specially calibrated tile or plaque which will give a good white diffuse surface for zeroing the instrument. An advantage of this is that the surface of the tile will not fade or darken over a considerable period of time and thus the standard of zero will not change. Such durable tiles are particularly suitable for zeroing densitometers on a universal basis, so that measurements on one reflection densitometer can be directly related to those made on another, both having been calibrated to the same standard. (see also paragraphs 11.36 and 11.37.)

The standard by which the tiles are calibrated will be one that reflects more white light than a typical unexposed but processed print margin. Therefore if the reflection densitometer is zeroed by using a standard calibrated tile, the plotted characteristic curve will show an appreciable D_{min}. On the other hand, if the print margin is used for zeroing, the curve will show this as $D_{min} = 0.0$. Printing paper characteristic curves published in manufacturers' literature and in textbooks are often shown in this way, with the curve going down to zero density at the threshold point.

Characteristics of photographic printing paper

5.5 The characteristic curve of a typical black-and-white printing paper emulsion (Figure 5.1) follows the same general pattern and has a similar shape to that of a film curve, except for a few important differences. The differences are largely brought about because:

(a) The printing paper emulsion is a low-speed fine-grain type.
(b) Light reflected from the silver image and from the print base (baryta or polyethylene substrate layer) has travelled through the emulsion not once, as with a transmission density, but at least twice. It

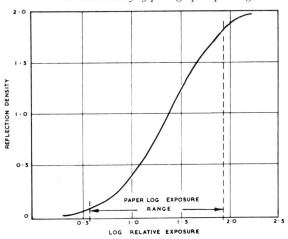

Fig. 5.1 The S-shaped characteristic curve of a typical glossy printing paper. The paper log exposure range indicates the part of the curve that can be most usefully employed in printing. Beyond this part the curve slope is, in general, too low to give acceptable highlight and shadow reproduction.

has also been refracted and scattered during its transit.
(c) Some of the light is reflected from the surface of the print without even entering the image.

The main differences between the characteristic curve of a typical black-and-white printing paper and that of a typical negative film are:

(a) Fog level (D_{min}): with normal development fog is very low.
(b) Curve shape: there is a somewhat extended toe to the curve, and often no region that can really be called straight. In addition, the shoulder is short and turns fairly abruptly into the maximum density.
(c) Curve slope: the maximum slope of the curve is comparatively steep.
(d) Density range: the fog level is very low, so the density range is numerically similar to the maximum density.
(e) Useful log exposure range: often called the paper log exposure range, this covers most of the curve but is shorter than that of a typical negative film curve.
(f) Maximum density: D_{max} is limited to about density 2.0. This upper limit of reflection density is controlled by:
   (1) The reflectance from the silver grains themselves and from the surface of the gelatin layer containing them. Consequently (no matter how much silver deposit is present) the reflectance value cannot be less than about one per cent.

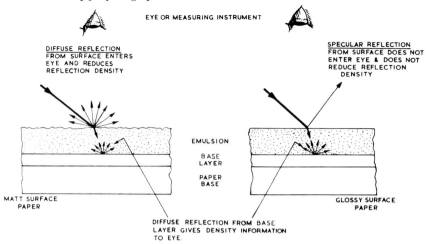

Fig. 5.2 A representation of the reflection of light from photographic paper prints with different surface finishes.

(2) The reflectance of the substrate layer. If the unexposed print margin is taken as being the zero density, density range (and therefore to some extent the measured maximum density) depends on the reflectance of the layer underlying the emulsion in the unexposed margin.

(3) The surface finish of the paper. Glossy paper produces a higher general and maximum density than matt paper, although both may contain equal amounts of silver grains. Figure 5.2 explains this and other effects.

When a print is measured on a reflection densitometer, the measured value of maximum density and of the darker areas of the print is greater than the density seen when the print is viewed. This is because the lighting in a densitometer is arranged so that little or no specularly reflected light from the surface of the print enters the receptor (see paragraph 2.46). On the other hand, in typical viewing conditions a print is illuminated by light from all directions, so wherever the eye is placed it sees some specular reflection; this lowers the visible density.

We can think of reflected light from a print (or what we see when we look at a print) as being the sum of reflectance from the three sources depicted in Figure 5.3. The percentage of each factor that goes to the sum depends on the density of the particular area.

5.6 *Paper log exposure range.* The extremes of the characteristic curve may not be used because of the insufficient tone separation (compression of contrast) that occurs in these areas as the curve

flattens. Because of this, paper curves have two limiting points, one on the toe and one on the lower part of the shoulder, beyond which the gradient is considered to be too low to give an acceptable contrast for viewing. The paper log exposure range is the distance along the log exposure axis between the two points. Of course this does not necessarily apply when prints are made for pictorial or aesthetic purposes, when a good white and a maximum black are often required (see paragraph 7.33 and Appendix C). In practice, the amount of

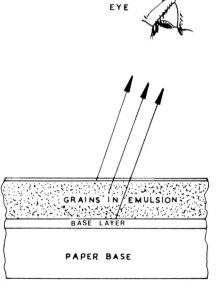

Fig. 5.3 A diagrammatic representation of the reflection of light from the base, the grain clusters in the emulsion and the surface of a photographic print. For simplicity of illustration, the refraction and scattering of light is not shown.

contrast lowering that can be accepted depends on the requirements of the task for which the print is made. For example, in wedding photography (in colour or black-and-white) the subtle tone grada- tions in the white dress of the bride must be visible, and the extreme toe of the print curve must be avoided. In the photography of the dark recesses of an iron foundry the slight differences in the dark tones may need to be emphasized, and the shoulder of the curve should be avoided.

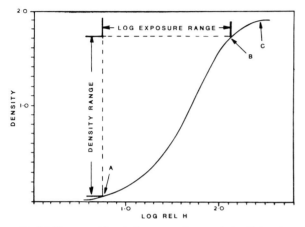

Fig. 5.4 Photographic printing paper characteristics. Points A and B indicate the limits of the useful log exposure range and the useful density range of the paper. Below A and above B, the characteristic curve gradient is considered to be too low to produce satisfactory highlight and shadow detail respectively, when the print is viewed. The point C approximates D_{max} and is used to locate point B.

For general-purpose photography the limits given in the current ANSI standard (Figure 5.4) can be used as a guide. However, for some tasks, such as printing for subsequent camera copying, and when making prints for photographic inter- pretation, the paper log exposure range is usually less than it would be for general-purpose photogra- phy (see paragraph 5.8).

5.7 *Printing paper criteria.* The requirements for producing good general-purpose prints are used as the criteria for assessing the characteristics of photographic printing paper. The current method (ANSI standard PH 2.2) for determining log exposure range and other relevant characteristics is outlined in Figure 5.4. The data for defining a 'good quality print' was obtained by a study of the opinions of a group of observers who carried out practical viewing tests on a large number of prints.

The lower limiting point is at A, which is a density of 0.04 above base-plus-fog. The upper

limiting point is B, which is a density equal to 0.9 of the density at C. We can consider C as being D_{max}, but because it is difficult to position D_{max} precisely on a paper curve, C is a point on the shoulder where the curve gradient is 0.05.

The portion of the characteristic curve between A and B is the part that can be used to make a satisfactory general-purpose print showing adequ- ate detail, and the paper log exposure range is the distance along the log H axis between points A and B.

The upper limit is lower than may be thought necessary because:

(a) Extensive practical viewing tests have shown that at densities beyond this the human eye is unable to distinguish small but significant differ- ences in density.
(b) Resolving power falls away before any marked reduction in curve gradient can be seen. This is partly due to the light-scattering effect of the substrate layer during exposure.

5.8 *Prints made for interpretation purposes.* Prints that are to be used for detailed inspection or photographic interpretation include aerial photo- graphs, and prints for scientific and police investigation. For this type of print the lower toe and upper shoulder of the characteristic curve must not be used. In these areas of low gradient the contrast of the image and resolving power of the processed emulsion is not satisfactory, and detail present in the negative will be degraded or lost if they are used. In particular, the upper shoulder must be avoided because small differences in density in this region cannot be visually distin- guished. This is evident if you look at a measured grey scale and compare the visual appearance of the upper shoulder with the actual density measurements.

No precise standards can be set or achieved in practice because of the different characteristics of printing papers, but in general, prints for photo- graphic interpretation should not extend beyond the range $D_{min} + 0.1$ to $D_{max} - 0.2$. A similar type of print but with a more restricted density range is required when prints are made specially for subsequent camera copying and printing, where further tone degradation will occur. (See Figure 7.10 and associated paragraphs.)

Self-assessment questions

5.9 If you want to test your learning, study Figure 5.1 and answer the following questions:

(a)   How does the shape of the characteristic curve compare with that of the film curves you constructed and studied previously?

(b)   Again by comparison, why is there a lower fog level with this emulsion?

(c)   Why is the D_{max} (maximum density) lower than that of a typical film?

(d)   If a characteristic curve for a typical general-purpose film were to be plotted on this graph, would it be to the left or right of the paper curve, and why?

(e)   Transmitted light is used to measure a film density. What light is used to measure a print density, and why?

(f)   Why, in most cases, should the extreme toe and shoulder of the characteristic curve not be used in printing?

(g)   When measuring reflection density, what is the angle of the incident light and the angle of the reflected light from the print surface, and why?

(h)   Explain why the paper log exposure range is usually less when making prints for photographic interpretation than it is when making prints for pictorial or aesthetic purposes.

Paper latitude in printing

5.10   The conditions of development for photographic printing paper should be such that a fairly high maximum density is obtained together with good image tones. The quality of a positive is for the most part dependent on these two factors, both of which will tend to deteriorate as development times are shortened. A family of characteristic curves can be made, and plotted to show the effect on the material of variation in development time. Several pieces of the same printing paper are given an identical range of exposures through a step wedge. They are then processed in the same developer but for different development times. The resultant densities are measured, and a characteristic curve for each is plotted on one piece of graph paper. The change caused by development time increase can be seen and measured by comparison of the curves.

The family of curves depicted in Figure 5.5 is for an enlarging paper emulsion, typical of most papers when developed at 20°C, using standard dish agitation (see paragraph 6.9(b)). For some polythene-coated papers, which are designed to speed up the printing process, much shorter development times are used; but similar principles apply.

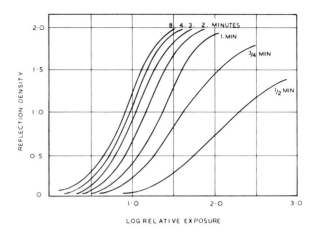

Fig. 5.5 Typical characteristic curves for a glossy printing paper at different development times. Between 2 and 4 minutes development the curve moves to the left without any significant change in shape, slope, D_{max} or D_{min}. This indicates that in printing there is an exposure latitude and an associated development latitude within which satisfactory prints can be obtained.

Perusal of the characteristic curves in Figure 5.5 enables us to describe the effects of development progression. Before maximum density is reached, the print has a low contrast. It contains no full black and is therefore of little practical use. Maximum density is achieved at 2 minutes development. Between 2 and 4 minutes the curve remains fairly constant in shape but moves steadily to the left. If the development time much exceeds 4 minutes, the unexposed parts may begin to show fog.

5.11   *Practical effect of development progression and printing latitude.*   A comparison of the characteristic curves in Figure 5.5 shows that:

(a)   There is a range of development times between which print quality will be satisfactory. In Figure 5.5 this range is from 2 to 4 minutes. Above and below these times prints are unsatifactory because of inadequate contrast (underdevelopment) or fog (overdevelopment). Therefore the recommended development time for this paper would be 3 minutes.

(b)   Between 2 and 4 minutes the paper log exposure range does not change significantly.

(c)   Between 2 minutes and 4 minutes the slope of the curve increases very little and maximum density does not change. The printing paper thus has a development latitude between these times, where development time can be varied with only a very small change occurring in the resultant curve slope. Although the increase in slope between 2 and 4 minutes is very small, it may still be sufficient to be of practical value when a very slight increase or decrease in the contrast of the print is required.

(d)   Between 2 and 4 minutes the curve moves to the left, the horizontal distance between the curves indicating an increase in emulsion speed. Therefore within these times the paper can be considered as having a printing exposure latitude. The effect of slight variations in printing exposure can be corrected by increasing or decreasing the development time between 2 and 4 minutes with negligible effect on print quality.

The above conclusions refer to fresh printing paper. As paper ages, its latitude may decrease and the onset of fog increase. The processing times given above are intended as examples only. Many printing papers can produce good prints at development times below 2 minutes and should therefore be processed in accordance with the makers' instructions.

In practice the printing latitude differs slightly for different grades and types of paper. As an example, with most photographic printing papers an approximate 20 per cent increase or decrease in exposure can be compensated for by increasing or decreasing development time.

Paper grade characteristics

5.12   Unlike black-and-white negative materials, which can be developed to produce varying contrasts, the contrast and therefore the exposure range of a photographic printing paper is more or less fixed. In order to accommodate negatives having different density ranges, printing papers are made with emulsions of different grades, which possess different log exposure ranges. The characteristic curves of the three main grades of paper, as shown in Figure 5.6, produce different slopes and thus have different paper log exposure ranges. Grade 1 (soft) paper has a long log exposure range, and grade 3 (hard) paper has a short log exposure range. Grades of paper having a similar finished surface produce a similar but not identical maximum density, hard and extra-hard grades sometimes having a slightly higher value than the softer grades. Approximate figures for typical log exposure ranges might be:

		Log exp range
Grade 0	Extra-soft	1.4–1.6
Grade 1	Soft	1.2–1.4
Grade 2	Normal (or medium)	1.0–1.2
Grade 3	Hard	0.8–1.0
Grade 4	Extra-hard	0.6–0.8

The higher the grade number and contrast, the shorter the log exposure range.

A satisfactory contact print can, in general terms, be achieved by using a grade of paper with a log exposure range numerically similar to the density range of the negative. Because density itself is a logarithmic function, a density range can be related directly to a logarithmic exposure range. You may like to satisfy yourself of the logic of these two statements. The density range of a negative can be found by using a densitometer to measure first the darkest highlight area, then the lightest shadow area, and subtracting one measurement from the other.

5.13   *Speeds of paper-based emulsions.* It is not usually necessary to specify a figure for paper speeds, but if a comparison between different papers is required a line from a mid-density point (say 0.6 to 0.7) on each characteristic curve can be drawn perpendicularly to the log H axis and the difference measured. Manufacturers aim to produce the main grades of printing paper so that they all have the same speed value in printing; the exceptions are the extra-hard grades, which are usually half the speed of the other grades.

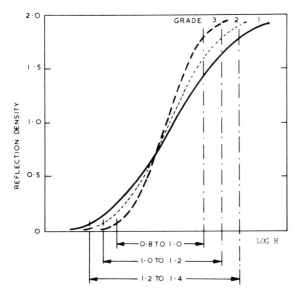

Fig. 5.6 Typical log exposure ranges for the three main grades of glossy printing paper. The steeper the slope of the characteristic curve, the harder the grade and the shorter the log exposure range.

5.14   *Determining a paper's effective log exposure range.*   The effective log exposure range of a photographic printing paper can best be obtained by carrying out a test on the printer or enlarger, under the same conditions as those to be used in practice. A step wedge with known increments of density is suitably masked around its edges to minimize the effect of any flare light. This is then printed onto the paper in the same way as a negative would be printed. After processing, the print of the step wedge will show which step is visually just below D_{max} and which is just above D_{min}. The effective log exposure range of the printing paper will correspond to the density range between the steps on the wedge which have been visually noted. For example, if the step wedge has 20 density increments of 0.15, and if the step number 4 and step number 11 are those noted, there will be seven increments showing, and the paper log exposure range will thus be $7 \times 0.15 = 1.05$. This means that under similar conditions negatives having a density range of about 1.05 will give satisfactory prints on this particular printing paper.

5.15   If a step wedge is not available an approximate assessment or a comparison with other printing papers can be made quite easily. The paper is given a series of progressively increasing time exposures and then processed using standard conditions. The exposure range is just less than the ratio of the time required to produce the maximum visible black to that required to produce a just visible density.

Modifying the exposure range of printing paper

5.16   Up to now we have considered the exposure range of ordinary printing paper as being a more or less fixed factor, and so it is under normal conditions. However, there are ways of modifying the exposure range, and hence the contrast, when necessary. They involve a degree of experimentation to obtain the desired result and (other than with variable-contrast papers) should only be used when, for example, the correct grade of printing paper is unavailable.

In addition, while not affecting the exposure range of the printing paper, the exposure range of the image being printed can be changed by modifying the illumination system of the enlarger (see paragraph 9.15).

5.17   *Modifying contrast by development.*   One method of modifying the contrast grade of black-and-white printing paper involves using either a high-contrast or a soft-working developer, which may increase or decrease the contrast of a print by, say, half a grade. Another method that may be used to reduce contrast involves increasing exposure, pre-soaking in warm water to swell the emulsion, and then developing in the normal solution diluted with, say, five times the amount of water. Both methods are feasible but should not be considered a normal practice. It is more convenient and reliable to have several paper grades than to experiment with development.

5.18   *Modifying contrast by controlled flashing.*   The contrast given by a grade of printing paper can be reduced, and the exposure range increased, by controlled 'flashing'. This involves giving a brief subsidiary exposure to the paper before, during or after the normal printing exposure. An evenly diffused light is used, and the flashing exposure is just below that which would fog or visibly affect the emulsion. The method can also be used with colour materials and with films – for example when duplicating colour transparencies, which are essentially of high contrast. Flashing is most effective on photographic materials having a sharply turning

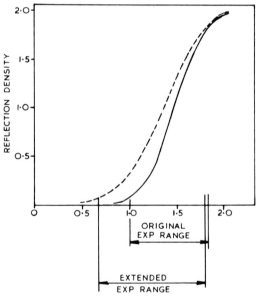

Fig. 5.7 The general effect of flashing on a typical hard grade of printing paper. As the proportion of flashing to normal exposure is increased, the sensitivity of the emulsion to low exposures is increased. This extends the paper log exposure range and also lowers the contrast.

toe, such as some of the harder grades of printing paper.

A controlled flash exposure in effect increases the sensitivity of the emulsion, particularly to low exposure levels. The toe of the characteristic curve is thus flattened and extended, and the exposure range is increased. The effect is the same as that caused by flare and stray light during enlarging (see paragraph 7.13). The general response of a hard grade of printing paper to flashing is shown by the dashed characteristic curve in Figure 5.7. The effect is increased as the flash exposure is increased, because it progressively diminishes the exposure inertia of the emulsion. However, if exposure is carried beyond the threshold point, visible fog occurs.

With some printing papers the increase in exposure range can be similar to going from a hard to a soft grade of paper, the amount of increase being controlled by varying the flashing exposure. Although the exposure range is increased, the effect on the resultant print will not be exactly the same as if the correct grade of paper had been used in the first instance. This is because flashing causes the highlights to be printed with less relative contrast than the shadows.

5.19 *Practical application of flashing.* The flashing exposure must be made to a uniform and even light. This can be produced, for example, by the printer or by a separate lamp. The intensity of the light must be low enough to permit the control of exposure times. A typical method, when enlarging, is either to expose with the negative removed or to diffuse the projected image with tracing or tissue paper. The correct time for the flashing exposure is found by exposing and processing a test strip. The exposure just below that which produces a visible fog is the longest that can be given, and will obtain the maximum paper exposure range. Intermediate ranges can of course be obtained by giving less exposure. A typical flash exposure might be equivalent to, say, five per cent of the normal exposure.

For colour materials, unless a particular colour effect or colour correction is required, the light used for flashing must be that for which the material is balanced. It is usually convenient to flash colour materials after the main exposure. The negative or transparency is removed and a suitable neutral-density filter (say between $D\,1.3$ and $D\,2.0$) is fitted in the light path, preferably where it will be out of focus. A flashing exposure is then made for the same time as for the main exposure.

As flashing raises the sensitivity of the emulsion to low exposure levels, it also raises the density of any age or storage fog that may not have been previously evident. In addition, safelighting considered as adequate for normal work may not be satisfactory when flashing is used.

Variable-contrast printing paper

5.20 Variable-contrast printing papers that can produce a variety of log exposure ranges are available. They differ from conventional papers in that negatives of almost any density range can all be printed on paper from the same box. This obviates the need for having several different grades of printing paper, some of which may seldom be used.

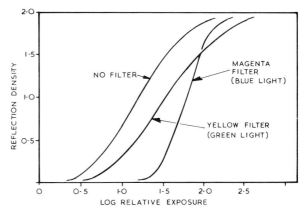

Fig. 5.8 The general effect on a typical variable-contrast printing paper of exposure to different coloured light during printing, A mixture of two emulsions having slightly different colour sensitivities is used. One part of the combined emulsion responds to blue light exposure and gives a contrasty result; the other responds mainly to green light exposure and gives a softer result. Varying the colour of the exposure light by filtration produces a variation in contrast and in log exposure range. There is also a lowering of relative speed. With unfiltered tungsten printing light a normal-grade contrast is produced.

A typical variable-contrast printing paper is coated with a mixture of two emulsions of different colour sensitivity. One emulsion is sensitive to blue light only and the other to blue and green light. With this combination of emulsions, the contrast of the resultant print depends on the colour of the exposing light. Several manufacturers produce variable-contrast papers, all similar in their application. With a typical variable-contrast paper, a high contrast is obtained by exposing only the blue-sensitive part of the emulsion, and a lower contrast by exposing the green-sensitive part. By varying the proportion of blue and green light, a variety of intermediate contrasts and exposure ranges can be obtained.

The colour of the exposing light can be varied either by using specially designed colour filters, or by using the yellow and magenta filters of a colour enlarger. The yellow filter absorbs blue light and transmits green, so it is used when a low-contrast image is required. The magenta filter absorbs green and transmits blue, and is used when a high-contrast image is required. With an unfiltered tungsten printing light, the paper gives a contrast equal to about grade 2 normal paper. The relative speed of the paper is lowered when filteration is used, but of course this can be easily compensated for by adjusting the printing exposure.

Another advantage of variable-contrast paper is that two or more contrast grades can be obtained on the same print. For example, one part of the image could be exposed to give a normal contrast and other parts to have a lower or higher contrast. This facility thus offers a particular control of print quality. The normal printing safelights may be used, provided that standard precautions are observed.

Self-assessment questions

5.21 If you want to test your learning, study Figure 5.5 and answer the following:

(a) What are the development time limits between which good prints can be produced on this particular paper?
(b) What would a half-minute print look like?
(c) What would an 8-minute print look like?
(d) What difference in middle-tone contrast is there between a 2-minute and a 4-minute print made from the same negative?
(e) Explain the practical relationship between paper development latitude and paper exposure latitude.
(f) Does the paper log exposure range change between 2 and 4 minutes?
(g) If the paper log exposure range does not change much between 2 minutes and 4 minutes, how can negatives having different density ranges be printed satisfactorily?

Now study Figure 5.6 and answer the following:

(h) Could you produce a satisfactory contact print on grade 3 (hard) paper from a negative with a density range of 1.4? Give a reason for your answer.
(i) Why is it often necessary to have at least three different grades of printing paper?

(j) What part of the paper characteristic curve is used to produce prints that will be satisfactory for photographic interpretation? Give a reason for your answer.
(k) To obtain a good contact print, what should the relationship be between the paper log exposure range and the density range of a negative?
(l) Presuming that you have a calibrated step wedge, how would you find the effective log exposure range of a particular grade of printing paper?
(m) A 'flashing' technique may be used to modify the contrast of prints, particularly if a hard grade of paper is being used. Describe the effect of controlled flashing and how you might carry it out in a practical situation.
(n) Explain the function of a variable-contrast printing paper, and then describe how it could be used with a colour enlarger.

Relationship of negative and print characteristic curves

5.22 The photographic process usually involves the making of a negative and the production of a print from the negative: in the simplest case, a contact print. There is therefore a need to show the effect of the two processes together on one graph.

To show the relationship of the negative-material characteristic curve and the printing-paper curve as a sensitometric diagram, the negative curve is first drawn in the normal manner. Then, as the density range of the negative is the same as the log exposure range of the optical image to be printed on the paper, the paper curve is turned clockwise through 90° and drawn on its side with its exposure axis parallel with the negative density axis as shown in Figure 5.9. The log exposure range of the optical image can then be transferred directly onto the paper characteristic curve. The same method is used if the original negative is printed onto film, that is, if a positive transparency is made.

An extension of this system is also used to show the relationship between the tonal characteristics of the original subject and the tones of the final print. This is explained in Chapter 7.

Figure 5.9 shows the same subject exposed onto three separate pieces of film which have been processed to give negatives of high, medium and low $\bar{G}$, and thus also of high, medium and low contrast. The negatives have been contact printed onto soft, normal and hard grades of paper

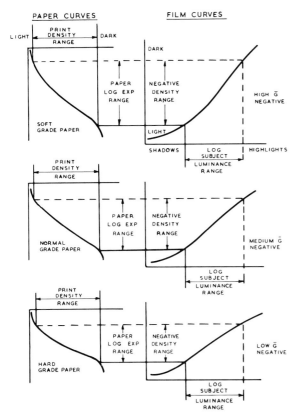

PAPER CURVES   FILM CURVES

Fig. 5.9 The relationship of negative and printing paper characteristic curves. In printing, the density range of a negative provides the exposure range received by the printing paper. To show this graphically, the paper curve is drawn on its side so that the density range of the negative is transferred directly to the paper log exposure axis. The figure shows three negatives made of the same subject, but having low, medium and high contrast: printed onto hard, normal and soft grades of printing paper respectively. Because in each case the negative density range and the paper log exposure range match each other, the resultant prints all have a similar density range.

respectively. Because of the corresponding relationship between negative and printing paper characteristics, the density ranges of the resultant prints are all similar.

5.23   A study of the characteristic curves in Figure 5.9 produces the following conclusions:

(a)   In general a soft-grade paper is suitable for a hard negative, that is a negative with a long density range. A hard-grade paper is suitable for a soft negative, that is a negative with a short density range.

(b)   To obtain a good contact print properly containing all the detail in the negative, the density range of the negative must not be measurably

greater or less than the log exposure range of the paper.

(c)   If the log luminance range of a subject is known, a film can be developed to a $\overline{G}$ (or gamma) that will produce a negative with a density range suitable for printing onto a particular grade of paper.

The formula that can be used as a guide for finding the $\overline{G}$ contrast (or the gamma) for the negative, to enable it to be printed onto a particular grade of paper, is:

Required $\overline{G}$ or gamma

$$= \frac{\text{paper log exposure range}}{\text{log subject luminance range}}$$

The two known quantities are the paper log exposure range and the log subject luminance range, and the relationship between the two can be used to decide the required $\overline{G}$, as shown in Figure 5.9.

This simple formula ignores the varying loss of contrast that occurs between subject and optical image owing to the camera lens flare and (in aerial and landscape photography) the additional effect of atmospheric haze. Also, in the strictest sense, it can only be applied to contact printing, as the characteristics of an enlarger may slightly modify the printing effect of the negative density range. However, practical tests have established that in the majority of cases the effects of these additional factors are not of great significance in general-purpose photography, and this simple formula is therefore of practical value. We shall consider the effects of the additional factors in paragraphs 7.5 to 7.8 and 7.13.

The essence of this is that in practical photography, whether the subject presents a long or short subject luminance range, we can apply the formula and produce negatives that in the majority of cases will give satisfactory prints on, say, grade 2 (normal) paper.

5.24   *The relationship of subject luminance range, negative density range and $\overline{G}$ (or gamma).*   We can relate the formula given in paragraph 5.23 to the examples shown in Figure 5.9. Let us presume that the subject represented in Figure 5.9 was measured using a light meter, and showed a ratio of highlight to shadow of 20 to 1. The logarithm of 20 is 1.3, so the log subject luminance range is 1.3. We need to know to what $\overline{G}$ or gamma a negative must be processed to produce a satisfactory print on:

Grade 1 (soft) paper with a log exposure range of, say, 1.4
Grade 2 (normal) paper with a log exposure range of, say, 1.2
Grade 3 (hard) paper with a log exposure range of, say, 1.0

Using the formula and working out the $\overline{G}$ to the nearest 0.05, the required $\overline{G}$ or gamma values are:

For grade 1 (soft) paper $\overline{G} = 1.4/1.3 = 1.1$
For grade 2 (normal) paper $\overline{G} = 1.2/1.3 = 0.9$
For grade 3 (hard) paper $\overline{G} = 1.0/1.3 = 0.75$

As the negative density range is directly related to the paper log exposure range, it follows that:

Negative density range
$= \overline{G}$ (or gamma) $\times$ log subject luminance range

Log subject luminance range
$$= \frac{\text{negative density range}}{\overline{G} \text{ (or gamma)}}$$

If the formula is depicted in the form of a simple triangular diagram (Figure 5.10), the $\overline{G}$ or gamma, negative density range and log subject luminance range can be found by covering up the factor wanted and then multiplying or dividing as shown.

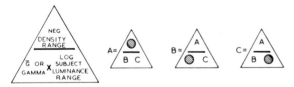

Fig. 5.10 A diagram that can be used to find the required $\overline{G}$ or gamma, negative density range or log subject luminance range, by covering it and then completing the equation.

Introduction to tone reproduction

5.25   Photographic tone reproduction refers to the relationship between the luminances presented by the various tones of the original subject photographed, and those of the final print. It is often thought that the aim in photography is to obtain a true overall tone reproduction, where the tones of the print match those of the original subject, but except for special copying or duplicating processes this is seldom the case. The aim is to obtain a visually satisfactory reproduction. This may mean that the tone scale of a good print is similar to that of the subject, but it may also be that it is less than, or even greater than, that of the subject. Furthermore, the individual tones of the shadows, middle-tones and highlights may be modified. The

primary means of obtaining the desired tone reproduction in printing is of course to use the correct grade of printing paper.

If it was necessary to obtain an accurate reproduction of the tone scale of a subject, each tone on the print would need to be in its correct position on the scale, relative to the corresponding tone of the original subject. Now, if the sensitometric characteristics of the camera-exposed film and the printing paper were either straight lines or curved lines that were 'mirror images' of each other, this could automatically be obtained as shown in Figure 5.11. However, the characteristics are usually curves and the curves are of differing shapes, so some change in the presentation of tones is inevitable.

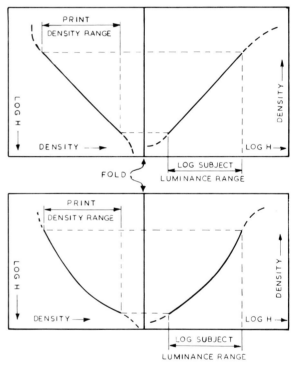

Fig. 5.11 Accurate tone scale reproduction can be obtained when film and paper characteristic curves are mirror images of each other. An easy way to understand this is to imagine one curve drawn using wet ink, and the paper folded to produce the reciprocal curve.

Figure 5.12 shows the tone scale reproduction of a contact print made from a negative developed to a gamma of 1.0. Comparing the tones of the subject and the print, not only are the middle-tones of the print separated to too great an extent (i.e. elongated), but both the highlight tones and the extreme shadow tones are insufficiently separated (i.e. compressed). This is a direct consequence of

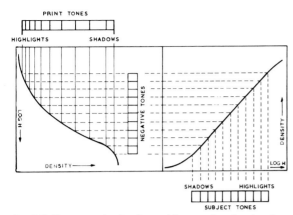

Fig. 5.12 Tone reproduction from subject to print, showing the change in tone scale caused by the curved sensitometric characteristic curve of the printing paper.

the S-shape of the paper characteristic curve. Camera lens flare during exposure also causes a compression of tones, particularly in the shadow areas of the negative. We shall consider this effect later.

5.26 *Result of the curved sensitometric characteristic of a negative being reproduced on paper.* The distortion of a tone scale caused by the characteristic curve of the printing paper can in fact be partly prevented by the curved nature of the negative characteristic as shown in Figure 5.13. A correctly exposed negative may have the highlights of the subject recorded on a comparatively steeper portion of its characteristic curve, but with the shadows on the toe region, which has a concave shape. Thus, the contrast in the shadows is less than that in the highlights. However, when these tones are printed onto the

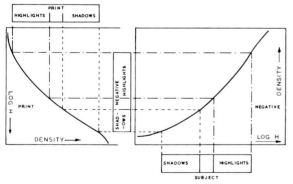

Fig. 5.13 Tone scale reproduction when part of the negative toe is used. Compression of the shadow tones, caused by the shape of the characteristic curve of the negative, is compensated in printing by placing them on the steeper part of the paper characteristic curve. At the same time, the elongation of highlight tones in the negative is compensated by printing onto the less steep part of the paper curve.

paper, the portion of the negative image that has recorded the highlights appears on the less steep toe region of the print curve and loses contrast. On the other hand, the shadow parts of the subject, which have recorded with a low contrast on the negative, appear on the steepest part of the paper characteristic curve and therefore gain in contrast. This opposing effect of the negative and paper characteristic curves accounts for three facts when paper prints are to be made:

(a) When making negatives, it is feasible to use part of the toe of the characteristic curve.

(b) Because the subject shadows are recorded on a less steep part of the characteristic curve, the overall contrast of the negative is lowered. This makes it easier to accommodate it on the restricted exposure range of printing paper.

(c) Provided that the top part of the paper characteristic curve is not used, a print may well show a more realistic tone separation in the shadows as well as the highlights, when compared with the negative itself. Figure 5.13 depicts this situation when a typical negative is printed.

5.27 *Effect of using curved characteristics in duplicating.* A similar situation to that shown in Figure 5.13 can exist in a duplicating process, for example when a duplicate negative is to be made from an original negative. If the characteristic curves in Figure 5.13 are assumed to be those of the same type of film, the right-hand curve will represent the intermediate positive and the left-hand curve the duplicate negative. The subject will of course be the original negative. The curves are almost mirror images of each other so the duplicate negative will be an almost true scale copy of the original negative.

We should remember that except for some aspects of film duplicating, true overall tone scale reproduction is not the aim in photography; it is seldom obtained and is not often needed. A print that well satisfies the requirements of a photographic task may approach true scale tonal reproduction or it may have a greater or less contrast than that of the original subject. Tone reproduction in printing, film duplicating and camera copying is dealt with in more detail in Chapter 7.

Tone modification in photographic printing

5.28 During printing it is often necessary to modify tone reproduction in order to obtain a satisfactory print. This is usually done by manually 'shading' and 'printing in' the image of the negative, to give less exposure to some areas and more to others. It may also be done by 'electronic printing' or by 'masking'. These techniques are all concerned with controlling the exposure given to different parts of the image in order to obtain the required result.

Other methods, which may not be strictly considered as methods of tone modification in printing but which can be used to affect the resultant print, are: the use of variable-contrast printing paper, 'flashing' to increase the exposure range of the printing material (described in paragraphs 5.18 to 5.20), and also modifying the enlarger to vary the contrast of the projected image, as described in paragraph 9.15.

5.29   *Shading and printing-in (dodging).*   When using an enlarger, shading and printing-in is carried out by obscuring some of the image-forming light, using and moving the hands or a piece of suitably shaped card during part of the exposure time. Shading of some areas necessarily involves printing-in the areas that are not shaded, and vice versa. The combined action is called 'dodging'. Shading and printing-in is most often used when the density range of a negative is greater than the log exposure range of the paper on which it is being enlarged. The highlight areas receive more exposure, and the shadow areas less exposure, than the rest of the print. Figure 5.14 depicts this situation in diagrammatic form. The action compresses the ends of the exposure range that would normally be

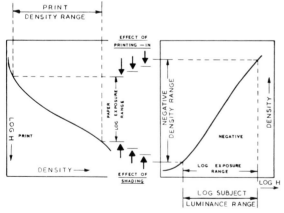

Fig. 5.14 The effect of shading and printing-in (dodging). Dodging may be used when the printing exposure range of the negative is too great to fit into the paper log exposure range. By controlling the exposure given to the shadows and highlights, the ends of the exposure range are compressed so that it can fit onto the printing paper. All the subject tones recorded in the negative are thus reproduced as tones in the print.

given, so that the range now fits into the paper exposure range. This of course may cause some variation in the highlight and shadow tones, but will leave the middle-tones unchanged. Because fairly large areas receive the modified exposure, only the contrast between large areas is affected.

The contrast of small detail within the large areas is not compressed and is therefore still well defined on the print. The retention of small and fine detail contrast in printing is particularly important because it will have already been reduced in the negative by light scatter during exposure, and other contrast-reducing factors. (See also Figure 2.34 and its associated paragraphs.)

Manual dodging is a crude procedure for obtaining tonal modification because it is usually impossible to shape precisely and to move one's hands so as to fit and properly control the exposure of different areas of the image. The result may be visually satisfactory but there will be some variation of both highlight and shadow tones. Tone modification during printing can be obtained in a more effective way by using an electronic printer or by using 'unsharp masking' techniques. We can consider these in turn.

5.30   *Electronic dodging.*   A similar effect to that obtained by manual dodging, but with minimum variation of highlight and shadow quality, can be obtained in a more refined way by using an electronic printer. This is a printer that can be set up to give automatic exposure control and dodging by electronic means. The distinct advantage that electronic printing offers over manual dodging or unsharp masking techniques is that quantities of different negatives can be printed semi-automatically, one after the other, whereas with the other methods each negative has to be treated individually by hand.

In electronic printing the total log exposure range given by the large areas of the negative may be compressed to fit the log exposure range of the material on which a print is being made. As with manual dodging, the contrast of small detail within the large areas is not compressed. The effect on tone reproduction of electronic printing is dealt with in more detail in Chapter 7.

Tone modification by masking

5.31   An electronic printer is an expensive piece of equipment and is unlikely to be available for use by many photographers. However, for individual negatives the same result can be obtained easily, and without the use of special equipment, by printing the negative in combination with a photographic mask. This provides a simple and efficient way of modifying tone reproduction. A mask might, for example, be a positive on film made by contact from the original negative, but processed to produce a lower contrast. A photographic mask is thus a dimensionally equivalent copy of a photographic image but has different sensitometric characteristics. It can be made in either negative or positive form and can be used with either negatives or positives and with black-and-white or colour materials. The techniques and applications of masking are many, and offer almost unlimited possibilities in tone and colour modification. At present though, we need only be concerned with an understanding of the basic principles and sensitometry of masking.

5.32　The concept of using a mask when printing can be understood by thinking of an original negative as a mask, which indeed it is. When we use it to make a print it masks different parts of the printing paper to a greater or lesser extent, and thus allows different exposures to be made onto the printing paper.

As an example of masking, suppose we have a negative with a density range much greater than the log exposure range of the paper on which it is to be printed. A straightforward print would show overexposure of the shadows and underexposure of the highlights as shown in Figure 5.15A. We can overcome this by making a low-contrast positive mask, by contact-printing the negative (see Figure 5.15B), and superimposing mask and negative by sandwiching them together in register. The positive adds density to the negative, most density being added to the shadow areas, less to the middle tones and very little to the highlights. Therefore, when we make a print from the combination, contrast is decreased and the print is correctly exposed. The effect can be shown by combining the two different characteristic curves (see Figure 5.15C). For the purpose of illustration, the curves of the original, the mask and the combination are shown on Figure 5.15 as fairly straight lines.

For the example shown in Figure 5.15 a positive mask was used. If in a similar situation the original negative had insufficient density range for good-quality printing, we could superimpose a negative mask with it and repeat the procedure. The negative mask would add density mostly to the highlight areas, the contrast of the result would be increased, and the resultant print would be correctly exposed.

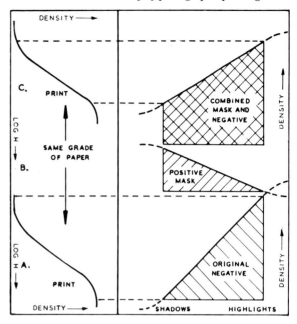

Fig. 5.15 Tone modification by printing a contrasty negative in combination with a positive mask. (A) Overexposure of shadows and underexposure of highlights results when printing the unmasked original negative. (B) A low-contrast positive mask made by contact-printing the original negative. (C) Correct exposure results when printing through the combined mask and negative together.

5.33　*Unsharp masks.*　Masking, like manual dodging and electronic printing, is most often used to reduce the overall large-area contrast of an image, without affecting the contrast of fine detail within the large areas. This is done quite easily by making the positive mask slightly unsharp. The unsharpness can be obtained by having a small separation between the original negative and the mask when it is being made. This causes a slight diffusion or spreading of the printed image, which means that the fine detail of the negative is not recorded (not resolved) on the mask, but shows as a fairly uniform density, while images of larger areas are recorded but have slightly diffused edges. The dashed line in Figure 5.16 shows this effect.

Figure 5.16 shows the principle and the effect of unsharp masking. It represents a plot of densities across a very small area of a negative and its associated unsharp mask, and shows the effect of the two in combination. In use, the unsharpness of the mask provides several advantages.

(a)　It is easier to position the unsharp mask in register with the original because registration is not as critical as it would be with a sharp mask.

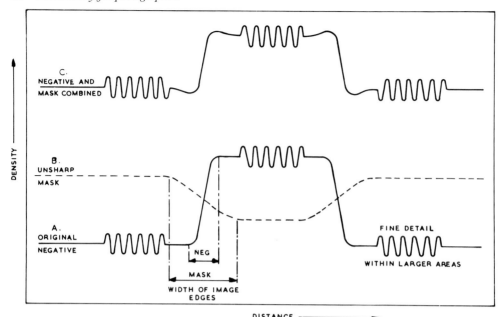

DISTANCE ⟶

Fig. 5.16 Representation of the effect of unsharp masking. (A) A cross-section of a very small area of a negative, containing fine detail within larger areas. (B) An unsharp mask made of the same area. (C) The effect on contrast and on image edges, of the negative and mask in combination. The fine detail of the negative is not recorded on the mask. The combined mask and negative therefore retain the contrast of fine detail but reduce the contrast between large areas.

(b)   An effect of the unsharp mask in combination with the original is that the contrast between large areas is decreased but that of fine detail is not changed.

(c)   The fine detail contrast is relatively greater than that between large areas; thus a print made from the combination appears sharper than a print made from the original image.

(d)   Because large-area contrast is reduced, the print can be made (if necessary) on a harder grade of paper than previously (or on a more contrasty film); thus the contrast of the fine detail will in fact be increased.

(e)   The slightly diffused edges of images recorded on the mask are in contact with the sharper edges of the same images on the original. The diffused edge causes less density to be added to the low-density side of the original edge, and more density to the high-density side. The resultant contrast between adjacent tones is thus greater than it would be if the mask was sharp.

The effect (as represented in Figure 5.16C) improves the visible sharpness of image edges and is similar to that produced by adjacency effects during development (see paragraph 2.103).

5.34   Making an unsharp mask is a fairly simple procedure. One method is to place a thin sheet of transparent material (such as clear film) as a spacer between the original and the material on which the mask is being made. The three are then sandwiched together in a printing frame and exposed to a diffuse (large-area) light source. A suitable exposing light would be that from an enlarger passing through a sheet of opal glass, plastic or tissue paper held above the printing frame. The intensity of the light can be controlled by adjusting the head of the enlarger and if necessary, using the lens stops. See Figure 5.17.

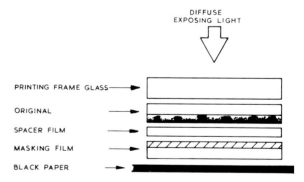

Fig. 5.17 A simple arrangement for making an unsharp mask by using a printing frame. Exposure is made by controlled-intensity light from an enlarger, passing through a diffusing screen. The degree of unsharpness is controlled by the spacer thickness.

A similar method is to print the original through its back, using for example a contact printer with a diffused exposing light, or printing the original in the normal manner but with a sheet of diffusing material between it and the masking film. Another method involves using a compact light source positioned obliquely at a distance from the combined original and mask material. The combination is rotated during exposure so that the light is spread evenly in all directions after it has passed through the original.

The degree of unsharpness required may need to be found by trial and error, and is of course controlled by the thickness of the spacer and the area or angle of the exposing light. The degree of large-area contrast reduction depends on the gamma of the mask relative to the gamma of the original. For example, suppose an original negative has an overall density range of 2.1 and we wish to reduce this to 1.1 in order to print it onto a particular grade of paper. The density range of the positive mask would need to be $2.1 - 1.1 = 1.0$. The gamma of the mask would therefore be $1.0/2.1 = 0.48$ as shown in Figure 5.18.

Because of image spread and other factors during making, the image on an unsharp mask

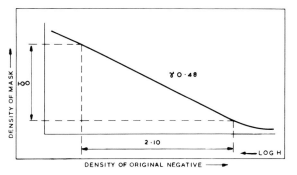

Fig. 5.18 The characteristic curve of a positive mask. Gamma = $1.0/2.1 = 0.48$.

may be very slightly larger than the original. To counteract this when the combination is enlarged, the mask is usually positioned nearer the exposing light source than is the original.

5.35 *Films and processing for mask making.* Special 'masking' films are obtainable. Because they are specifically designed for mask making they are preferable, particularly for use with colour materials. The manufacturers of these films provide detailed information on masking techniques. However, any moderate- to low-speed fine-grain

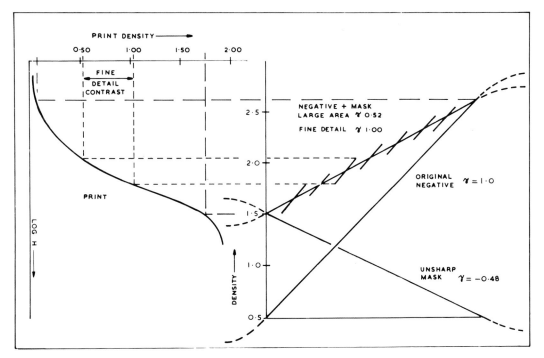

Fig. 5.19 The effect on large-area contrast and on fine detail contrast when an unsharp mask is used in printing. The gamma of the combined negative and mask is $1.0 - 0.48 = 0.52$. Large-area contrast is thus compressed. Fine detail, represented by the several short lines at 45°, is not resolved on the mask. Thus its gamma remains at 1.0, as on the original negative, and its contrast is not compressed. Both large areas and small details are thus contained and well represented on the print.

film, capable of producing a suitable range of contrast, should suffice for experiments, or for less exacting work. For low-contrast masks there may be some difficulty encountered in obtaining uniform development. This can usually be overcome by using a fine-grain developer diluted with, say, five times the amount of water, and prolonging the development time.

5.36 *The sensitometry of unsharp masking.* As an example of the sensitometry of unsharp masking we can consider the original negative and the unsharp mask described in the previous paragraph. The unsharp positive mask can be used to reduce the contrast between large areas, without changing the contrast of the fine detail within the large areas. This can better be understood by reference to Figure 5.19.

The density range of the negative and mask together is $DR_{neg} - DR_{mask} = 2.1 - 1.0 = 1.1$, and this is suitable for printing on the particular grade of paper. The gamma of the negative and mask together is $\gamma_{neg} - \gamma_{mask} = 1.0 - 0.48 = 0.52$. However, the fine detail of the negative is not resolved by the unsharp mask and thus retains its original contrast of $\gamma = 1.0$. This is represented by the several short lines at 45° on the negative-plus-mask curve. Thus in the print the large-area contrast is compressed and contained within the density range of the paper, whereas the contrast of the fine detail is not compressed and is therefore more visible on the print than it would otherwise be. In addition, the visible sharpness of image edges is improved as described in paragraph 5.33 (e).

5.37 *Some other uses of masks.* To increase the overall contrast of a negative, negative masks can be made, but these are used less frequently than positive masks. This is because it is usually more convenient to make a duplicate negative directly to the required contrast and then to print that (see Chapter 7). By this means, the contrast of both large areas and of small detail within the large areas is increased.

Masks are most often used to reduce the overall contrast of negatives (or positives) that are too contrasty for normal printing, but they can be used for modifying tone reproduction in a variety of ways. If we make a mask of, say, the shadows only or the shadows and middle-tones only (by adjusting the exposure when making the mask), we can control the contrast in selected tonal areas of the image. We can also reduce or increase the density of selected areas, for example to subdue but not completely block out unimportant background detail.

The significance of tone modification and masking

5.38 There are many ways in which tone modification and masking methods are used to improve images in both black-and-white and colour photography, and in the graphic arts. By using photographic masking techniques during printing we can, for example:

(a) Increase or decrease contrast overall or in selected tone areas only.
(b) Decrease the contrast between large areas while at the same time retaining the contrast of fine detail.
(c) Increase or decrease the density of selected areas of an image.
(d) Produce bas-relief, tone-line images, posterization, and other graphic effects: for example, by using high-contrast masks or by having a mask slightly out of register.

In colour photography, both black-and-white and coloured masks may be used to produce the above and similar effects. They can be used to control contrast and to compensate for colour deficiencies respectively, and to create special effects.

Tone modification in printing, whether carried out by crude manual dodging, electronic printing or photographic masking, involves the same sensitometric principles. The essence of the technique is that the results obtained are variable and to a great extent under the control of the user. A further advantage is that the original image is not changed in a permanent manner as it would be if, say, chemical reduction or intensification had been used to modify the tone reproduction.

Self-assessment questions

5.39 If you want to test your learning, write out answers to the following questions:

(a) A subject is photographed and presents a ratio of highlight to shadow readings of 25:1 to the film. To what $\bar{G}$ should the exposed film be developed in order to contact-print satisfactorily onto paper having a log exposure range of 1.2?
(b) Complete the following statement. The shadows of a subject have been recorded on part of the toe of the characteristic curve of a negative, and the

highlights on the straight-line region. However, an undodged paper print made from the negative shows an almost true tone-scale reproduction. This is explained as follows:

(c) By dodging during printing, or by using an unsharp mask, the photographer can control the log exposure range given by the negative so that it fits into the log exposure range of the printing paper. Explain the effect that this has on the contrast between large areas on the print, and on the contrast of fine detail within the large areas.

(d) A negative with a shadow density of 0.2 and a maximum highlight density of 2.3 needs to be printed in combination with an unsharp mask to produce a log exposure range of 1.2. To what gamma will the mask be processed?

Fine detail in second-generation images

5.40 Whatever system is used to produce a print from a negative, there is bound to be some slight loss of information in the fine detail because of the turbidity (light-scattering effect) of the positive emulsion (see Figure 2.34 and associated paragraphs) and imperfections in the printing apparatus. The effect of turbidity is worse in a paper print than in a transparent positive because, in addition, the substrate layer scatters light back into the emulsion by diffuse reflection (see Figure 5.2). Nevertheless the printing operation also enables the tone separation between images to be expanded if necessary. This, by increasing the contrast, can make small images more readily discernible.

5.41 The question might still be asked, 'If some information is lost in second-generation images, why not view the negative directly?' The answer could be, 'Look at a negative and its positive side-by-side and find out for yourself.' The function of the human brain is such that negative images present a psychological obstacle to the extraction of information by a viewer. A print or transparency, because it presents images in a natural, positive form, is much more easily observed.

5.42 To obtain the best possible transfer of fine detail from negative to print on a contact printer, the contact of negative and positive must be true. In projection printing the lens must give its optimum performance. In both cases direct illumination will produce a better resolution than diffuse illumination.

To facilitate composition and fine focusing of the projected image, the matt-white reverse side of a piece of printing paper is often placed on the enlarger easel. However, difficulty in focusing may be encountered if a piece of polythene-coated paper is used for this purpose, because the coating tends to scatter projected light so that fine detail in the image cannot be visibly focused.

Emphasis of detail contrast can be obtained by making a positive transparency on film; because this is viewed by transmitted light it presents a greater density range than a print on paper. The material used for making such 'diapositives' should preferably be a fairly high contrast 'positive' film, with its associated high resolving power and low turbidity.

Another way to emphasize detail contrast is to make separate paper prints for, say, shadows, middle-tones and highlights, each at optimum contrast.

6

Sensitometry in practice

6.1   We have now reached a stage where we can consider some aspects of sensitometry in practice, before going on to study other applications of sensitometric curves. As in all sections of the book, it is most important to bear in mind that although the accent here is on sensitometric testing, what happens in sensitometry also happens in practical photography when we use a camera, a printer, or a processing system.

Considerations in sensitometric testing

6.2   To be of practical value, sensitometric tests must utilize, or at least simulate as far as possible, the conditions of exposure and processing (including drying) that the material will receive in actural use. The advantage of carrying out tests under practical conditions is that all the many factors that can affect the response of photographic material will be automatically included in the result. Emulsion sensitivity changes with temperature and humidity, so a simulation of practical conditions should also include the ambient conditions before, during and after exposure.

6.3   *Random errors.* In ordinary sensitometric procedure, results cannot be determined with absolute accuracy owing to imperfections in the procedure, for instance:

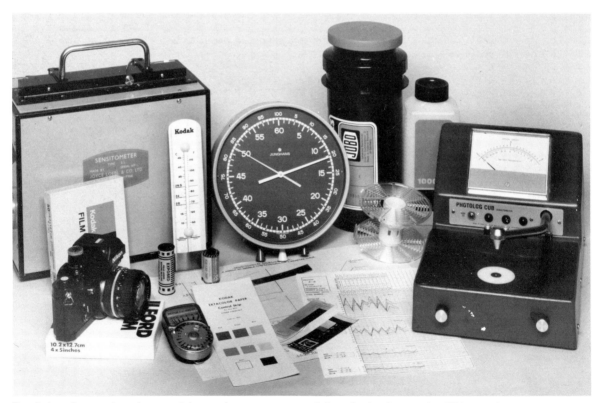

Practical sensitometry is used to control the complete photographic process, from the manufacture of materials to their use by the photographer. This control enables us to achieve the best possible results at all times.

(a) Variations in the characteristics of the emulsion from batch to batch, or even within a single batch.

(b) Experimental error in the measuring apparatus.

(c) Irregularities in the action of processing solutions and small unpredictable fluctuations in processing procedure.

Possibly the greatest problem is in obtaining uniform development, in order to obtain an even density in all the areas that have received the same exposure. This particularly applies when processing sensitometric strips under practical conditions, for example in continuous or roller-transport processing machines. Development methods that are quite satisfactory for normal photographic processing are not always adequate for sensitometric testing because, as well as the effects of processing variation, they may not produce sufficiently even densities. The varying effect on test results of such random errors and fluctuations can be minimized by making at least five separate tests and taking the mean of the measured values.

6.4 *Serviceability of sensitometric equipment.* All equipment used, especially sensitometers and densitometers, must be optically clean, serviceable, and set up accurately. Periodic tests must be made to check the accuracy of instruments in accordance with the manufacturers' instructions. Lamps used in instruments must be clean and free from fingerprints, grease marks, etc. Sensitometric wedges are particularly liable to damage. They must be free from fingerprints, scratches and dirt-filled scratches, grease marks, etc., which would adversely affect the results. In darkroom conditions it is easy to unintentionally touch the surface of a wedge or of the material under test. Care must be taken to avoid this, but if it is likely to happen you should wear clean lint-free cotton gloves. Wedges can be protected from damage by covering them with a thin sheet of transparent plastic, which itself can be changed at intervals. Plastic sheets are not identical in their transmission characteristics, so several covers for later use should be cut from the same original sheet.

Thermometers, timing devices etc. should be checked for accuracy periodically. Filters, grey scales, wedges, calibration plaques, reference strips and colour charts should be treated with the same care as lenses. Surfaces must not be touched, and when not in use they must be stored in a dry place away from dirt, dust, heat and light in special 'photographic' storage envelopes, as postal-type and other envelopes may contain glues that can affect photographic materials.

In a sensitometric laboratory, where for example precise film testing is carried out, the consistency of test equipment performance will be checked regularly. Records of the small variations in the reproducibility of calibrated sensitometers, densitometers and associated equipment will be kept, and the results averaged and correlated as necessary, so that a standard of precision can be established and then maintained (see paragraphs 2.14, 2.43 and 6.38). When the reproducibility characteristics of sensitometric and photographic equipment are being established, it is usual to have the same person carry out all the tests in order to minimize the possibility of human errors and variations between different operators. The calibration of sensitometers is further considered and described in Appendix B.

6.5 *Storage and ageing of materials before exposure and processing.* Light-sensitive photographic materials are unstable in both their unexposed and exposed states. At normal room temperature, both the speed and the contrast of unexposed photographic emulsions are slowly reduced and the fog level is slowly increased with age. For example, with film a loss of speed of one stop (0.3 log exposure units) in three years is a reasonable estimate. These ageing effects are aggravated by high temperature and humidity. Conversely, storage at low temperatures retards the effects of age. Thus materials that have been stored under different conditions of temperature and humidity cannot be expected to give comparable results, even though they may have been from the same batch of emulsion. Colour materials in particular need proper conditions of storage, if possible well below freezing point. They consist of several separate and differently sensitized layers of emulsion that have been balanced in manufacture to give optimum results. Poor storage conditions will cause changes in speed and contrast which can affect each emulsion differently, thus changing the colour balance of resultant photographs. Black-and-white printing paper, and 'slow' emulsions in general, are more resistant to ageing effects than are faster emulsions. With most photographic materials the effects of ageing and poor storage show first as loss of contrast, particularly in the toe region of the characteristic curve, and then in visible fog as the effects increase.

The speed (sensitivity to light) of most materials will vary slightly with temperature. Therefore materials that have been stored in a frozen state must be allowed to reach the ambient working temperature before being exposed. Overnight or 4–5 hours should suffice for most packages of material, but tightly rolled motion-picture film in cans, or long rolls of aerial film, may need up to 24 hours.

Manufacturers provide specific instructions for the correct storage and treatment of photographic materials before exposure, after exposure, and after processing (see Appendix G).

6.6   *Delay between exposure and processing of materials.* At temperatures above freezing point the latent image fades very slowly. The effect, called 'latent image regression', is in general most active during the first hour or so after exposure, but after this time has elapsed it reaches a plateau where any changes are extremely slow. Because of this, test samples on film should be processed only after more than one hour has elapsed since exposure, particularly if several samples have been exposed at different times. A delay of one hour or so will ensure that all the samples reach equilibrium. In many aspects of photography, of course, delays of this order are usual, so this treatment will not be very different from normal practice. Regression of the latent image is aggravated in conditions of high temperature and humidity.

Printing paper, on the other hand, is usually processed within a moment or two of exposure and should so be treated in sensitometric tests. In all cases the correct system is to duplicate the conditions that exist in normal practice. The effect of latent image regression on regular colour material is considered in more detail in paragraph 11.120.

Processing techniques

6.7   The processing conditions for sensitometric testing should be the same as those the material will receive in practice. However, actual operating conditions are not always available or feasible. The points given below should be used as a guide in such circumstances and when tanks, dishes, trays or spiral processing methods have to be used. The aim throughout is to adopt a suitable standard procedure that will give consistent and reproducible results. For colour materials, the various processing steps do not of course have the same function as those for black-and-white materials. Therefore the procedures recommended by the manufacturers of colour material and processing equipment must be followed as closely as possible.

(a)   *Size of tank, dish or tray.* Tanks, dishes and trays should be of a generous size in order to contain sufficient developer for thermal stability and to minimize uneven development.

(b)   *Developer.* The developer should be freshly mixed and of ample quantity for the test in hand. The addition of wetting agent and the use of pre-soaking techniques is not recommended unless such are to be used in practice later.

(c)   *Temperature.* Developer temperature must typically be controlled within $\pm 0.5°C$; other solutions should be within 5°C of the developer temperature or, for colour materials, $\pm 0.25°C$ and 1°C or less (but see manufacturer's instruction leaflet for a specific process). For black-and-white processing this is best achieved by control of the laboratory room temperature and by allowing solutions and equipment used to reach the ambient temperature. If this method is not suitable, a temperature-controlled water-bath surrounding the tank or dish should be used. Large quantities of developer, for example in a tank, must be thoroughly stirred immediately before use to ensure a stable level of activity and temperature. For some colour processes the developer temperature latitude may be only $\pm 0.15°C$ at temperatures up to 38°C. In order to achieve control in these conditions, the best practicable method is to use an efficient colour-processing machine.

(d)   *Insertion, positioning and removal of samples in tanks, dishes, trays, processing machines and roll-film spirals.* Sensitometric strips must be inserted and positioned so that they will receive the same processing conditions as the regular material.

(1)   *Tanks.*   The high-density end of the strip should be towards the bottom of the tank. By doing this, the by-products of the process, which retard development, will have less effect as they flow downwards from the lower-density areas. Strips should be kept away from the sides of the tanks and be well and equally separated, with the emulsion of each facing the same way.

(2)   *Dishes and trays.* Strips should be central in the dish or tray, emulsion up, and remain fully immersed throughout processing. They should be taped or held in position, for example on a piece of rigid plastic sheet, to prevent them from moving with the flow of solution during agitation.

(3) *Continuous or roller-transport processing machines.* The low-density end of the strip should enter the machine first, with the emulsion facing the same way as the regular material.

(4) *Roll-film spirals.* The use of roll-film spirals is not recommended for sensitometric testing because of the uneven processing results usually produced. However, if they have to be used, the strips should be positioned with the emulsion facing the same way as the regular material and with a space between each pair of strips.

If tanks, trays or dishes have to be used for test processing a series of sensitometric strips, it is preferable to insert the strips into the developer at timed intervals and then to remove them all together for insertion in the next solution. This method is particularly applicable to colour materials, as the subsequent colour-processing procedures are then more easily carried out. When this method is used, the required universal standard of agitation for the strips may in some circumstances be difficult to achieve. If this is so, the strips will have to be inserted together as a unit, agitated together and then removed individually at timed intervals. Which procedure is adopted depends upon the type of process, the equipment, and the method used.

Agitation

6.8 The three main factors in development and processing are time, temperature and agitation; of the three, manual agitation is often the one most difficult to control. Efficient agitation is essential if we are to obtain uniform processing and development. Furthermore, once the proper agitation has been obtained, it must be standardized for all the sensitometric strips or samples of any particular test so that the action is reproducible (see paragraphs 3.14 and 3.15).

6.9 Unlike development time and temperature, the degree of agitation cannot be precisely specified, but in general a turbulent flow of developer giving fairly vigorous yet random agitation is best for producing uniform development. Agitation techniques recommended for black-and-white and colour material processing are different and depend on the particular process and method used. Colour materials require a specific rate of agitation, and special techniques are invariably recommended by the manufacturer. This is because the materials consist of several layers of emulsion, and even slight changes in

agitation will affect each layer to a different extent and can upset the colour balance. If no specific instructions are available, the suggested agitation methods given below may be used. You are advised to practice the procedure several times before actual use, so that it will be familiar when carried out in darkroom conditions.

(a) *For frames in tanks (Figure 6.1).* Insert quickly and smoothly, and tap the frame(s) sharply four or five times on the tank edge to remove any air-bells. Follow by continuous, gentle, full up-and-down agitation for the first 15 seconds, then every 30 seconds lift clear, and (keeping the film plane vertical) turn the frame one-eighth of a turn, drain, turn back and lower, taking 5 seconds. The turn should be alternately to the left and then to the right so that the solution is drained from alternate bottom corners.

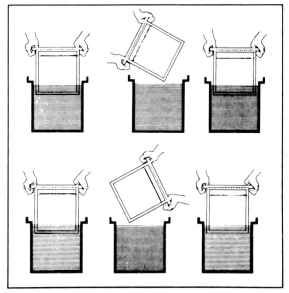

Fig. 6.1 Agitation cycle for tank development (courtesy Kodak Ltd).

(b) *In dishes or trays.* A continuous, irregular, four-way rocking cycle of about 4 to 8 seconds, by lifting and lowering each edge of the dish in turn. Or lift and lower left side, lift and lower near side, lift and lower right side, lift and lower near side, and then repeat the procedure (Figure 6.2). Larger dishes require the longer rocking cycle. Uniform development can probably be best achieved by brushing the surface of the emulsion immersed in the developer with a soft broad brush. The method of agitation adopted depends on the reason for the test.

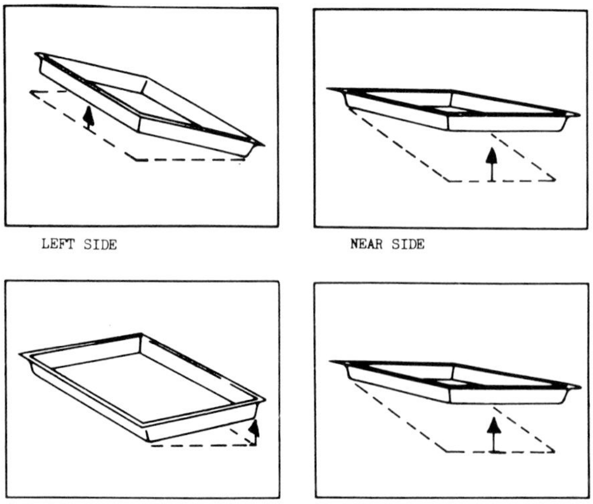

LEFT SIDE

NEAR SIDE

RIGHT SIDE

NEAR SIDE

Fig. 6.2 Agitation cycle for dish or tray development (courtesy of Kodak Ltd).

(c) *In roll-film (daylight-developing) spirals.* Processing in daylight-developing tanks using spiral spools usually produces uneven results, despite the most careful agitation. The agitation method recommended by the manufacturers of the unit should be adopted, but in general an inversion method should have a more uniform effect than agitation by rotation or other means. For accurate timing of development, the immersion of the film spiral into the developer and then into the stop-bath should be as swift and even as possible. This is best done by processing in the darkroom conditions using a series of tank bodies in a line, and by using the same system of agitation as recommended for frames in tanks.

(d) *Nitrogen-burst agitation.* The most efficient and controllable method of agitation is given by the nitrogen-burst system. It can be used in tanks, large dishes and processing machines, but is not really suitable for films on spirals which trap the bubbles. The system requires special apparatus. Bursts of nitrogen gas are introduced into the bottom of a processing tank at controlled intervals through a special distribution unit. The bubbles of gas rising through the solution give automatic agitation, and the degree of agitation can be regulated to obtain standard results. Once the desired agitation is achieved it can be repeated at any time. Nitrogen gas is used because it is odourless, non-toxic and has no chemical effect on the processing solutions.

When a nitrogen-burst system is used, air-bells still need to be removed; wherever feasible, agitation

for the first 15 seconds is carried out by hand, as described in paragraph 6.9(a).

Development and processing times

6.10 The duration of development depends on the requirements of the test, but short development times should be avoided as much as possible because of variations in the initiation of development, which will produce uneven results. As a general rule, development times longer than 4 minutes will give more precise, meaningful and reproducible results than times of less than four minutes. Development times for producing a family of characteristic curves depend on the spread of the results required. For an initial test it is usual to choose a series of times that increase proportionally. For example: for a 40 per cent increase, approximate development times for a film emulsion might be 3, 4¼, 6, 8¼, 11½ and 16 minutes. For a 20 per cent increase, approximate times might be 3, 3½, 4¼, 5¼, 6¼ and 7½ minutes.

The timing of development, processing and agitation can be awkward in darkroom conditions, especially when several samples are processed together. To ensure correct timing you can use a clearly visible luminous (darkroom) clock situated directly in front of the operator, or an electronic process timer which can be preset to indicate a range of different times. Visible timing devices must be positioned to avoid any possible fogging of photographic material. Another method is to use a tape recorder set to play a prepared tape of instructions and suitable time intervals. The tape must be of a type that will not stretch and thus give a wrong time scale. Failing this, an assistant can pass on instructions from outside the darkroom.

Processing instruction tapes are particularly suitable for carrying out manual colour processing because they enable the user to give full attention to the procedure without being distracted by the constant need to read and check instructions.

For colour materials the duration of immersion in each of the processing solutions is particularly critical, and must be timed as accurately as possible. Processing time covers the period from immersion in a solution to immersion in the next solution. Automatic processing machines have timed mechanisms which ensure that the duration of each different step in the process is accurately controlled.

6.11 *Draining and stop-bath.* Draining time after development should be standardized at about 5 seconds, and is considered as part of the development time. After this, the material is quickly immersed and continuously agitated for about 10 seconds in a fresh 3 per cent acetic acid stop-bath, or put into the next solution.

6.12 *Fixation.* The fixer should be reasonably fresh and of the same formulation as that used in practice. Samples should be agitated fairly vigorously for at least 15 seconds, and must not be left in the fix for much longer than twice the clearing time.

6.13 *Rinsing and washing.* Samples should be rinsed separate from the wash tank, and then washed for at least 10 minutes in a gentle stream of water at a temperature within about 5°C of that of the previous solution. If samples or sensitometric strips are to be retained as a record, a longer period of washing is necessary.

6.14 *Film drying.* A correct method and rate of drying is of particular importance, as density differences will occur if it is changed significantly or if drying is uneven. Water spots must be avoided, as the swelling of the emulsion under the spot may cause the silver grains of the image to be moved out of place and thus cause an unwanted change in density. Film strips should be immersed in a fresh wetting-agent solution for about one minute, and allowed to drain from one corner before insertion in well-separated positions in a drying cabinet. Although 'natural' slow drying is best, standard and reproducible conditions can be obtained more effectively by using a drying cabinet for all film drying.

The effect of drying should be such that the image contained in the swollen emulsion shrinks back into the exact position that it held during the precise moment of exposure. This aspect in film drying is particularly important for the photography and correct reproduction of fine detail.

6.15 *Print drying.* To obtain meaningful density measurements, print surfaces must be clean, flat and scratch-free, so care must be taken in drying (and particularly in glazing) paper prints and sensitometric strips. Glazing sheets invariably have minute scratch marks, so a sheet of good-quality glass should be used if glazing is required. Polyethylene (PE) coated printing papers and papers that do not require glazing must be dried with care so that the surface to be measured is flat, otherwise reflection density measurements will be inaccurate.

6.16 *Practical working conditions.* It is emphasized that although consideration of the above points will assist the production of consistent and reproducible results, sensitometric tests are usually made to find out what will happen in practice. In such conditions meaningful results can only be obtained by using the same processing method for the test.

Safelight testing

6.17 In sensitometric testing, unprocessed materials must be protected as much as possible from exposure to light and radiation other than that used in the test. This is particularly important with colour printing paper, because latensification due to long exposure to a safelight can cause colour casts to show on the finished print. If a safelight is necessary or useful in working conditions, it should be tested to ensure that it is in fact safe to use. The test must be carried out using the fastest material that is to be exposed to the safelight.

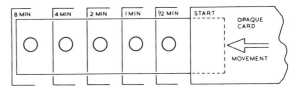

Fig. 6.3 A method for testing a safelight. A piece of slightly pre-fogged photographic material is partly covered and then exposed to the safelight. Exposure increase is made in several steps and the material is then processed in total darkness. An increase in density above that of the originally covered area indicates an unsafe exposure time.

A simple method is to pre-fog evenly a piece of the material, such that if processed it would produce a density of 0.5 or so. This action overcomes the inherent exposure inertia of the emulsion and thus makes it more sensitive to additional light, a state that is applicable to any latent image. It also ensures that the effect of any subsequent exposure is emphasized by being on the steep part of the characteristic curve. Approximately one-sixth of the material is close-covered with a thin opaque card and it is placed in the required position facing the safelight. The remaining area of emulsion is then exposed in five steps, by moving the card forward after, say, ½, 1, 2, 4 and 8 minutes on the clock. The material is then processed for the normal time in total darkness. The safe exposure time is determined by visual side-by-side or densitometric comparison of the steps, to find the longest exposure that does not produce an increase in density. If this time is halved, the result can be considered a safe exposure time.

Density differences can be made more apparent if five coins are also placed along the material as distance markers before exposure to the safelight, one coin being covered each time the card is moved. A similar method is to line up several coins and to remove them one by one at intervals. After processing, the outline of the coin-covered area will contrast with the surrounding area.

When colour printing safelights are to be tested it is often convenient to carry out a similar procedure by using paper process-control strips. Individual control strips are exposed to the safelighting for different times; after identical processing, the low-density steps are compared with each other and with the low-density step of the manufacturer's reference strip.

Safelights are often overlooked in the general check of laboratory serviceability. Because certain types of safelight tend to crack and leak, and the dyes used in the filters fade with age, they should be examined and tested at least once every year and whenever a lamp is renewed. The date and result of the test should be indicated on the safelight filter for future reference.

For conventional safelights, a 25 watt lamp is usually the maximum recommended for use with a 200 to 250 volt mains supply, and a 15 watt lamp with a 110 to 120 volt supply; in all cases the material manufacturer's instruction sheet should be consulted.

Process quality control

6.18   Quality control in processing refers to the establishing of processing conditions that produce optimum results and then ensuring that subsequent processing has the same effect. It is used for all photographic materials, film and paper, and its application is based on comparative sensitometry, as described in paragraphs 2.120 and 121. If you are particularly interested in process control, you may wish to reread those paragraphs before continuing here. Processing a single film to a high standard is not too difficult. The problem is to maintain the same high standard for many films over a long period of time. A process thus needs to be initially correct and reliable, and then to be consistent at all times. This consistency can best be checked by using sensitometric monitoring.

You may think that this type of quality-control monitoring is not in your province, that it is more the concern of the large-scale processing units that compete with each other to produce the best results. This is not so; process quality control is just as necessary for the keen photographer who wants to produce optimum results. Continue reading here, and then if necessary refer to Chapter 13 in which a method of simplified quality-control monitoring is described.

Sensitometric monitoring methods are used in obtaining accurate and consistent results in photographic processing, particularly where replenishing of solutions is carried out – for example, with tank lines or in batch processing or continuous processing machines. Standard pre-exposed sensitometric strips called 'process-control strips' are processed at intervals, and by using a quick method of measuring on a densitometer and comparison with predetermined values, the efficiency of the process is monitored. The quality of processing can then be maintained by corrective action. As it may be included with regular films, the control strip also enables the operator to distinguish between an error in processing and an error in exposure. The measuring and comparison of process-control strips may be carried out by conventional methods, but in large-scale regular use results are often obtained automatically by using a computer-directed process-control densitometer.

6.19   *Process control: measuring and recording.* The monitoring procedure is similar for black-and-white and colour materials. The densitometric values of the control strips are plotted on a progressive chart (called a 'process control record' or simply a 'control chart') either side of a datum line representing the optimum standard process. The control chart provides a sensitometric record of what occurred during processing, and when it occurred. It also shows whether or not the process is operating normally. For example, a typical chart for black-and-white aerial film processing (Figure 6.4) will show separate records of contrast ($\bar{G}$), relative speed, and fog; the plotted values are contained within predetermined tolerance levels defined by control limit lines (dashed lines in Figure 6.4). The tolerance levels and the mean (average) of the values to be expected depend on the particular process in use and the needs of the task. They can be decided by experience or, if necessary, by a statistical study of the random changes that occur when the process is operating normally. These include, for example, small unavoidable fluctuations in contrast and speed. In

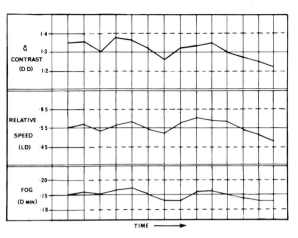

Fig. 6.4 A typical process-control chart for black-and-white aerial film. The results of periodic sensitometric tests are plotted on the chart alongside a datum line representing optimum performance, and within lines indicating the tolerance that can be accepted. The chart provides a record of processing and an indication of present effects and also of future trends that may need preventive action.

operation such small random changes are normal, but with a continuous process, for example, remedial action would be taken as soon as a significant downward or upward trend from a mean value was seen. To assist the operator, some process control charts have additional lines (called 'action limits'), drawn just inside the control limit lines. If the action limit lines are crossed, the operator will take remedial action. If the control limit lines outside them are crossed, the processing of photographic material must be stopped, because the system is then 'out of control'.

A plotted process control chart thus provides:

(a) Datum lines representing the optimum quality level.
(b) A systematic record of the behaviour of the processing system.
(c) An indication of the degree of tolerance allowable under practical operating conditions.
(d) Both an indication and a prediction of the possible need for preventive or remedial action.

The chart, or a separate record, will also be used to record the processing time (or, for a processing machine, the running speed), solution state, temperatures, replenishment action, etc., so that they can be related to the sensitometric results, and indicate the possible cause of a variation in standards. Although sensitometric findings can indicate a change in processing they cannot show the cause of the change, so the recording of these

interrelated mechanical, physical and chemical variables is important. Furthermore there may be a situation in which one condition, say a decrease in agitation, is temporarily countered by an increase in temperature. Such faults may not be evident on the control strip but will show on the running record.

The accuracy of results depends first on the stability of the original process-control strips and then on accurate density measurements (see paragraphs 2.43 and 2.51). The densitometer used for measuring the results must therefore be reliable and be properly calibrated and used. Otherwise any error in the setting-up or any variation in readings may be misinterpreted as an error in processing. This is particularly important, because it is the one step in the process that is not being investigated and it can easily be overlooked.

The manufacturers of photographic materials usually supply detailed instructions, process-control charts and pre-exposed control strips to suit their products and procedures, together with a 'reference strip' that has been correctly processed. These must be used in colour process monitoring in particular. Different materials and processes have their own particular reference strips, control strips and standards of tolerance.

6.20 *Colour process monitoring.* The monitoring of colour processes for both film and paper is similar to that used for black-and-white photography. However, it is a little more difficult because of the several different image layers of the colour control strip, and the more complex chemistry used in the process. After processing, a colour densitometer fitted with red, green and blue filters is used to measure the densities of the cyan, magenta and yellow dyes of the control strip. The three separate readings are made and recorded, in order to monitor the balance of colour reproduction. Colour photographic processing and its sensitometry are explained in Chapter 11.

Correctly exposed and processed reference strips are provided by the film manufacturer, together with a quantity of unprocessed control strips that have received the same exposure as the reference strip. In use, density readings from the newly processed control strips are compared with those of the reference strip and any differences expressed in terms of plus or minus values. The figures are plotted on the control chart either side of a datum line representing the optimum standard process. Variations from the datum line indicate the extent of processing changes. Figures 6.6 and 6.7 show typical plotted control charts for colour film processing.

Because of its standard characteristics the reference strip used in colour processing must be handled with care, and when not in use it must be kept in its storage envelope in a dry place, away from light and heat.

Colour-processing quality control is used extensively in the motion-picture film industry and in photographic processing laboratories, particularly where long rolls of colour material are concerned. In the film industry, the original negatives may be processed and then printed to produce master positives, which are then printed and so on, to produce several generations of images. In this sort of procedure, process quality control is operated at each stage, the control strips and the densitometer used being appropriate to the particular stage of the operation. The practice in this and in related procedures is always to use densitometry that simulates the intended use of the material being processed. This type of densitometry is explained in paragraph 11.37.

6.21   *Interpretation and action.*   The correct interpretation of control chart recordings and the decision on what action to take is fairly self-evident for black-and-white processing. However this is not necessarily so for colour processing. Each colour process has its own characteristic responses and the manufacturer's advice and action must be followed to ensure optimum results. (See also paragraphs 6.27 to 6.37.)

6.22   *Locally made process-control strips.*   If the manufacturer's control strips are unavailable or unsuitable for a particular process, your own locally exposed process control strips may be used. They must be made from film of the same type as that to be used in practice. It is important that the strips are all standardized with regard to emulsion characteristics and exposure, at the time of processing. This can be achieved by exposing a quantity at one time. They must all be from the same batch, preferably from the same roll or box, and all exposed on the same sensitometer. The complete film or the separate strips should be stored in a cool place for at least 48 hours before use so that the latent images reach equilibrium. A means of making and using 'home-made' control strips, and in particular for monitoring the processing of colour materials, is described in paragraph 13.30.

If control strips are to be used over a considerable period of time they should be put in an airtight container and stored in deep-freeze conditions ($-18°C$). On removal, each strip must be allowed to reach the ambient working temperature before processing (see paragraph 6.5). For more precise control the exposed control strips should be mixed in a haphazard manner and processed in pairs. This action allows for the possible effects of slight changes in sensitivity that may be present throughout the roll or batch of films used.

6.23   *Processing record of individual films.*   In addition to process-control monitoring, and particularly for long lengths of film, sensitometric exposures may be made on each end of the film. This provides a permanent and integrated record of the characteristics and processing of individual films, and also enables identification to be made between possible processing errors and exposure errors. To ensure standardization the same sensitometer must be used to expose all the sensitometric records.

6.24   *Quick evaluation of speed and $\bar{G}$.*   Approximate but consistent and sufficiently accurate values of contrast ($\bar{G}$), relative speed produced and D_{min}, both for control strips and for sensitometric test strip exposures, may be determined directly from the strip without plotting a characteristic curve. This speedy acquisition of data is essential with long lengths of aerial film so that any necessary remedial action can be carried out without the delay encountered in plotting a full characteristic curve. The same densitometer, accurately calibrated and zeroed, should be used to measure all the strips. The procedure is:

(a)   Read and note the fog level (D_{min}).

(b)   Find the step that has a density of approximately 0.4 above D_{min} and note its density. This is called the low-density (LD) step.

(c)   By reference to the sensitometer masterwedge, find the step that has received 1.0 log exposure more than the $0.4 + D_{min}$ step and note its density. This is called the high-density (HD) step.

(d)   Subtract the low density from the high density (HD − LD) to obtain the density difference (DD). The result substantially equates to finding the $\bar{G}$ contrast for aerial films (see paragraph 4.13).

Similar procedures, and a similar interpretation of results, can be used in the process-control monitoring of other photographic material (film or paper), for example black-and-white general-purpose films and colour films, which are processed to different values. These are described in paragraphs 6.29 to 6.36 (and also in 2.120 and 2.121).

6.25 *Interpreting the findings.* The value of relative speed produced for aerial films that are in the same speed group, or for process control strips, is sufficiently indicated by the actual density value of the low-density $(0.4 + D_{min})$ step. For example, when identical sensitometric exposures on two different films are compared after identical processing, the film producing the higher density value is the faster film. True differences in speed can only be found by constructing and plotting back through characteristic curves (see Figures 2.38 and 2.40, and associated paragraphs).

When pre-exposed control strips are processed, the original characteristics of each strip will be identical; therefore variation in the values found will indicate variation in the activity of processing only.

The three values found ($\bar{G}$ contrast, relative speed produced, and D_{min}) are together important indicators of a change in the processing. The temptation to simplify the procedure by attempting to rely on one value (for example D_{min}) is a risk that must not be taken.

6.26 *Data determination in practice.* With practice, an operator will be able to choose the low-density (LD) and the high-density (HD) steps and carry out the monitoring procedure speedily and with certainty. As an aid to identification, the relevant steps are usually indicated by arrow-head markings on the sensitometer wedge. When this is done, the operator can quickly read and record D_{min}, relative speed produced, and $\bar{G}$ contrast.

In large-scale processing units and sensitometric laboratories this sort of procedure is often carried out by using a computer-controlled densitometer, which may incorporate a graph and data printout facility. The data obtained, for both black-and-white and colour processes, may also be interpreted automatically.

Process monitoring

6.27 The following information and the four process control charts (Figures 6.5 to 6.8) explain in outline a typical process-monitoring system. Further information, process-control strips, process-control charts, and processing manuals that give detailed instructions on individual processes

and the interpretation of control plots, are usually available from the manufacturers of photographic materials.

6.28 Reliable and consistent photographic processing depends very much on standardized conditions and the careful, correct maintenance of the processing solutions and equipment. It is therefore advantageous to know whether these conditions have been obtained and whether the process is giving optimum results. Process monitoring using control strips provides this information by using a simple method of comparative sensitometry (see paragraph 6.18). It is then only necessary to evaluate the results of the comparison to decide what action, if any, to take.

The following describes in outline a Kodak process-monitoring system, but it is typical of other manufacturers' systems of process quality control. By processing, plotting, and evaluating control strips regularly, any change or drift towards the established processing tolerance limits will be noticed and can therefore be corrected before the ordinary photographic material is visibly affected. If the control strip plots fall outside the tolerance limits, no more photographic material should be processed until a second control check is carried out. Then if the results from the first strip are confirmed, the cause of the trouble must be established before any more material is processed. If the cause of the trouble cannot be located the processing solutions must be discarded, fresh solutions made up, and a further test carried out before regular photographic material is processed (see also paragraph 6.37).

Monitoring on its own cannot ensure accurate processing. This can only be obtained when the information supplied by regular process monitoring is correctly interpreted and the appropriate action is taken.

6.29 *Black-and-white process control strips.* Ten-step process-control strips are recommended for Kodak professional black-and-white processes. They are pieces of film that have been pre-exposed to give a ten-step sensitometric strip. One high-density (HD) step and one low-density (LD) step are each marked with an arrow-head, and these steps may be used for routine process control. The full ten-step scale and D_{min} need only be used when more detailed information is required.

After optimum processing, the selected steps are measured on a densitometer, and reference values are established for the low-density step (LD), the

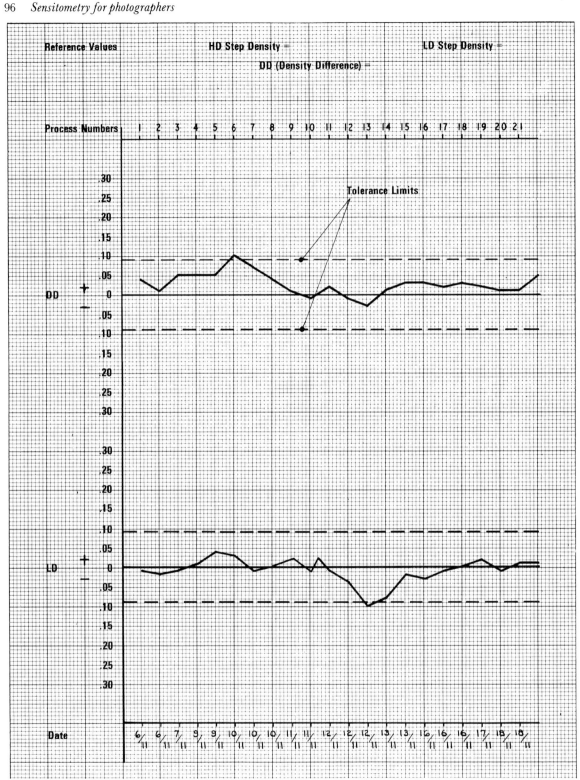

Fig. 6.5 A typical process-control chart plotted for a black-and-white film process (courtesy Kodak Ltd).

high-density step (HD) and the difference between them (DD). Control strips processed subsequently are measured in the same way, and the difference between the reference values and the control strip values are plotted on a process-control chart. An example is shown in Figure 6.5. Limit lines have been drawn on this chart to indicate the degree of processing variation that will probably be the maximum acceptable. Should the plots fall outside these lines the process is considered to be out of control. Experience, however, may establish that for individual processing requirements these limit lines can be modified without noticeably affecting the quality of results.

6.30 *Colour process-control strips.* Colour process-control strips are available for monitoring the processing of both colour reversal and negative films, and for colour printing papers. Each colour material and process has its own particular process-control strip, and the details of the monitoring procedure vary somewhat; therefore the instructions in the relevant processing manual must be carried out for a particular process. Although the process-control strips vary in their format, most incorporate a small grey-scale sensitometric strip, with steps of differing density. These represent the highlights, middle-tones and shadows of a typical colour reproduction, After processing, the red, green and blue densities of selected steps of the control strip are measured on a densitometer, and the results plotted on a process-control chart.

For reversal film processing, the density values of the minimum density (D_{min}), a low-density step (LD), a fairly high-density step (HD) and the maximum density (D_{max}) are measured. The differences between the control strip values and the values of the appropriate reference strip are then plotted on the process-control chart, in terms of a plus or minus value (see paragraph 6.20 and Figure 6.6).

For colour negative film and printing paper processing, the density differences between a high-density step and a low-density step (HD − LD), the density values of a low-density step (LD) and the values of the minimum density (D_{min}) are measured. The differences between the control strip values and the values of the appropriate reference strip are then plotted on the process-control chart in terms of plus or minus values.

These values establish the relative colour contrasts of the three emulsion layers, the speed produced in the photographic material by the colour process, and the level of fog or stain. Figure 6.6 shows a typical process-control chart and plots for a colour reversal film process, and Figures 6.7 and 6.8 show the same for colour negative and colour print processing respectively.

The B-HDC red value plots, at the top of the chart in Figure 6.8, were used to indicate the effect of a bleach-fix problem which may have caused reddish shadows on colour prints.

6.31 *Process-control monitoring and photographic quality.* When carrying out any sensitometric process control, it is important to bear in mind that control strips and plots on a process-control chart simply provide a means of checking and recording the accuracy of processing. They do not by themselves indicate the quality of the processed material. Therefore the results of process-control monitoring must always be supplemented by a regular visual quality check on the final product.

Interpreting colour process control records

6.32 In an ideal situation the dye density readings taken of a processed control strip will coincide with the readings of the reference strip. Therefore, plots made on the process-control chart will all be on the datum line, as this represents the reference values for optimum processing. In practice, of course, this ideal situation is seldom achieved. Some variation in processing is unavoidable, so plots that are within the control limit lines on the chart are considered to be satisfactory and indicate the production of colour material that has been processed to an acceptable standard.

When interpreting process-control charts, the actual processing method used is a factor in deciding the relative importance of the plots. For instance, when batch processing machines or tank lines are used, by definition processing is intermittent. Therefore the measurement of the control strips for each batch and the vertical position on the chart of control plots are important. This is because any decisions concerning replenishment rates and processing times, etc., have to be made before the next batch of material is processed. On the other hand, when continuous processing machines are used, replenishment rate and machine speed etc. may vary or be adjusted during a processing run. Therefore the trend patterns, horizontally along the chart, of a series of plots are often more important than are individual plots.

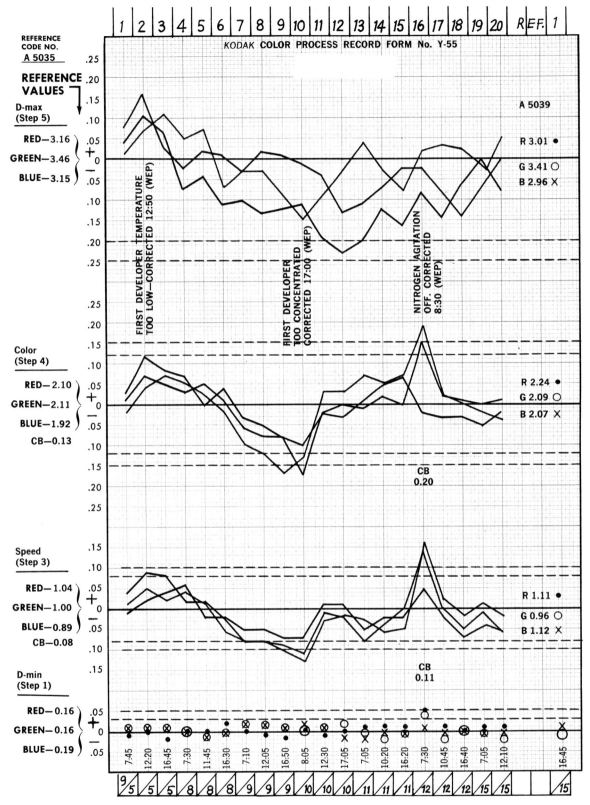

Fig. 6.6 A typical process-control chart plotted for a colour
reversal film process (courtesy Kodak Ltd).

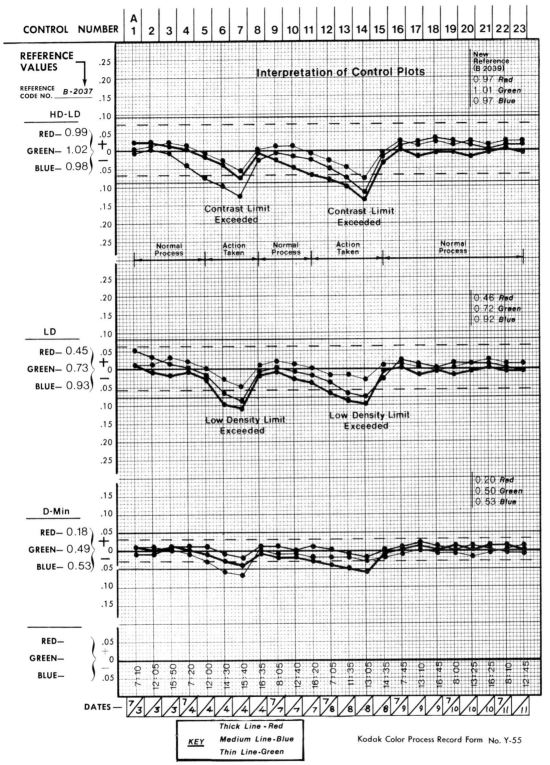

Fig. 6.7 A typical process-control chart plotted for a colour
negative film process (courtesy Kodak Ltd).

6.33   When interpreting the results plotted on a process-control chart, it is advantageous to recognize which plotting variations are significant and which are not so important. The three main types of colour material and processes that may be used are reversal, negative and print. Incorrect processing of these materials may cause an incorrect overall density and/or an incorrect colour balance. With regard to the quality of results, the significance of each of these two variables depends upon the type of material that has been processed – whether it is an end product in itself, such as a transparency, or only a means to an end, such as a negative, where some corrections for processing variations can be applied during printing.

Because of the difference in usage of each type of photographic material we will consider the basic interpretation of control charts for the processing of each of the three main types of colour material in turn.

6.34   *Interpretation for reversal film processing (Figure 6.6).*   Being an end product, a correctly processed colour transparency, unlike a negative, must be visually satisfactory. If all three vertical plots (red, green and blue) of each step plotted on the control chart are close together and either above or below the datum line the effect will be relatively unimportant, because this simply indicates that the transparencies processed, along with the plotted control strip, may be a little too light or too dark. Within limits, such transparencies will be visually satisfactory. However, if the three plots (red, green and blue) are spread apart this is significant, particularly if the spreading occurs in the middle steps of the process-control strip, because these steps represent the most visually noticeable part of the transparency. This particular pattern of plots is called a 'colour spread' (see Figure 6.9) and indicates that a colour cast has been produced in the processed transparencies. Even a small colour cast will be very evident on the transparency, whereas a small change in overall density will still be visually acceptable.

6.35   *Interpretation for negative film processing (Figure 6.7).*   Some corrections for the effect of processing variations are carried out automatically when colour negatives are printed. These include using a suitable level of exposure, which will compensate for slight variations in overall negative density and D_{min}, and using suitable filtration, which will compensate for slight variations in individual emulsion speeds. Therefore plots on the process-control chart that indicate these variations, for example as a colour spread, are relatively unimportant for colour negative films. However, plots that indicate a difference in contrast $(HD - LD)$ between the individual red, green and blue readings are important, because the effect of such variation cannot be corrected during printing.

Plots indicating an equal change in contrast for all three emulsion layers are also significant, because the resultant increase or decrease in overall negative contrast may not normally be corrected in printing. This is because there is usually only one specific grade of colour printing paper available (see paragraph 11.58).

6.36   *Interpretation for colour printing paper processing (Figure 6.8).*   A colour print is the final product of a negative–positive process and must be capable of producing good colour fidelity. However, even with non-optimum but consistent processing, it is often possible to produce colour prints of an acceptable standard. This is because some correction for the effects of the processing of both negative and print are carried out automatically as part of the printing process. These include the printing exposure, which will compensate for slight variations in paper speed, and printing filtration, which will compensate for slight variations in speed between the colour paper emulsions. Therefore plots on the process-control chart that indicate these variations are relatively unimportant. However, plots indicating variations in contrast between each individual emulsion layer $(HD - LD)$ are important. This is because any contrast variation between layers will cause colour balance changes, which may show as one colour cast in the highlights and a different colour cast in the shadows of the colour photograph. Also of importance is any rise in the level of D_{min} density, because this indicates degraded whites or an increase in colour stain, which would be very noticeable on the colour print.

Successful colour printing demands precise processing control, because the only two corrections that can usually be made are those given at the exposing stage, by using a suitable exposure level and filtration. Therefore a similar level of processing must be given to each successive batch of colour printing paper. When colour paper is processed, the allowable batch-to-batch processing tolerances are relatively small, so the process control chart is interpreted with the aim of keeping processing variation to a minimum.

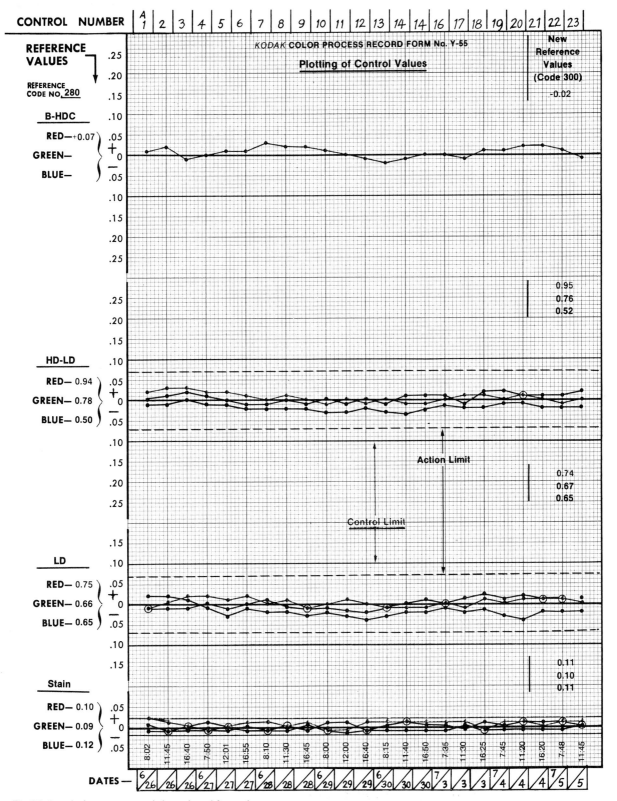

Fig. 6.8 A typical process-control chart plotted for a colour
printing paper process; for B-HDC see paragraph 6.30.
(courtesy Kodak Ltd).

Process-control manuals and terminology used

6.37   The information on colour process control given in this book can only be of a general nature, since colour processes and the monitoring procedures used to control them are changed from time to time. Specific information can only be obtained from up-to-date processing manuals covering the particular process in use. Each process-control manual describes a particular colour process in detail and also gives full instructions for measuring control strips, plotting the process-control chart, and using it. Typical processing problems and their probable causes and corrections are described, and the manuals include many diagrams showing what the problems look like on a process-control chart. In addition, there is usually a list of specific problems and their probable solutions. The manuals also include advice on using various processing methods, solution mixing instructions, replenishment rates and silver recovery techniques.

Many of the descriptive terms used in process-monitoring and process-control manuals are self-explanatory. However, some of the terminology used to describe plot patterns on the process-control chart, and associated situations, may be confusing unless supported by illustrations. Information regarding the interpretation and significance of particular plots and plot patterns is of course best obtained from the appropriate manual. However, we can consider briefly some of the typical terms used and how the effects they describe may look on a process-control chart.

Any group of three vertically positioned plot points on a colour process-control chart represents the response of one particular process-control strip to a processing situation at a particular time. A number of groups of three plot points are joined by lines to form a pattern indicating the response to a series of processing situations over a period of time. Plots that are displaced from the central (datum) line indicate the extent and probable visual effect on the control strip, and on the associated regular photographic material, of colour processing variations. Some typical plot patterns are illustrated in Figure 6.9. The terms often used to describe these patterns are given below, together with a brief description of the probable visual appearance of colour prints or transparencies that have been processed along with the control strips. It is easier to recognize and understand the visual appearance of the effects of these patterns on colour prints or transparencies than on colour negatives.

(a)   *Trend patterns:* a gradual upward or downward drift with all three density plots fairly close to each other. Trend patterns show as an increase or decrease in overall density or contrast, but with an acceptable colour balance.

(b)   *Jump patterns:* abrupt changes in the grouped plot positions. Jump patterns show as sudden random changes in overall density or contrast, and possible small changes in colour balance, with each successive processing run.

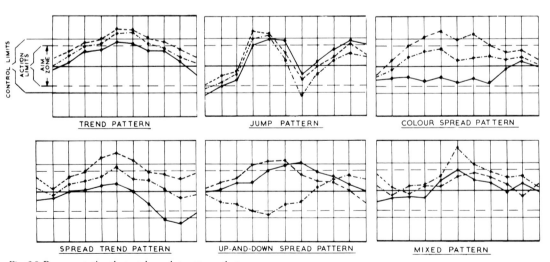

Fig. 6.9 Representative three-colour plot patterns that may occur on a process-control chart used for colour process monitoring.

(c) *Colour spread patterns:* the three density plots are spread apart more than is usual. They appear as an incorrect colour balance, which may be different in light and dark areas.

(d) *Spread trend patterns:* the density plot points are gradually spread apart with movement in a general upward or downward direction. These patterns show as a colour cast that increases gradually with each successive processing run, and may be different in light and dark areas.

(e) *Up-and-down spread patterns:* the density plot points are out of their normal vertical sequence, with one moving away from the other two. Lines joining the plots may cross each other. They appear as a gradually increasing or decreasing colour cast that changes with each successive processing run. The colour casts may be different in light and dark areas.

(f) *Mixed patterns:* a combination of two or more types of pattern occurring over a short period of time. They show as random changes in density and colour balance, over a range of processing runs.

The descriptive terms and the interpretations given above are only of a general nature. Specific information and probable reasons for a particular situation can be obtained from the process-control manual describing the relevant colour process. The majority of processing problems can be solved by logical deduction and can be easily corrected, but it is important that expensive colour chemical solutions are not needlessly discarded when attempting a correction. For example, if it is suspected that an out-of-control situation is caused by a particular solution in the processing sequence, the manual will probably suggest that a 'by-pass test' be made before a possibly large quantity of expensive solution is discarded. A by-pass test is carried out by processing a control strip in a freshly prepared, small quantity of the suspect solution. The control strip is processed as normal up to the suspected step and is then removed, and processing is continued in the fresh solution (for example, in a small dish, tray or beaker, using gentle agitation). The strip is then returned to the normal process. On completion, comparison with the out-of-control strip will indicate whether or not the suspected solution is at fault.

Obtaining accurate sensitometric results

6.38 Four factors determine the results we obtain from a sensitometric test strip:

(a) The inherent characteristics of the photographic material used.

(b) The conditions of the exposure it receives.

(c) The conditions of the processing it receives.

(d) The characteristics of the density-measuring device.

In sensitometric testing, the aim is usually to hold three of these factors constant in order to properly evaluate the effect of the other. For example, in process quality control, the characteristics of the exposed control strips are held as constant as possible and the densitometer used in measuring is consistent. Therefore any variation in results can be directly attributed to the processing conditions.

6.39 For precise tests of photographic materials, such as those carried out by film manufacturers and for scientific investigation, the need is to hold the conditions of exposure, processing and measuring constant. Any variation in results will then be directly attributable to the characteristics of the material under test. The exposure and measuring conditions can be reasonably established as a constant. Sensitometers are capable of giving standard and repeatable exposure conditions with very little variation, and precision densitometers, properly used, give accurate and repeatable results. The main problem is to maintain the processing conditions as a constant. As we already know, this is an almost impossible task when using ordinary processing techniques. Although these techniques are adequate for normal photographic work, and with care can be used for practical sensitometric tests, they cannot be considered as being constant over a period of time, or of producing sufficiently uniform development.

For the precise processing of photographic materials, the processing stage must be held as constant as possible so that it does not contribute any significant variation to the result of a test. Therefore, for tests of this type, special processing devices or small machines are used. These are designed so that their effect in processing can be considered as almost constant. The variations met in normal processing techniques are brought into control by processing under special 'laboratory conditions' and using:

(a) Precisely formulated, measured and mixed solutions.

(b) Accurate control of solution temperatures throughout.

(c) Precise immersion times.

(d) Efficient and consistently reproducible agitation methods.

(e) Controlled drying.

(f) Conditions of processing either as close as possible to those the material is expected to receive in practice, or such that the results can be correlated to practical photographic conditions.

The main feature of sensitometric processing devices is that the processing conditions are controlled, uniform, and consistent.

As with ordinary sensitometric procedures, there will still be some small random variations in the results owing to the varying characteristics of photographic materials and slight imperfections in the sensitometric procedure. However, if the same test is repeated several times and the results are averaged, the effect of any random variability can be minimized.

The ISO method of developing black-and-white negative materials for still photography, when determining an ISO speed, is given in the standard leaflet ISO-6. The ISO standard requires a method equivalent in agitation and overall efficiency to that produced by a prescribed system of processing. In essence this consists of using a specially formulated developer solution, which in use fills all but a quarter of a vacuum flask. A vacuum flask is used so that the temperature of the solution in it can be held constant at 20°C during development. The test sample is fastened to a glass strip, which is fixed to the stopper of the flask and inserted centrally in the vessel. Agitation may be carried out manually by tilting and rotating the flask strictly in accordance with a prescribed technique.

Exposure control in camera and printer

6.40   When using a sensitometer, exposure control is a straightforward matter as the same standard subject is recorded each time the sensitometer is used. The step wedge provides a regular range of illuminances, and the duration of exposure is usually a fixed factor. Furthermore, there is no need to confine the exposure range to a particular part of the characteristic curve of the test material. In practical photography, however, where exposures are made in a camera or printer, there will be variations in the illuminance range of each subject recorded. Furthermore, the aim when photographing or printing a subject is to place the resultant image densities onto a particular part of the characteristic curve of the photographic material in order to obtain an optimum result. Because of this and other variables, practical photography demands a fairly precise control of exposure. The achievement of correct exposure

applies particularly to colour materials, and this aspect is further considered in Chapter 11.

6.41   *Correct camera exposure.*   When taking photographs with a camera, the correct placing of exposure on the film characteristic curve depends principally on the illuminance range of the subject's image and the camera settings used (lens aperture and shutter speed). Thus for a particular film and processing, the quality of the final reproduction depends to a large extent on giving the correct camera exposure. An exposure-estimating device such as a light meter (exposure meter) can be used to compute the combined effect of most of the exposure variables, such as the intensity of light and the emulsion speed of the film. Other variables, such as the effect of modified processing, can be assessed and taken into account by using a decision based on sensitometric knowledge. A most reliable way of ensuring optimum results is to make a series of exposures bracketing an estimated correct exposure – for example, by giving the estimated exposure and others half a stop or so either side of this. The method is reliable because it incorporates the sensitometric effect of all the small and indeterminable factors in both exposure and processing that can influence the end result (see also paragraph 11.116). Exposure bracketing is often used for critical photography. However, it is wasteful and often impracticable, so for general work more direct methods of exposure assessment are usually adopted.

6.42   *Exposure meter calibration.*   Methods of determining camera exposure are many and varied, but in the main depend on the use of photoelectric exposure meters which convert light energy into electrical energy. Photoelectric meters respond to light falling on a photocell, the amount of response varying in proportion to the intensity of light received. Depending on the type of meter, the photoelectric effect either causes the generation of a small electric current (photogenerative) or causes the photocell to change its resistance to an existing current (photoresistive). The meter may be calibrated to indicate the measured level as a 'light value', and this can then be used in association with the film speed to determine camera exposure in terms of lens aperture and shutter speed. An exposure meter may be used external to the camera or as part of a through-the-lens (TTL) system. The best position for measuring the light that will reach the film is inside the camera, because the effect of the camera lens (lens flare, etc.) is then taken into account. The use of TTL exposure meters is described in more detail in paragraph 11.115.

The majority of external (hand-held) exposure meters are used to measure the average luminance of the scene to be recorded on the film, and all are designed and calibrated by the manufacturer to interpret light values based on a particular standard. This standard is usually an average neutral middle-tone reflecting 18 per cent of the incident light. TTL meters are at present usually calibrated on a statistical basis for colour reversal film, assuming that the majority of exposures will be made on colour film. A TTL meter calibrated to give correct exposure on colour reversal film (with its limited exposure latitude and critical exposure requirements) will also provide a satisfactory exposure level for other types of film. Some exposure meters are designed or used to give an emphasis to the central area (centre-weighted) or main part of the subject; others can be used to measure a selected small area of the subject, or of its image in the camera. The light measurement made by the meter is then used in conjunction with the film speed, to determine the camera exposure as a combination of lens aperture and shutter speed.

An exposure meter is used to decide the critical first step in the photographic process, so it must be operated properly and in accordance with the manufacturer's instructions. Furthermore, because of the variations that occur in individual cameras and working conditions, it is usually necessary to adjust or 'calibrate' an exposure meter to suit one's own equipment and working methods. This can be done by finding, and then using on the meter, a film speed setting suitable for the combined effect on exposure of the particular film characteristics, the camera lens and shutter operation, and typical conditions of photography. When the exposure meter is calibrated, there will be a satisfactory relationship between the meter exposure indications and the actual camera exposure required to place the subject image on the best part of the film characteristic curve.

Individual meter calibration can be obtained by carrying out practical tests under the expected conditions of use, and making a series of (e.g. half-stop) camera exposures bracketing an estimated 'correct exposure', based on the film manufacturer's recommended film speed. After processing the test film (and if applicable printing), the exposure that gave the best result can be used as a basis for calibrating the meter. For example, if the exposure that gave the best result was one stop less than that indicated by the exposure meter, the film speed setting used should be increased by a factor of 2. If it was one stop greater, the setting should be decreased by a factor of 2. This method of exposure meter calibration takes into account the effects of any variations that may be present in a particular lens or shutter, and in the photographer's own working conditions and requirements (see also paragraph 11.116).

6.43 *Using exposure meters.* The way in which an exposure meter is used is very important if accurate results are to be obtained. The method of use depends for the most part on the type of subject and the kind of photograph required. There are four commonly used methods, each appropriate to a particular photographic situation and each offering advantages under differing subject conditions. The photographer must decide which method is best for the task in hand. In this book we need to consider each method only briefly, as all have the same basic sensitometric aim of placing the exposure range on the best part of the characteristic curve. More detailed information can be obtained from exposure-meter and camera manufacturers' instruction pamphlets and from books concerned specifically with exposure meters and exposure control. The use of an exposure meter in obtaining the correct exposure of colour materials, and the associated sensitometry of colour photography, is considered in more detail in Chapter 11.

6.44 *General (or integrated) reading.* The most commonly used method of estimating exposure is based on a general reading of the subject. This is an average overall measurement of all the light reaching the exposure meter from the subject (an integrated measurement). The reading is simple and convenient to make, but only suitable for subjects that have a fairly average luminance distribution. With such subjects, the luminance range will be positioned suitably on the film characteristic curve. With other subjects, such as those of high or low average luminance, the exposure indication will be inaccurate. For example, if large dark areas predominate in the subject the result will be overexposed. Conversely, with large light areas the result will be underexposed. Figure 7.4 shows some examples of this type of subject.

6.45 *Luminance-range reading.* A more accurate indication of the required exposure may be obtained by taking a luminance-range reading. Separate and selected measurements are taken of the lightest and darkest important parts of the subject. The exposure given is then based on a point midway between the two readings. A luminance-range reading is less convenient to make than a general reading but offers more control over exposure. With non-average subjects in particular, the luminance range can be measured; if it is found to be too long or too short, remedial action can be taken. For example, by modifying the subject lighting or the film processing time the resultant image may be positioned correctly on the film characteristic curve (see also Figure 11.19).

6.46 *Key-tone reading.* This is a reading of one important tone of the subject (for example, the face in portraiture), or of a substitute tone temporarily included in the scene. A mid-grey or a white card, or the palm of one's hand, may be used for this purpose. The reading made of this key tone is adjusted, so that the exposure given positions the key-tone area on the appropriate part of the film characteristic curve. The method is not suitable for accurately recording the highlight and shadow areas of subjects with a long or short luminance range.

6.47 *Incident-light reading.* An incident-light reading is an integrated measurement of the light that is incident on the subject. A specially shaped disc or hemisphere of diffusing plastic is usually fitted over the light-sensitive cell, and the meter is pointed towards the camera from the subject position. The diffuser is designed so that an exposure based on the reading given will automatically place the subject highlights on the correct part of the characteristic curve. The method is generally accepted as being especially suitable for determining the exposure for colour reversal films.

6.48 *Correct printing exposure.* Compared with most film materials, printing paper has a limited exposure range and thus very little exposure latitude. Therefore control of exposure, although often simpler to achieve, is just as essential in projection printing as it is in camera operating. When detail is required in both shadows and highlights, the aim is to place the projected image onto the paper characteristic curve, so that only the extreme ends of the curve are not used (see paragraph 5.6). This involves using a grade of printing paper that has an exposure range suitable

for accommodating the exposures given by the projected image. Exposure control in colour printing is considered in more detail in Chapter 11.

6.49 *Printing test strip.* The most reliable means of obtaining the required result is to make an exposure test strip. This involves using the desired lens aperture and degree of enlargement, and making a suitable range of exposures on the paper, followed by standard processing. By this means, the sensitometric effect of all the many factors that can influence the result are automatically taken into account. In practice, a strip of printing paper is exposed in steps of, say 2, 4, 8 and 16 seconds, or 2, 3, 4, 6, 8 and 12 seconds. This can be achieved by first exposing the whole strip and then progressively covering it with a piece of opaque black card. The procedure is shown in Figure 6.10 and can be considered as an application of time scale sensitometry (see paragraph 2.5).

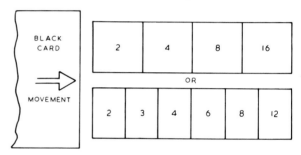

Fig. 6.10 A method of exposing a test strip when using an enlarger. Expose all of the paper for 2 seconds, then quickly cover one-quarter; continue count to 4 seconds then cover half; continue count to 8 seconds then cover three-quarters, and continue count up to 16 seconds. This will give an exposure series in steps of 2, 4, 8 and 16 seconds.

As far as possible, each step of a printing exposure test strip should include representative areas of the image, from highlights to shadows. The processed strip is then viewed in daylight in order to assess the correct exposure. A print covering the whole image can then be made using the selected exposure, and viewed to see if any local variation (shading or dodging) is necessary. In black-and-white printing the exposure test strip may also be used to check that the correct grade of printing paper has been used.

The test strip method is reliable but takes time and uses expensive material. Therefore, after first establishing correct exposure by test strip, it is often more convenient to obtain a direct indication of the exposure for other different negatives by using an enlarger exposure meter.

6.50 *Enlarger exposure meters.* There are several types of photometer (exposure meter) and various ways of using them to estimate printing exposure. With the photoelectric type of meter, the instrument is first set up (calibrated) to suit the exposure characteristics of the enlarger and the speed of the printing paper. An average (or 'master') negative is printed and the exposure is adjusted by trial and error until an optimum print is obtained. A light reading is then taken of the projected image and the meter scale adjusted to a particular value. Thus, when a different negative is in position, the difference in readings will indicate the exposure adjustment required. The reading will also take into account the effect of any change in lens aperture or degree of enlargement.

Photometers and electronic devices are used in commercial printing laboratories where quality, consistent with speed of output and minimum waste, is the main consideration. Because the prints are made on long rolls of paper which are machine processed, correct exposure without the need for trial and error is essential. Many exposure-calculating instruments are suitable for black-and-white, colour reversal, or colour negative printing and are designed to switch off the exposure light after the selected exposure has been given. The two main methods of measuring the illuminance of the image are the integration (or large-area) reading method, and the spot (or small-area) reading method. We can consider each briefly. (The estimation of exposure for colour printing is further considered in Chapter 11.)

6.51 *Integrated (large area) reading.* An integrated reading is an average overall measurement of all or most of the image illuminance. In a typical system the image light from the enlarger lens is integrated (scrambled) by a diffusing material and measurement is made with the meter probe on the easel. The system is comparable with that used for an integrated reading made for camera exposure. It also has the same disadvantage, that if the illuminances of the image are unevenly distributed (i.e. if large areas of high or low illuminance predominate) then the exposure will be inaccurate.

6.52 *Spot (small area) reading.* Spot measurements can be made of any selected image area or key tone; a shadow or a highlight area is often used. The measuring probe is placed on the enlarger easel in the image of the selected area, and this measurement is used for calculating the required exposure.

Zone system of exposure and tone control

6.53 Several tone control systems have been designed for controlling exposure and development so that preconceived tonal arrangements can be achieved in the final result. Probably the best known is the Zone System devised by Ansel Adams and expounded by Minor White and other eminent photographers. The Zone System depends on the application of a basic sensitometric understanding to practical creative photography. It is a method by which the variables of the photographic process can be systematically controlled and manipulated to obtain the desired tonal and textural quality in the finished production. The system helps the photographer to look at the scene to be photographed and to visualize it as it will appear in the final print. It thus relates the luminances of the subject to the tonal values of the print, and the photographer can in many instances plan each photograph in advance. In practice, individual luminances in the subject are measured, and the final tonal rendering visualized. The necessary exposure and development can then be given to obtain the visualized result. A representation of the fundamental sensitometry of a typical zone system is shown in Figure 6.11. See also Figure 1.5.

In the updated zone system there are eleven basic exposure zones designated as 0, I, II, III and so on, up to X. Roman numerals are used so that they will not be confused with the Arabic numbers used for film speeds, lens stops, etc. The exposure zones can be depicted as a series of short distances along the log exposure scale of the film characteristic curve, starting from D_{min}, the centre of each being log 0.3 (one *f*-stop) different from its adjacent zone. They can thus represent a series of equally spaced subject luminances, each zone covering a short part of the complete range of required tones presented by a subject or its image. The zones, from 0 through to X, are related to similarly designated zone 'values' from black to white in the final print. A 'value' can be thought of as the mid-point of a zone. The 0 and X values are, respectively, total black in the print and the white of the paper base, so they do not show any texture or image detail. The extreme useful range of values is therefore from I to IX, with V as a mid-point. The range that is considered to give an acceptable quality in the reproduction of texture and detail (as shown by satisfactory contrast in the print) is from II to VIII. Zone and value V relate to a middle-grey and represent an average tone in the subject, or an 18 per cent reflectance from a grey test card (see paragraphs 6.42, 6.46 and 11.65).

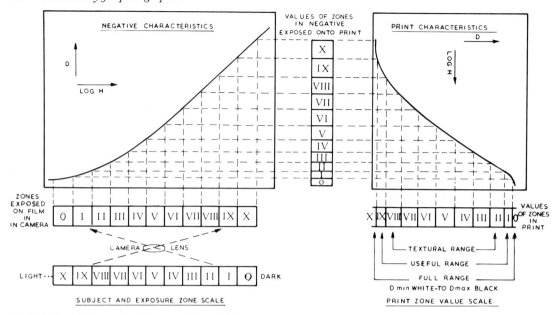

Fig. 6.11 The fundamental sensitometry of a typical Zone System of exposure and tone control, used with a negative–positive process. By using a system based on a series of tonal zones, the subject to be photographed is first previsualized as it is required to appear in the finished print. Then by an application of sensitometric understanding, reproduction of the tonal range from subject to print can be controlled by exposure and processing to obtain the visualized result.

A typical exposure meter will contain a series of scale values such that each represents a change in luminance by a factor of two (0.3 log) or one *f*-stop exposure change. This represents a change of one zone in the zone system. Thus, by changing camera exposure by one *f*-stop, all the tones in the subject will be moved along the full zone scale. With such a calibrated exposure meter, the luminances of the required tones of a subject can be measured and the readings compared with the scale of exposure zones and print values. The subject can therefore be evaluated with regard to its tonal reproduction in the final print. An application of sensitometric knowledge will indicate whether any modification in camera exposure or film development is necessary to achieve the desired result. The Zone System can be applied to the use of half-zones or thirds of zones if these can be related to the particular camera exposure settings.

When considering a tone control system we should bear in mind that in some cases the full range of subject luminances is not viewed, assessed or measured by the photographer. In fact there are many occasions, particularly in pictorial photography, where in order to obtain an aesthetically pleasing result, the full subject luminance range is not recorded in the final print. This particular aspect of tone reproduction is considered in Appendix C.

A full description of a typical Zone System and its practical application is given in *The New Ansel Adams Photographic Series* published by the New York Graphic Society, and *The New Zone System Manual* published by Morgan and Morgan.

Applications of sensitometry

6.54　Sensitometric knowledge can be applied to all photographic tasks and to all systems that involve photographic recording, whether they are large or small, simple or complex.

Typical useful information that can be obtained from existing sensitometric data is:

(a)　The type of film most suitable for a particular photographic task.
(b)　The grade of paper or type of film that will suit a particular printing situation.
(c)　Comparisons of speed, gamma, $\bar{G}$ contrast, contrast index, fog level, maximum density and characteristic curve shape, for different emulsions or processing conditions.
(d)　The tone scale reproduction that will be obtained by changing emulsions, exposure, or processing characteristics.
(e)　The exposure latitude for given subjects.
(f)　The effect of processing time and temperature variations on contrast, speed and density.

Manufacturers use sensitometry to analyse the performance of photographic materials, to study the effect of storage conditions before and after exposure, and to maintain definite standards of:

(a) Emulsion speed, fog level, curve shape and gradient, and useful exposure range.
(b) Colour reproduction and long-term keeping quality.

Sensitometry is used for comparing photographic systems, materials and processes, to obtain conditions that will produce optimum results, for example by:

(a) Comparing the speed, contrast, tone and colour reproduction of different materials.
(b) Estimating possible loss of speed, growth of fog and changes in colour rendition etc., due to age or bad storage.
(c) Determining the exposure factors and effect of light filters under various lighting conditions.

Some uses of sensitometry in photographic exposure, processing and printing are:

(a) For establishing and then maintaining conditions that will achieve optimum results.
(b) To determine correct exposure and exposure conditions for camera films.
(c) To study and evaluate the effect of different processing times and temperatures, or of different processing solutions.
(d) To obtain reliable and comparable results under different processing or printing conditions, for example in machine and hand processing.
(e) To study comparatively the effect of different processing methods, for example hand processing of lengths of film in spool tanks or processing on spiral units.
(f) To evaluate and determine correct exposure conditions for the printing of both black-and-white and colour materials.
(g) To measure the effect of after-treatments, such as masking, reduction and intensification.
(h) In the analysis of exposure and processing faults.

Sensitometry is used also in the control of all activities that involve photographic recording, such as the graphic arts, cinematography, television, optical sound recording on film, film duplicating, reprography, radiography, spectrosensitometry, audio-visual techniques and so on.

Self-assessment questions

6.55 If you want to test your learning, answer the following:

(a) Explain why sensitometric tests should be carried out under conditions of exposure and processing similar to those expected in practice.
(b) When carrying out sensitometric tests, results cannot be determined with absolute accuracy. Why is this so, and how can the effects of variation be minimized?
(c) List the effects that age and poor storage conditions may have on a high-speed panchromatic film.
(d) Give two reasons why you should wait an hour or so before processing sensitometric strips for a family of curves.
(e) Describe a method of achieving uniform development when processing sensitometric strips in: (1) tanks, (2) dishes, (3) roll-film spirals.
(f) List the three main factors in development that control the results of a sensitometric test made using fresh developer.
(g) How would you test a safelight to find its 'safe exposure' time?
(h) What are a 'process control strip' and a 'reference strip', and how are they used in process quality control?
(i) List the information that can be obtained from measuring the following significant steps on a process control strip: (1) D_{min}, (2) LD, (3) HD − LD.
(j) What does a 'colour spread' pattern on a process control chart indicate?
(k) Refer to Figure 6.6. Explain the probable effect on the control strip and on the associated transparencies indicated by the plots made on 5 September.
(l) Describe the function of a 'by-pass' test and how you might carry it out when processing colour materials.
(m) How would you calibrate an external hand-held exposure meter to suit your own equipment and working conditions?
(n) Explain the advantages and disadvantages of using an exposure meter for making: (1) a general (integrated) reading; (2) a luminance-range reading; (3) an incident-light reading.

7

Tone reproduction

7.1 The relationship between the tonal characteristics of the subject and those of the final print can be illustrated and investigated sensitometrically by the use of a 'tone reproduction quadrant diagram'. This can relate to either black-and-white or colour processes. The diagram gives a graphical representation of the photographic process, from the subject, through camera exposure and negative, to printing and viewing the final print. Tone reproduction diagrams enable the photographer to study the practical applications necessary to obtain the desired end product, whether it be a print for viewing or interpretation, a positive transparency for projection or a duplicate negative.

A tone reproduction diagram brings together all the principles of sensitometry that we have already considered, so the construction, interpretation and use of the diagram will give you a further appreciation of how you can use sensitometry to manipulate and control the photographic process. The system of studying tone reproduction by the use of quadrant diagrams was first introduced by Dr Lloyd A. Jones, an American physicist who specialized in sensitometry.

The construction of a tone reproduction diagram of a photographic process is made easier if a calibrated step wedge (or grey scale) is included in the original scene. The function of the step wedge is simply to represent the tones of the subject in an easily measured form, and thus enable us to plot the results of the process accurately. The step wedge or grey scale should present a range of densities at least equal to the luminance range of the subject. The steps of this range can then be used to construct graphs representing the progressive stages in tone reproduction, from the original subject via the negative and positive, through to viewing of the final print.

Basic tone reproduction diagram

7.2 The basic diagram (Figure 7.1) consists of four quadrants, which are interrelated graphs representing each of the stages of the photographic

110

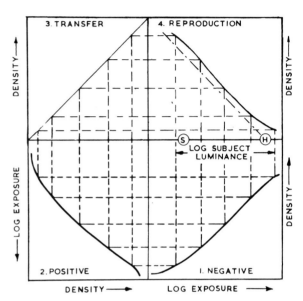

Fig. 7.1 A basic tone reproduction diagram. S denotes the shadows and H the highlights. The diagram shows the sensitometry of a photographic process, as explained in the text. The curve in quadrant 4 relates the log luminance range of the original subject to the final print density range. It thus represents the combined effect on tone reproduction of the negative and positive characteristic curves. Where the reproduction curve is steeper than 45°, the contrast of the reproduction is higher than that of the corresponding area on the original subject. Where it is less than 45°, the contrast of the reproduction is lower than that of the subject.

process proceeding in a clockwise direction. The arrangement is such that the data output from one graph is transferred directly as the input to the next graph. The representative quadrants in this basic diagram are:

(1) Negative material.
(2) Positive material.
(3) Transfer line.
(4) Overall tone reproduction.

You will notice that the dashed lines, representing exposure received on the negative and on the positive, come down from above the characteristic curve instead of up from below. This makes no difference, as a log exposure axis can be drawn above or below a curve, just as a density axis can be to the left or right of a curve.

A tone reproduction diagram has no practical value unless details of its production are given, so in practice all the relevant details of the photographic materials, exposure method, processing conditions etc. must be recorded on or with the diagram.

7.3   To understand the diagram you should think of a simple photographic task in which a negative is made and then contact-printed onto paper. Now relate this task to the diagram, beginning at the top of quadrant 1 and proceeding clockwise.

Quadrant 1

(a) *Subject and exposure*. Begin with the log luminance range (representing the tones of the subject). S denotes the shadows and H the highlights. Notice that the image of the subject is positioned (by the camera exposure) to give correct exposure on the negative material characteristic curve. As the upper part of the curve is not used it is not included, and any reduction in the log exposure range due to camera lens flare has also been ignored in this basic diagram.
(b) *Development and negative characteristics*. The negative has been developed to a $\bar{G}$ contrast that can be measured if necessary, and this produces the density range of the negative.

Quadrant 2

(c) *Choice of paper grade*. The density range of the negative is equivalent to the log exposure range of the image to be printed onto the paper, so a grade of paper is chosen with a log exposure range approximately equal to the density range of the negative.
(d) *Paper characteristics and exposure*. The characteristic curve of the printing paper is drawn on its side, so that the log exposure range given by the density range of the negative image can be transferred directly onto it. The log exposure range is positioned (by the printing exposure) to give correct exposure on the positive material characteristic curve. After processing, the print consists of a range of reflection densities.

Quadrant 3

(e) *Transfer of print densities to meet subject log luminance values*. The print densities (tones) are to

be compared with the original subject log luminances; lines representing various densities are therefore turned through 90° in the transfer quadrant so that they are in a position to meet the corresponding lines taken up from the subject log luminances, in the reproduction quadrant.

The transfer quadrant could be used to represent the viewing conditions. The straight line at 45° would then depict viewing of the print under conditions similar to the conditions of measuring used in the reflection densitometer. Different viewing arrangements might produce a curved line, depending on how the densities are seen by the viewer's eyes.

Quadrant 4

(f) *Overall tone reproduction characteristics*. After plotting the meeting points of lines representing the print densities and the corresponding subject log luminances, a curve is made in the reproduction quadrant indicating the overall tone reproduction characteristics of the complete photographic process. With true overall tone scale reproduction, the curve will be a straight line at an angle of 45° to the horizontal axis, that is parallel to the dashed and dotted line on the diagram. In this state, contrast of subject and contrast of print will be equal throughout the whole range. If the ends of the curve are joined with a straight line, and this is at 45°, the overall contrast of the subject and print are equal, but with an elongation and a corresponding compression of tones occurring within the range. When considering this interpretation, we should bear in mind that a true tone scale reproduction is not often wanted in general-purpose photography (see paragraph 5.25). A reproduction appearing as a straight line at an angle smaller or greater than 45° indicates, respectively, a compression or an elongation of the tone scale, but with the tones still in correct proportion to one another.

The tone reproduction curve itself incorporates the effect of all the relevant events that have occurred in the photographic process, from the input of a range of illuminances from the subject to the film in the camera, through to output to the viewer of a range of densities or tones on the final print.

Note that some tone reproduction diagrams you may see in photographic literature are constructed so that they present the reproduction curve with its general slope on an opposite diagonal to that shown in Figure 7.1, and with the print density scale values increasing downward instead of

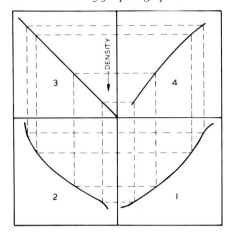
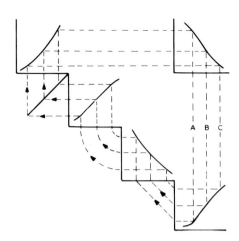

Fig. 7.2 Some alternative ways of presenting tone reproduction diagrams. These diagrams have no particular sensitometric significance and are intended only to illustrate different methods of construction and presentation.

upward. This form of presentation could be obtained in Figure 7.1 by changing the diagonal of the transfer line. If this is done it makes no difference at all to the effects or the results. It is simply a different way of presentation and may be more convenient for interpretation in certain cases. This and other alternative forms of construction and presentation are shown in Figure 7.2.

(g) *Reproduction characteristics of fine detail.* The tone reproduction curve, like the basic characteristic curve, strictly applies only to macro contrast: the contrast of micro detail will be somewhat lower than indicated. However, increases or decreases in the gradient of the tone reproduction curve indicate similar increases or decreases in the contrast of fine detail (provided that development adjacency effects are not significant). Do not be concerned about the statement in brackets; it is inserted only to make the full statement precise. See paragraphs 2.102, 2.103 and 2.106 on the reproduction of fine detail.

The tone reproduction quadrant diagram in Figure 7.1 shows only the effect of negative and positive characteristics under the related conditions of exposure, processing and measuring. Other influencing factors (such as the effect of atmospheric haze, lens flare, enlarger or printer characteristics, and viewing or projection conditions) can be incorporated if required.

Interpreting the quadrant diagram

7.4 An interpretation of the tone reproduction quadrant diagram will indicate several facts and features, all relevant to a typical photographic process.

(a) To obtain true scale (not merely proportional) tonal reproduction, the following conditions are necessary:
(1) When the characteristic curves are straight lines, the product of the gamma values of negative and positive must equal unity ($\gamma_{negative} \times \gamma_{positive} = 1.0$).
(2) When the characteristic curves are not straight lines, the negative curve and the positive curve must be complementary to one another (have the same curvature or be 'mirror images' of each other).

It is again emphasized that true scale tonal reproduction is usually only required when, for example, duplicate negatives are to be produced (see also Figure 5.11).

(b) A gradient of less than 45° in any part of the reproduction curve indicates tonal compression: a gradient of more than 45° indicates tonal elongation.

(c) The reason for tonal distortion can be traced to either or both of the curves in quadrants 1 and 2.

(d) The gradient of the reproduction curve at any point is equal to the product of the gradients at the corresponding points on the other two curves.

(e) The average gradient of the reproduction curve is equal to the product of the average gradient of the other two curves ($\overline{G}_{reproduction} = \overline{G}_{negative} \times \overline{G}_{positive}$). This principle can be applied to any number of additional factors influencing the reproduction, for instance atmospheric haze, lens flare, printer characteristics.

(f) If the log subject luminance range is known, the density range of the positive can be given by:

Positive density range = log subject luminance range × average negative gradient × average positive gradient

(g) The effect of exposure changes given to the negative or positive material can be shown by lateral movement of the characteristic curve along the respective log exposure axis. Such exposure changes may change the shape of the reproduction curve. When considering this it may be helpful to think of the curve as being a length of bent wire laid on the graph and able to be moved around.

(h) The contrast of the negative can be controlled (by development time variation) so that the negative density range matches the paper log exposure range:

$$\text{Negative } \bar{G} \text{ or } \gamma = \frac{\text{paper log exposure range}}{\text{log subject luminance range}}$$

(This formula ignores any loss of contrast that may be caused by camera lens flare. See also paragraph 5.23.)

It is worth remembering that, as with the plotting of single characteristic curves, the above findings are possible because uniformly scaled logarithmic axes are used throughout. This enables the tonal effect of variables involved in the photographic process and the relationship between them to be measured and given a numerical value at any stage, from the original subject through to the final print.

Flare and haze effects in the tone reproduction diagram

7.5 In many aspects of photography – particularly in aerial and long-distance photography – the effects of camera lens flare and atmospheric haze between the subject and the camera lens are very important, and may therefore be included in a tone reproduction diagram. First let us consider how flare and haze affect the camera image.

7.6 *Camera and lens flare.* The image received by the film in the camera is not an exact luminous reproduction of the scene being photographed, as it is made up of two parts:

(a) The image-forming light, or 'focused light' from the scene.
(b) The non-image-forming light or 'flare light', i.e. light scattered or reflected inside the camera by

the lens surfaces, diaphragm edges, lens barrel, emulsion surface, etc. Note that lenses that have multiple-layer anti-reflection coatings and an efficient lens hood may still produce a considerable amount of flare light by internal reflection inside the camera. (Figure 7.3).

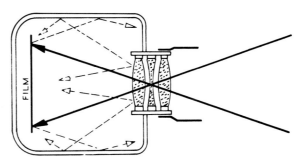

Fig. 7.3 Camera and lens flare. The dashed lines represent some of the non-image-forming flare light that is scattered within a camera body and falls on the film surface. Its effect is to degrade the image formed by the properly focused light.

Flare light degrades the image formed by the focused light. Its overall effect is to compress the tonal range and thus reduce the contrast of the camera image, particularly in the shadow areas. For example, if the focused light gives 10 units of light in the image highlights and 1 unit of light in the shadows, and if the flare light is 1 unit of light over all the image, then:

Highlights = 10 + 1,
        i.e. 10% increase in illuminance
Shadows = 1 + 1,
        i.e. 100% increase in illuminance

The overall contrast of the image is also reduced from 10:1 to 11:2

The amount and distribution of flare light received on the film will vary, depending on the camera and its optical system. It will also depend on the subject luminance range and on the area of high luminance in the scene, as shown in Figure 7.4.

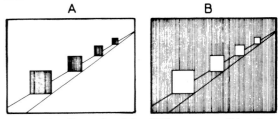

Fig. 7.4 The effect on flare light of different scenes. Although the two scenes present the same luminance range of say, 50 to 1 (1.7 log), scene A will cause more flare light in the camera than B because of its greater area of high illuminance.

Large areas of highly illuminated light background and the back-lighting of objects will produce a great deal of flare light and should therefore be avoided if at all possible. For example, in colour photography the flare light from a brightly lit coloured background can cause a colour cast that can affect the shadow areas of the image.

7.7   Camera lens flare curve.   The characteristics of lens flare can be shown by a lens flare curve, which is a plot of the image log illuminances produced by the lens against the subject log luminances. In Figure 7.5 'log relative subject luminance' represents the log of the luminance of different parts of the subject from shadows to highlights; 'log relative image illuminance' represents the log of the illuminance of the image of the same parts, plus the flare light received on the film in the camera. The dashed line at 45° indicates an ideal situation with no flare.

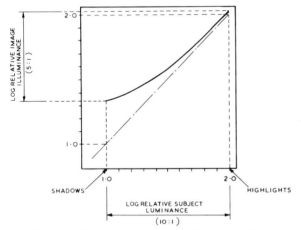

Fig. 7.5 A typical camera lens flare curve, showing how the image of the original subject luminances is affected by lens and internal flare light during exposure. Owing to the addition of non-image-forming flare light in the camera, the contrast of the image recorded on the film is lower that that of the subject itself. The curve shows that contrast loss is greater in the shadow areas, becoming gradually less towards the highlights. The dashed line at 45° represents a situation with no flare effect.

We can see in Figure 7.5 that flare light reduces the contrast of the image received on the film. The gradient of the curve shows that the contrast reduction is greatest in the darker shadow areas, becoming progressively less in the middle-tones, and is least of all in the highlights. The amount of flare relative to a camera and an average scene can be given as the 'flare factor'. This is found by dividing the luminance range of the subject by the illuminance range of the image. In the example shown in Figure 7.5, the flare factor is 10/5 = 2.

7.8   Atmospheric haze.   The effect of atmospheric haze between the subject and the camera is to scatter back into the camera lens some of the light that would have fallen on the subject. Because the shorter wavelengths of light are scattered more than the longer, the haze often looks bluish (hence the blue appearance of the sky). Its effect on the film can be minimized by using a yellow (minus blue) filter on the camera lens. Haze causes a degradation in the image, particularly in the shadow areas, and compresses the tonal range. Its effect on the camera image is essentially the same as that of camera lens flare, so, if necessary, both effects can be combined and an appropriate curve designated as 'flare and haze characteristics'.

7.9   Flare and haze curve.   The degree of haze varies with the weather and the distance of objects from the camera, so the curve representing flare and haze is of necessity an assumption based on average conditions. This indicates that the camera image contrast must also be an assumption.

7.10   Including flare effect in the tone reproduction diagram.   The effect of flare light is often incorporated directly into the negative material characteristic curve. This is because the exposure range

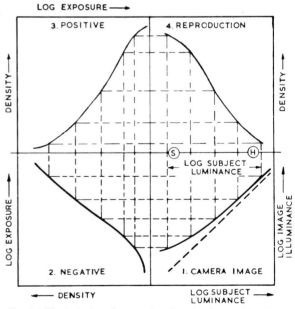

Fig. 7.6 The inclusion of camera lens flare (or flare and haze) effect in a quadrant diagram. The effect occurs during camera exposure and before processing, so it is shown in the first quadrant. The other factors that control tone reproduction are moved round to accommodate it. The dashed line in the first quadrant represents the transfer from subject to image when no flare effect is present.

received by the film will have already been reduced by flare. However, separate inclusion in a tone reproduction quadrant diagram can be made by using the first quadrant for the flare, or the flare and haze characteristics, moving the negative and positive characteristics forward and eliminating the transfer quadrant (see Figure 7.6).

7.11   *Minimizing the effect of flare and haze.*   The effect of atmospheric haze is first reduced during exposure by using an efficient hood and a yellow filter on the camera lens to prevent an excess of blue light reaching the film (see paragraph 7.8). In practice, the contrast-reducing effect of flare or haze can be minimized by developing the negative to a relatively high value of $\overline{G}$ contrast. Notice that the $\overline{G}$ of the negative in Figure 7.6 has been increased (compared with that in Figure 7.1) so that the reproduction curve is satisfactory. Notice also that the effect of lens flare and haze, which is greatest in the shadow areas, has been minimized by:

(a)   Choice of a film with a shortish toe and fairly high contrast characteristics.
(b)   Correct camera exposure (for aerial film, shadows above *D* 0.4 + fog) and suitable development.
(c)   Printing the shadows on the steepest part of the positive (printing paper) characteristic. This action also ties in with normal avoidance of the extreme parts of the paper curve shoulder, as explained in paragraphs 5.6 to 5.8.

There is, of course, a limit to using contrast increase to minimize the effect of tonal compression in the shadows. If it is used to excess the highlights will be overexposed, with a consequent loss of resolution, and the negative will have an overall contrast too high for normal printing. It is therefore crucial to choose an original film that has a short toe, and can therefore obtain maximum contrast low on the characteristic curve, where the shadows will be recorded.

7.12   *Enlarger lens flare.*   A flare curve for an enlarger lens is a plot of the image log illuminances produced by the lens in the plane of the focused image, against the subject log luminances (i.e. the negative density range reversed), as measured with the negative in the enlarger.

7.13   *Effect of enlarger lens flare.*   A flare curve for an enlarger lens will show tone compression in the highlights, that is in the image of the denser parts of the negative. Thus the camera lens flare and the enlarger lens flare tend to oppose each other, the first giving most compression in the shadows and the second most compression in the highlights. The net result is a reduction in tone scale and contrast at both ends of the range instead of at one particular end, resulting in a slightly S-shaped distortion of what ideally would be a straight line. In practice, stray light that reaches the emulsion will emphasize this effect. Such light might be from unmasked areas around a negative, or light reflected from shiny internal or external surfaces of the enlarger.

In a well-maintained and properly used enlarger the problem and effect of flare is not as significant as in a camera, since the luminance range projected is usually much lower that that of the average scene.

7.14   *Including enlarger lens flare curve in the tone reproduction diagram.*   If an enlarger lens flare curve (or any other characteristic curve) is to be separately included, and there are not enough quadrants to accommodate all the separate characteristics, the curve may be plotted outside the diagram. The image log illuminance values can then be fed into the quadrant representing the printing material characteristics (see Figure 7.2).

Effect of flare light in practice

7.15   The effect of flare light in the camera and in any optical system used in photography may be significant, and therefore must be considered in practice. The response to flare light is difficult to predict. It may be uniform over the surface of the photographic emulsion or it may be distributed in a random fashion. Nevertheless, the general effect on the emulsion's characteristic curve is to make the toe region longer and more shallow, and thus to reduce the effective length of the straight-line region. With this in mind, the photographer can choose suitable photographic material and, if necessary, adjust exposure and processing to compensate for the general effect of flare light.

7.16   Flare effect is a factor that in most cases we should like to be rid of. In some circumstances it may, however, have one redeeming feature, in that it helps to keep under control the density range of negatives made of different subjects. In general, the longer the subject luminance range, the greater is the tone-compressing effect of flare light on the camera image. Therefore flare tends to minimize the differences between the density ranges of negatives made of widely varying scenes. Because of this built-in tone compression, we are more likely to obtain such negatives on a roll of film that will print directly onto one or two grades of paper. Of course this does not compensate for the detrimental effect of camera lens flare on the shadow detail.

Automatic inclusion of influencing factors

7.17   As far as possible, tone reproduction diagrams are compiled from data obtained by using the exposure and processing conditions and procedures that the material will receive in actual use. Under these conditions the characteristics of influencing factors such as lens flare, colour quality of illuminance received, processing agitation and Callier effect (considered later) will be automatically included in the negative and positive characteristic curves. The result will be a true graphical representation of the particular process under consideration. If the reproduction is a transparency intended for projection, consideration will also be required of the relationship between its range of densities and the luminances of the image projected onto, or reflected from, a viewing screen.

7.18   A tone reproduction diagram can only properly relate to one specific set of conditions in photography. If a diagram is needed to show the general tone reproduction to be expected in a particular type of task, some assumptions have to be made concerning the effects that can occur relative to the subject, the camera lens and the image received by the film. The amount and the effect of flare light falling on the film will depend to a great extent on the subject itself. For example, in aerial photography the effect of the changing atmospheric haze and camera lens flare conditions (see paragraphs 7.6 and 7.9) preclude the use of a measured image illuminance range, so an assumption is made based on the average conditions.

Practical applications of tone reproduction diagrams

7.19   A tone reproduction quadrant diagram shows a comparison of all the original subject luminances with their corresponding densities in the final positive. It is a means of illustrating the macro contrast transfer between the two, for all levels of subject luminance. The construction of a quadrant diagram enables the relevant effect of each event or stage in the photographic process to be directly linked to the next. The y-axis (usually vertical) of the first graph becomes the x-axis (usually horizontal) of the second graph and so on, thus depicting in succession all the stages of the photographic process. The principles can be applied to any photographic system provided that the transfer characteristic of each stage is known. In colour photography, for example, the normal events of the process, plus the effects of adding or removing colour filters on the camera or printer, can be illustrated by a colour tone reproduction quadrant diagram. (See Figure 11.17 and associated paragraphs.)

7.20   A tone reproduction quadrant diagram is used principally to study the effect on the reproduction curve of a change in one or more of the measurable variables, such as the effect of varying the type of negative material, varying the make or grade of the printing material, or adjusting the exposure or processing. Thus the system enables us to predict what will happen, or what we can do if changes are proposed, without having to carry them out in practice on a trial-and-error basis. It also enables us to plan techniques to suit particular applications and requirements.

The graphical presentation of the photographic process is also very convenient when we are required to explain it to someone who is not conversant with the succession of events that occur in photography.

Film duplicating

7.21   The study of tone reproduction applies particularly to photographic duplicating tasks, where precise results are usually required. Duplicate copies of original negatives are often made, so that more than one copy of the information contained in the original is available for use. They may be almost exact duplicate copies (facsimiles), or improved copies of the original. The same situation applies, of course, when making duplicate positives from original positives. The main reasons for producing duplicate copies are:

(a)   The originals may be costly, difficult or impossible to replace should they be damaged.
(b)   Several copies may be required for use at the same time in different localities.
(c)   To prevent wear and damage to the original.
(d)   To obtain improved negatives that will produce better prints than the original negative.

These situations are often met in aerial photography and in the motion-picture and audio-visual industries.

7.22 The easiest way of producing duplicate copies is by contact printing. Optical projection printing may be used, and offers advantages if it is, but the complications caused by lens flare and other factors will also occur. The original negative is printed onto film to produce an 'intermediate' (or master) positive; this is then printed to produce one or more duplicate negatives (although, for quantities of work, direct reversal films that produce direct copies in one operation are available). The control of tone reproduction is simplified by using special fine-grain duplicating films that have a high resolution. These have characteristic curves with a fairly long, straight-line region so that the tone-distorting curved toe and shoulder can be avoided in printing. Manufacturers supply such films and associated gamma/time curves, but for many black-and-white duplicating tasks any fine-grain low-speed film capable of producing a gamma of 1.0 or so, and covering the required density range, will suffice. If necessary, gammas higher or lower than normal can usually be obtained without deterioration in quality, by processing in either a high-contrast (high-activity) or a low-contrast (low-activity) developer respectively.

To enable the results to be measured, a calibrated step wedge with a density range similar to the density range of the original should be attached to the original and printed with it. If a step wedge is not available, the density range of the original is measured and noted for comparison with the density range of the same areas on the duplicate. Copies of single negatives or short lengths of film can be most easily produced by using a contact printer, but for duplicating long lengths of film a continuous-strip printer may be used. The basic principle of a printing machine is that the original negative and the film on which it is to be printed are drawn together in contact, emulsion to emulsion, past an exposing light. After processing, the procedure is repeated using the inter-positive for printing. The end product is thus a duplicate negative.

7.23   *Obtaining true tone scale reproduction.* We know from our study of tone reproduction diagrams (paragraph 7.4) that, to obtain true tone scale reproduction, the product of the two gammas obtained must equal unity. The easiest way to achieve this is to use the same type of film for each printing and to process the images on both films under identical conditions. However, if for example the inter-positive is processed, to say, gamma 1.1,

the duplicate negative will need to be processed to gamma 0.9, which is the reciprocal of 1.1 (i.e. 1/1.1). The product of the two gammas will thus be $1.1 \times 0.9 = 1.0$ (approximately). Figure 7.7 shows this example, the two characteristic curves being idealized for the purpose of illustration. The films can be developed to different gammas as long as the product of the two is unity, and provided that the images on each film are recorded only on the straight-line region. The same condition applies when producing, for example, a transparency from an existing negative.

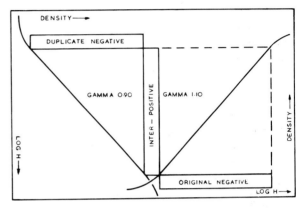

Fig. 7.7 The sensitometry of film duplicating by contact printing. To obtain true tone scale reproduction, only the straight-line region of each characteristic curve is used and the product of the two gammas must equal unity. In this case, $1.1 \times 0.9 = 1.0$ (almost).

When producing duplicates, the necessity of confining images to the straight-line region of the characteristic curves, and avoiding the curved toe region, may result in an overall density difference between the original and the duplicate (e.g. the duplicate looking denser than the original). However, as long as this is not excessive, such a change in overall density is relatively unimportant. This illustrates the difference between a 'duplicate tone scale' reproduction of an original, and a 'facsimile' reproduction. In a facsimile the densities themselves are identical, not just the density increments and tone scale.

A satisfactory technique for the production in quantity of black-and-white duplicates, is to use a gamma of about 1.5 for the intermediate (or master) positive and a lower value of about gamma 0.7 for the duplicate negative ($1.5 \times 0.7 = 1.05$). Manufacturers supply special master positive and duplicate negative films for this purpose. These films have characteristics that produce somewhat better definition than would be obtained if one particular type of film was used for both positive and negative.

7.24 *Duplicating colour films.* In the duplication of colour films the basic conditions still apply, but because of the need for correct colour reproduction, the material and procedures recommended by the film manufacturers should be used. These usually involve colour filtration, and may include the use of 'colour correction masking' and techniques to control the resultant contrast, particularly in the highlight areas.

In the duplicating of inherently high-contrast colour transparencies, special inter-negative materials may be used. Typically these materials are designed to produce characteristic curves with the required medium contrast in the middle-tones but with an increasing contrast in the highlight areas. The inherent increase in highlight contrast of the inter-negative material compensates for the compression of highlight tones on the toe of the original transparency. In some applications duplicate colour transparencies are made without using an inter-negative, by printing directly on special colour-reversal duplicating films that give a reduced contrast, together with good tone and colour reproduction. If ordinary (camera) colour-reversal film has to be used for duplicating, a flashing technique may be employed to reduce the inherent high contrast of such film (see paragraphs 5.18 and 5.19).

7.25 *Obtaining improved tone scale reproduction.* The duplicating process may also be used to produce copies that are an improvement on the original. If the original negative is difficult to print because of its overall density or contrast, copies with improved characteristics can be made. Overall density can be changed by adjusting exposure, and contrast can be changed by increasing or decreasing the development of either or both films. Reference to a tone reproduction diagram, and possibly to gamma/time curves for the film, enable us to predict the effect of such changes, which can then be carried out in practice. The expressions given in paragraphs 7.4(a), (e) and (f) can also be used. As an example, improvement could be made if the original negative had a very short density range (say 0.65) and was unsuitable for printing on any available grade of paper. The contrast of either the inter-positive or the duplicate negative film, or both, could be increased so that the duplicate negative would give a good contact print on, say, a normal grade of paper. Using the familiar formula:

Required gamma

$$= \frac{\text{paper log exposure range (of normal paper)}}{\text{density range of negative}}$$

$$= \frac{1.10}{0.65} = 1.7 \text{ (approximately)}$$

The films could both be developed to a gamma of 1.3 (which is the square root of 1.7) so that the product is $1.3 \times 1.3 = 1.7$ as shown in Figure 7.8. Alternatively, they could be developed to any gamma within the sensitometric capabilities of the films (see paragraph 7.23) as long as the product of the two gammas equals 1.7. The same formula and

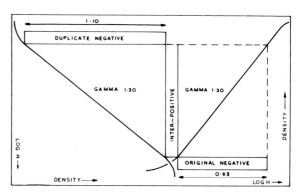

Fig. 7.8 Duplicating to improve tone reproduction when the contrast of the original is too low for satisfactory printing. The density range of the duplicate negative is the density range of the original negative multiplied by the product of the two gammas ($0.65 \times 1.7 = 1.10$). The improved duplicate is then suitable for printing on, say, grade 2 paper (see paragraph 7.25).

method can be used to obtain an improved duplicate negative from an original that has a density range too long for direct printing. Remember that faults such as uneven densities and marks on the original will appear on the duplicate, and may even be emphasized.

Note that copies produced in this manner will not, in the strictest sense, be duplicates of the original. When the product of the two gammas is either more than or less than unity, or when the toe region of either or both characteristic curves is used, the density range and increments of the original and duplicate will not be the same.

7.26 *Obtaining partial tone-scale modification.* If necessary, improvement in the duplicate negative can be obtained by using the toe region of either or both of the duplicating films to decrease the contrast (compress the tones) in the shadows or highlights, or both, relative to the contrast of the middle-tones. Reference to a tone reproduction diagram of the process will indicate the change in exposure needed to shift the highlights (dark areas) of the original negative on to the toe of the inter-positive, and the exposure needed to shift the shadows (dark areas) of the inter-positive on to the toe of the duplicate negative, as necessary. The diagram will also show the extent and degree of tonal compression, and if a reproduction curve is plotted it can be used to predict the effect on the final duplicate negative. For example, if the toe region of the inter-positive only is used, the highlight tones will be compressed; if the toe region of the duplicate negative only is used, the shadow tones will be compressed (Figure 7.9 shows both effects). You may like to use a suitable tone

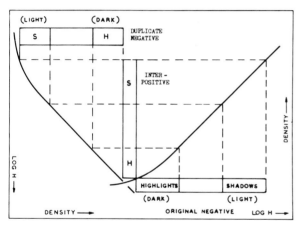

Fig. 7.9 Film duplicating, showing the effect of using the toe of the positive and negative characteristic curves in order to compress the tones of the highlights and shadows (see paragraph 7.26).

reproduction diagram (say Figure 7.1) and work out for yourself that this is so. Remember that the original subject is a negative, so the highlights are the dark areas of the negative and the shadows are the light areas.

When duplicating single negatives, simple shading, masking or retouching can be used. These are probably better introduced when producing the inter-positive, as the effect is directly evident on a positive image. For long lengths of film (or single negatives), problems requiring masking or shading may be overcome by using an electronic printer. The effect on tone reproduction of electronic printing is dealt with later.

7.27 Practical check of tone reproduction. The best means of checking the accuracy of results is to include a calibrated step wedge with the original to be duplicated, and to measure the results. For most purposes a complete tone reproduction diagram need not be constructed, as original densities can be plotted against final densities to provide the reproduction curve directly. If a step wedge is not available, the density range of the original $(D_{max} - D_{min})$ can be compared with the density range of the same areas on the duplicate negative. If the straight-line regions have been used, equality in density range indicates true tone scale reproduction. In both cases the same method can be used, if necessary, to check the gamma of the inter-positive before it is printed. However, note that if a step wedge is to be used on an electronic printer, the area of each step should be fairly square in shape and as large as possible (see paragraph 7.41).

If density-measuring methods are not available, a quick practical check on the duplicating process can be carried out as follows. Superimpose the original negative and the inter-positive on an illuminated viewing table. If a matching contrast has been achieved, the combination will show an almost even density overall. If the negative predominates, the gamma of the positive is less than 1.0; if a duplicate negative matching the original is wanted, development of the duplicate must be taken further than that of the inter-positive. The opposite procedure should be used if the positive predominates in the superimposition. The same check can be used with the inter-positive and the duplicate negative.

7.28   By understanding the factors involved in tone reproduction and applying sensitometry, we can make duplicate negatives that conform to the standards required and can give copies or prints identical to, or better than, those printed from the original negatives. However, we must bear in mind that, as in all second- or third-generation images, the reproduction of fine detail may be impaired. (See paragraphs 5.40 to 42.)

Camera copying and printing of positive originals

7.29   The term 'copying' is used for several techniques for the reproduction of photographs, documents, etc. Here it refers to using a camera to photograph a continuous-tone print on paper, and then printing the negative in order to produce copies. The use of a camera is particularly necessary when copies of a size different from that of the original are needed. We can consider the tone reproduction when producing a continuous-tone black-and-white print, but a similar condition also applies when colour materials are used.

When trying to obtain true tone scale reproduction in camera copying and printing, the same basic condition of '$\gamma_{negative} \times \gamma_{positve} = 1.0$' applies, just as it does in film duplicating. In other words, if the straight-line region of both the negative and positive materials can be used, and if they are processed so that the product of the two gammas is unity, then true tone scale reproduction will be obtained. If a suitable film is used in the camera, the copy negative may be made so that all or most of its densities are on the straight-line region of the film characteristic curve. There will be some slight

tonal compression of the shadows, owing to camera lens flare, but in a properly set up copying system the effect will be small.

7.30   *Tone distortion problems in printing.*   A problem arises when the negative is printed on paper. Tone-scale distortion will be caused by the curved sensitometric characteristics of the printing paper and, if the image is enlarged, by lens flare and other effects. A compression of contrast in the tone of highlight and shadow areas will be particularly evident if the extremes of the paper toe and shoulder are approached in printing. This tonal compression happens in any case when a negative is printed on paper, but in a camera copying process the effect may be exaggerated. If the

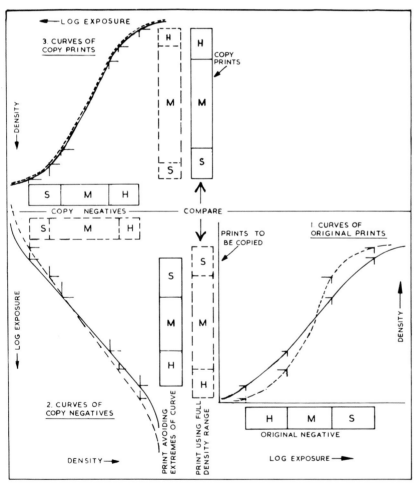

Fig. 7.10 Tonal reproduction in the camera-copying and reproduction of continuous-tone photographic prints. H, M and S refer to the highlights, middle-tones and shadows. (Remember that in a negative H represents dark areas, and S light areas.) The dashed lines and curves depict the situation and final tone

reproduction when a typical photographic print is made, camera-copied, and the copy negative printed. The solid lines depict the situation and final tone reproduction when a special print with a restricted density range is made, camera-copied, and the copy negative printed.

original photographic print itself contains almost-white highlights and near-black shadows, they will already show tonal compression. The second-generation print will compound the effect, and show further tonal compression of the highlight and shadow areas, and this will be emphasized by an increase in the tone separation of the middle-tones. The dashed lines and curves in Figure 7.10 show the general effect of this situation. This lack of quality can be seen on many copy prints of continuous-tone photographic originals, but other than avoiding the extreme toe and shoulder in printing there is little that can be done to remedy the condition.

7.31 *Minimizing the effect of tone distortion.* Better results will be obtained if the original photographic print to be copied can be specially made to suit the camera copying process. By this means, the compression of highlights and shadows can be minimized, and acceptable prints achieved. This is done simply by making the original print on a softer grade of printing paper than would normally be used. The softer grade paper has a longer exposure range, and thus the lower toe and upper shoulder of the characteristic curve can be avoided. The print will not be pleasing to look at, but its density range will be contained on the straighter part of the print characteristic curve and thus show the minimum tonal distortion. The overall loss of contrast obtained by using a softer grade of paper can be corrected if necessary by increasing the development and hence the gamma of the copy negative. The effect of this procedure, and the tone reproduction of the resultant print, is shown by the solid lines and curves in Figure 7.10. It can be seen that the tone reproduction of the copy print will be almost the same as that of a print made directly from the original negative (see 'compare' in Figure 7.10). This method is used, for example, when a montage or a mosaic of prints is made and then camera-copied and printed to produce smaller prints for distribution in quantity. It is also worth noting that the contrast of the middle shadow areas will be improved if the copy negative is printed using direct illumination in a condenser enlarger. This effect is explained in Chapter 9.

7.32 *Copying and reproducing black-and-white documents, line drawings, etc.* In sensitometric terms a special case exists when copying originals that consist essentially of the two extreme tones only, for example black lettering on a white background. The aim with this type of copying is to obtain

prints containing only D_{max} and D_{min} with no intermediate densities. To obtain this, the copy negative itself needs to have clear, almost transparent lettering on a fairly dense background with no in-between densities. This can be considered almost as a case of non-use of both the film and

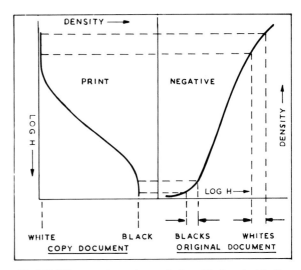

Fig. 7.11 When copying and reproducing a black-and-white line original, it is usual to require maximum contrast in the resultant print. The blacks of the original need to be of little or no density in the negative, and maximum density in the print. The whites need to be dense in the negative and not to record at all in the print. In an ideal case, most of the densities available between D_{max} and D_{min}, in both negative and print, are not used.

print characteristic curves, as shown in Figure 7.11. As we can see from the diagram, if the negative contrast is sufficiently high a soft grade of paper can be used to make the print.

Objective and subjective tone reproduction

7.33 In general terms, the comparison of log subject luminances with the final print densities is called 'objective tone reproduction', meaning that the relationship is measurable. However, the final evaluation often depends on how the print, transparency or projected image appears to an observer and whether or not it satisfies his requirements. This subjective assessment of quality cannot be expressed as a simple measurement, so when the human factor is also considered the term used is 'subjective tone reproduction'. The subjective judgement of observers can, if necessary, be used to modify the objective tone reproduction characteristics so that both agree. This in no way detracts from the value of objective tone reproduction in describing and analysing the photographic process. Extensive studies have indeed been carried out into the objectively measured tone reproduction of pictorial scenes that are subjectively preferred by human observers. The results of this investigation are of particular interest and are described in Appendix C.

7.34   For photographers and viewers, the two main factors to bear in mind with regard to viewing and obtaining information from photo-reproductions are:

(a)   *The response of the eye to viewing conditions.* Viewing conditions must be satisfactory. Our eyes can adapt to different lighting conditions within limits, but illuminance must not be too high or too low. Distractions, such as the white or coloured borders of a print, or the illuminated surrounds on a viewing table, should not be allowed to influence the eye. A photograph on a flat surface with no depth often presents a greater impression of reality when viewed using only one eye. This can also be done, and the borders avoided, by using a magnifying lens. In fact, small prints and small areas of prints are best viewed by using a magnifying lens so that the eyes are relaxed. A standard viewing light with a correlated colour temperature of 5000 K and a regularized intensity level is used in the commercial photography and graphic arts industries, particularly for viewing colour work. The viewing of reproductions in colour is further considered in paragraphs 11.79 to 11.82.

(b)   *The contrast sensitivity of the eye.* The response of our eyes to contrast is complex, but when viewing conditions are satisfactory the average unaided human eye is unable to distinguish, in adjacent areas of a photograph, density differences less than about 0.03 (particularly in the dark shadow areas), whereas a typical photoelectric densitometer can be used to distinguish density differences down to 0.01 or less. This particularly applies to reflection densities in the upper shoulder area of prints, where the eye soon loses its ability to discriminate between differing dark tones (see paragraphs 5.5 to 5.8).

Self-assessment questions

7.35   If you want to test your learning, study the basic tone reproduction diagram (Figure 7.1) and answer the following.

(a)   Describe in outline the photographic process represented in the diagram.
(b)   What is the $\bar{G}$ contrast of the negative?
(c)   What is the relationship between the negative density range and the paper log exposure range?
(d)   How should an increase in printing exposure be indicated on the diagram?
(e)   State how the tone reproduction curve is constructed.
(f)   What would represent:
  (1) True tone scale reproduction?
  (2) Proportional reproduction?
  (3) Tonal elongation over part of the print?
(g)   In Figure 7.1 what is the cause of the slight tonal compression in the highlights of the print?
(h)   Describe how the contrast in the shadows could be increased by using only exposure control.

Answer the following questions:

(i)   If a camera image log illuminance range is 1.4, the negative $\bar{G}$ is 0.75 and the average positive gradient is 1.6, what is the resultant reflection density range of the print? You can check your answer by drawing a graph similar to those in Figures 7.7 and 7.8.
(j)   How would the reproduction curve slope, with respect to the previous question?
(k)   What is the relationship between the negative and positive characteristic curves when true tone scale reproduction is obtained?
(l)   Describe the possible effect on the tonal range of:
  (1) Camera lens flare.
  (2) Atmospheric haze.
  (3) Enlarger lens flare.
(m)   The image of a subject is contained on the straight-line region of the characteristic curve when the negative has been developed to a gamma of 0.8. If a positive transparency giving true tone scale reproduction is required from the negative:
  (1) Where on the characteristic curve of the transparency film must the image be placed?
  (2) To what gamma must the transparency be developed?
  (3) How can the correct placing of the image on the transparency characteristic curve be achieved?

You can check you answers by drawing a graph similar to those in Figure 7.7 and 7.8.

(n)   A negative with a density range of 1.4 has been duplicated and the duplicate negative was processed to gamma 0.9 in order to achieve unity (have the same density range as the original).

What is the density range of the intermediate positive? You can check your answer by drawing a graph similar to those in Figures 7.7 and 7.8.

(o) To obtain improved tone scale reproduction, an intermediate positive was processed to gamma 1.4 and the duplicate negative film to gamma 1.1. If the original negative had a density range of 0.85:

(1) What is the density range of the improved 'duplicate' negative?

(2) To what gamma would the duplicate negative have been processed in order to obtain true tone scale reproduction of the original?

You can check your answers by drawing a graph similar to those in Figures 7.7 and 7.8.

Effects of electronic printing on tone reproduction

7.36 For photographic interpretation, paper prints and transparencies made from negatives should ideally contain all the detail and information that is in the negative and present it without any loss or degradation. The quality of this transfer of information will of course be limited by imperfections in the printing process (see paragraph 5.40). Other than this, difficulties in the production of optimum-quality prints and transparencies, for example from aerial photography negatives, are due in the main to four related factors which are also applicable to many general-purpose negatives:

(a) *Negative density range.* The density range of a negative is often too great for its image to be accommodated correctly on the log exposure range of the chosen printing material. This may result in loss of detail and contrast in the highlights and shadows of the print.

(b) *Subject illumination.* Variations in the density of a negative due to uneven illumination of the subject, caused by cloud shadow etc., may necessitate local exposure control at the printing stage by 'shading' (dodging).

(c) *Overall density differences.* Variations in negative density due to focal-plane shutter acceleration, or to fall-off in illumination towards the edges of the focal plane, may necessitate inverse variation of printing exposure.

(d) *Fine detail contrast.* Fine detail in a negative is often only discernible (resolved) because of the contrast between the images of different small areas of the subject. This contrast must be maintained or even increased in the print to obtain satisfactory resolution.

The factors listed above indicate that it may be necessary to compress the printing contrast of the large areas of the negative and to compensate for the uneven density produced by subject illumination differences, yet retain the contrast of small detail that might otherwise be lost. This can be achieved in an extremely crude fashion by manual shading and printing-in (dodging). It can also be achieved by using an unsharp contrast-reducing mask for each individual negative, and printing negative and mask together (see paragraph 5.33). Both the above methods are, however, extremely time-consuming and particularly difficult when dealing with negatives in quantity. By far the best method is to use an electronic printer. Electronic printing provides a means of obtaining refined and subtle shading and printing-in (dodging), and correct exposure, in an automatic manner. The principles of electronic printing apply to both black-and-white and colour photography, and it is used in many applications where precise exposure and the optimum reproduction of fine detail is important.

The effect of electronic printing on tone reproduction can be illustrated graphically by a tone reproduction diagram, but before we study the diagram we can briefly consider how an electronic printer operates and the results it can achieve.

7.37 Electronic printing is a means of making contact prints, transparencies, duplicates or enlargements, by using a moving-spot scanning light source to make the exposure, instead, of an overall continuous light source as used in a conventional printer. In a typical electronic printing system (Figure 7.12), the spot of light is imaged from the fluorescent face of a cathode-ray tube and is usually between 2 mm and 6 mm in diameter when incident on the negative. On many printers this size is controllable. The spot scans in a regular interlaced pattern and exposes one small area of the negative at a time onto the printing material. A photoreceptor (usually a photomultiplier tube) measures the intensity of light that has passed through the negative. It thus monitors the density of each area of the image continuously and produces a voltage output proportional to the light it receives. An instantaneous-feedback system from the photoreceptor to the cathode-ray tube modulates either the brightness or the speed of travel of the exposing spot, so that correct exposure for the printing material being used is given for each small area of the negative.

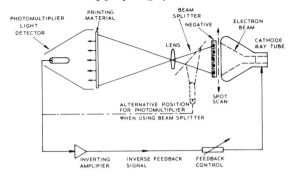

Fig. 7.12 Simplified schematic diagram of an electronic printing system. The spot of light produced on the face of the cathode-ray tube scans the negative in a regular overlapping pattern, and an image focused by the lens is formed on the printing material. The photomultiplier continuously measures the image light that passes through the printing material. The signal it generates is used to obtain correct exposure for each small area of the image. When printing a contrasty negative, the inverse feedback system from the photomultiplier to the cathode-ray tube modulates the exposing spot so that exposure is increased for very dark areas of the negative, and decreased for very light areas. It thus optimizes the overall exposure and the resultant contrast of the print. The degree of control is adjusted to suit the characteristics of the negative and printing material. As an alternative in some printers, sufficient light to activate the photomultiplier is diverted by a beam splitter situated near the lens.

For example, when the spot scans a dark negative area which would ordinarily print too light, the signal fed to the cathode-ray tube is such that exposure for the dark area is increased. When the spot scans a very light area which would ordinarily print too dark, the signal is such that exposure for the light area is decreased. Thus, in this case, the overall contrast of the printing image is lowered (this effect can be seen graphically in Figure 5.14). The feedback system can also be made to function in the opposite manner, so that the exposing spot gives less exposure through the darker areas of a negative and more exposure through the lighter areas. This increases the contrast of the printing image. Electronic printing can thus provide a very wide degree of exposure and contrast control.

On large-area contact printers, an image of the exposing spot is projected onto the negative by a lens. On small-area enlargers the face of the cathode-ray tube, and thus the exposing spot, may almost be in contact with the negative. In some printers the light is measured by the photoreceptor after it has passed through both negative and printing material. In others a small part of the light, after passing through the negative, is diverted to the receptor by a beam-splitting device,

positioned just above or just below the lens. Figure 7.12 illustrates this and the basic arrangement of an electronic printing system.

By giving correct exposure for individual areas of the negative, three things are achieved:

(a) *Large-area contrast compression.* The overall density range (large-area contrast) of the negative image is compressed (if necessary) so that it will match the log exposure range of the printing material.

(b) *Matching to printing material.* The degree of large-area tone compression may be matched to the characteristic curve of the printing material being used, so that, for example, the compression is greater in the areas printed onto the steepest part of the paper curve and less in the areas printed onto the shoulder and toe of the curve.

(c) *Retention of fine-detail contrast.* Density differences contained within areas smaller than the exposing spot size are not compressed. Thus the contrast and resolution of fine detail in all areas are preserved, and visual sharpness is improved.

Electronic printing tone reproduction diagram

7.38   The general effect of an electronic printing system can be shown graphically by a tone reproduction diagram (Figure 7.13). The basic principles depicted apply also to printing when using an unsharp positive mask in combination with the negative, as described in Chapter 5. The diagram's main purpose is to exercise your ability to interpret tone reproduction diagrams and therefore better appreciate the photographic process.

The situation depicted in Figure 7.13 is applicable to any photographic task in which the satisfactory reproduction of fine detail and tonal information is important. The subject, taken from aerial photography, provides a good example of the sensitometry of electronic printing.

Think of the original subject as a high-altitude vertical view of the ground, half of which is in direct sunlight and half in cloud shadow, with a road running through both sunlit and shadow areas. The fine detail could be pedestrian crossings (alternate dark and light bars), one in the sunlit half and another in the shadow half. Now, beginning in quadrant 1 and continuing in a clockwise direction, the diagram indicates:

(a) *Quadrant 1: characteristic curve of a typical aerial film negative.* The film has been correctly exposed

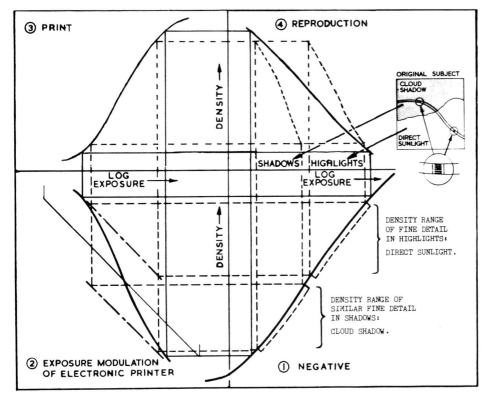

Solid lines and curves indicate the effect on large-area contrast.

Dashed lines and curves indicate the effect on fine-detail contrast.

Fig. 7.13 A tone reproduction diagram illustrating schematically that the general effect of electronic printing is to give correct exposure for all parts of the negative and at the same time to control the contrast of the large areas of the image without changing the contrast of fine detail. *Quadrant 1* shows the characteristic curve of a correctly exposed and processed negative with a high overall contrast and containing fine detail images. *Quadrant 2* shows that during electronic printing the contrast of the fine detail is not changed (dashed straight lines at 45°), while the contrast of the larger areas is compressed (solid curved line) so that it just fits onto the printing-paper exposure range. The degree of large-area contrast compression is matched to the contrast response of the printing paper, as shown by the curved line with an overall gradient well below 45°. *Quadrant 3* shows the characteristic curve of the correctly exposed and processed print. *Quadrant 4* shows the tone reproduction curves relating the original subject image tones to the final print densities, and indicates that satisfactory reproduction of both large areas and small detail has been achieved.

and developed to produce a suitable $\bar{G}$ in order to record the contrast of the fine detail of the terrain photographed. The negative has a long overall density range, caused by variations in the terrain illumination (i.e. the effect of cloud shadow and direct sunlight) and by development to the necessary $\bar{G}$ contrast. Therefore the average density of detail in the highlights is much higher than that of similar detail in the shadows. Any camera lens flare and atmospheric haze effects can be considered as being incorporated in the negative characteristic curve.

(b) *Quadrant 2: exposure modulation effect of the electronic printing system.* (The thin line drawn at 45° across the quadrant would represent the transfer line if electronic exposure modulation had not been used.) The position and slope of the exposure modulation curve of the electronic printer (solid curve) shows that the exposure through the shadow areas has been decreased, and the exposure through the highlight areas has been increased. Thus the overall density range (large-area contrast) of the negative image is compressed in its printing effect, so that it fits onto the paper's log exposure range. The shape of the exposure modulation curve shows that the degree of compression is matched to the characteristic curve of the printing material: compression is greatest in the areas that print onto the steepest part of the paper curve, and vice versa. The slope of the dashed lines at 45° shows that the contrast of fine detail within areas smaller than the exposing spot size is not changed. The position of the dashed lines is due to the decrease in exposure through the shadow areas and the increase in exposure through the highlight areas, and shows that the image of fine detail in both shadows and highlights has been exposed so that it fits onto the paper log exposure range.

(c) *Quadrant 3: characteristic curve of the printing material.* The characteristic curve of the printing material has received the contrast-adjusted exposure range from the large areas of the negative image, and the contrast-unadjusted but correctly exposed range from the fine detail in both shadows and highlights of the negative.

(d) *Quadrant 4: tone reproduction characteristics.* The tones of the large areas are all on a reasonably straight line. This indicates that the large-area tones of the subject (through the overall density range of the negative) are contained in the print, and that consecutive tonal reproduction is satisfactory. The reproduction curves for fine detail (dashed lines) show that the tones of fine detail are all on steep curves. This indicates that the tonal and density range of the fine detail is contained in the print and that the contrast between different areas of the fine detail has been both maintained and increased. The contrast of very fine detail, already reduced in the negative, will follow the same general pattern but at a somewhat lower gradient.

7.39   Electronic printing overcomes the difficulties often met in printing negatives that have different density ranges. It can be used to produce high-quality prints with a tonal and detail reproduction suitable for photographic interpretation. This is done by proportionally compressing the overall contrast (where necessary) without compressing the contrast of fine detail. The amount of feedback from the density-monitoring photomultiplier to the cathode-ray tube controls the degree of overall (large-area) contrast compression, and the size of the exposing spot controls the lower limit that this effect has on the contrast of small-area detail in the negative.

The 'fringing' effect in electronic printing

7.40   In electronic printing the size of the exposing spot also controls the amount of 'fringing', a smaller spot having less effect than a larger one. Fringing is the effect, sometimes seen in prints made on an electronic printer, where density is less than it should be at the border of a lighter area and greater than it should be at the border of an adjacent dark area. Because of its emphasis on edges, fringing improves the apparent sharpness of

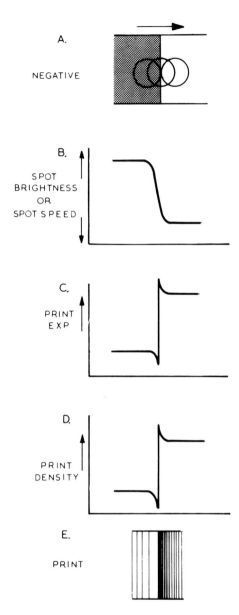

Fig. 7.14 The effect of fringing in electronic printing, showing how it improves the apparent sharpness of the printed image. (A) The exposing spot moves over the edge of a high-density area of the negative and into a low-density area. (B) As the average density that the spot scans decreases gradually, the instantaneous feedback system causes the spot brightness to decrease (or the spot speed to increase), also gradually. (C) The trailing part of the spot is still exposing the edge of the high-density area, so the edge receives less exposure than before. The leading part of the spot is already exposing the edge of the low-density area, so the edge receives more exposure than the area will later. (D, E) The result on the print is that density gradually decreases towards the edge of the light areas and gradually increases towards the edge of the darker area. The size of the exposing spot governs the amount of fringing, a smaller spot having less visible effect than a larger one.

the image (Figure 7.14). The effect is the same as that produced when an unsharp mask is used (paragraph 5.33) and similar to that produced by adjoining effects (Figure 2.35).

The step wedge in electronic printing

7.41   When a step wedge is being used on an electronic printer, the fringing effect will occur as the exposing spot moves over the edge of each step. Consequently correct exposure will only be obtained when the complete spot is on a step. Furthermore, the moving spot itself will not have a uniform luminance, and may also pass over the wedge in any direction across, along or diagonally in an overlapping and interlaced pattern. Therefore, when a step wedge is to be used on an electronic printer, the area of each step must be much greater than the area of the exposing spot and should be approximately square in shape. For a spot diameter of 6 mm, the minimum step size suggested is 35 × 35 mm. If the complete step

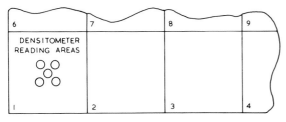

Fig. 7.15 A step tablet for use on an electronic printer. Because of the fringing effect that occurs at the edge between different densities and other factors during exposure, the step tablet must have steps of a fairly large area. Several large area measurements can then be made on the exposed and processed test material and the results averaged.

wedge cannot be accommodated within the printer format, steps can be exposed singly, one after the other, or in separate groups. When arranged as in Figure 7.15 the assembly is often called a 'step tablet'.

When measuring the densities produced, several (at least five) readings should be taken and the results averaged. The largest practical aperture of the densitometer should be used, and readings made near the centre of the step and at the same relative place on each step as indicated in Figure 7.15. Before carrying out sensitometric tests on electronic printers, you should experiment with step wedges having different step sizes to check for any fringing effect, and to decide a size suitable for the particular equipment being used.

Self-assessment questions

7.42   If you want to test your learning, write out answers to the following:

(a)   What is the main requirement in a photographic transparency or print that is to be interpreted?
(b)   In printing, what should the relationship be between the effective negative density range and the printing-paper log exposure range?
(c)   List three improvements that may be achieved by using an electronic printing system.
(d)   Study the tone reproduction quadrant diagram (Figure 7.13) and describe the procedure from exposure of the original subject through to viewing the final print. It is probably easier to describe first the effect that electronic printing has on large areas, and then the effect on fine detail.

8

Reciprocity failure

8.1 The reciprocity law was the first expressed by Bunsen and Roscoe in the early days of photography. It states that any photochemical effect depends only on the quantity of absorbed light. This means that the effect of exposure on a photographic emulsion is dependent on the product of the two variable factors involved, namely the illuminance and its duration. This product is known as the exposure, and the standard unit is the lux second. The law can be related to the equation (given in paragraph 2.3):

$$\text{Exposure} = \text{illuminance} \times \text{duration} \ (H = E \times t)$$

Reciprocity failure effects

8.2 The reciprocity law assumes that illuminance and duration are reciprocally interchangeable. This means, for example, that doubling the illuminance and halving the duration makes no difference to the photochemical effect. However, photographic emulsions do not strictly follow this law and show marked departures when the value of the illuminance is either very high or very low. Under these conditions the developed effect of exposure depends on the actual values of E and t and not simply on their product. For example, exposure to an illuminance of 10 lux for $1/10$ second may not produce the same density after development as an exposure to an illuminance of $1/10$ lux for 10 seconds, although the value of $E \times t$ is the same in each case. This failure in the reciprocal relationship of E and t is known as reciprocity law failure or, more correctly, as *reciprocity failure*. Reciprocity failure can also affect the resultant contrast of an emulsion.

Reciprocity failure has little significance in most practical applications of black-and-white photography, except when very short or very long exposures are used, but its effect must be considered in colour photography and in all aspects of sensitometric testing. If the conditions of exposure in a sensitometer vary greatly from the conditions that the material under test will receive

in practice, the effect of exposure may be quite different and thus make the results of a test invalid. The effect of reciprocity failure on a hypothetical photographic emulsion is illustrated in Figure 8.1.

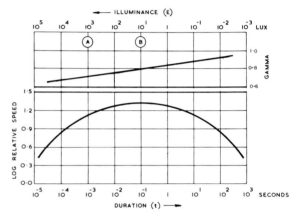

Fig. 8.1 The general effects of reciprocity failure on a hypothetical photographic emulsion. The graph shows the two factors that produce exposure ($H = Et$). Along the top scale, the values of illuminance increase from right to left. Along the bottom scale, the values of duration increase from left to right. The two factors have a reciprocal relationship, so all the vertical lines joining them indicate the same exposure value. The upper graph shows the effect of reciprocity failure on gamma (contrast produced), and the lower graph its effect on speed. Away from an optimum exposure in the centre of the graph, reciprocity failure will reduce the effective speed of the emulsion. Additionally, with short exposure times it will cause a reduction in contrast, and with long exposure times an increase in contrast.

In the figure the two factors E and t are shown as reciprocally interchangeable. Throughout the whole range, the value of $E \times t$ remains the same. The upper graph shows the varying effect on gamma and the lower graph the variation in effective emulsion speed. If there were no reciprocity failure, both curves would be horizontal straight lines.

The diagram indicates that an exposure to, say, an illuminance of 1000 lux for $1/1000$ second (line A on the diagram) gives less effective emulsion speed and a lower gamma than exposure to, say, 10 lux

128

for $\frac{1}{10}$ second (line B on the diagram), although $E \times t$ is the same in each case. We can deduce from Figure 8.1 that reciprocity failure:

(a) Reduces the effective speed of the photographic emulsion.
(b) Affects the resultant contrast of the emulsion: short exposure to high illuminance lowers contrast, and long exposure to low illuminance increases contrast.

Optimum conditions for this emulsion are given with exposure to an illuminance of about 10 lux for $\frac{1}{10}$ second (line B on the diagram).

It is emphasized that the diagram in figure 8.1 is for a hypothetical emulsion and is intended to illustrate only the general effect of reciprocity failure.

8.3 *Reciprocity failure in colour photography.* Reciprocity failure is particularly important in colour photography. The several different light-sensitive layers of a colour material are balanced in manufacture to give satisfactory results under average exposure conditions. Exposures other than average will cause reciprocity failure, which can have a different effect on each emulsion. The different changes in speed and contrast may cause unwanted colour casts in the resultant photography (see Chapter 11). Some colour material manufacturers therefore provide two types of colour film: one for short exposure times of, say, less than $\frac{1}{10}$ second, and a different type for long exposure times of, say, $\frac{1}{10}$ second to 1 minute or so.

8.4 *Summary of reciprocity failure effects.* The main effects of reciprocity failure can be summarized and compared with optimum conditions, as shown in Table 8.1. You can confirm these finding by relating them to Figure 8.1.

Table 8.1 Causes and effects of reciprocity failure.

| Exposure conditions | | Effects | |
Illuminance	Duration	Speed	Contrast
Optimum	Optimum	Highest	Intermediate
High	Short	Less	Lower
Low	Long	Less	Higher

8.5 All photographic emulsions are affected by reciprocity failure, but its effect is not significant in normal use because emulsions are manufactured to give a satisfactory performance under the likely conditions of exposure. For example:

(a) General-purpose films give a satisfactory performance in the region of, say, $\frac{1}{1000}$ to $\frac{1}{10}$ second, typical printing papers in the region of 1 to 10 seconds or so.
(b) Materials made for astronomical photography perform well at low illuminances and long exposure durations (e.g. exposures lasting several hours).
(c) Films made for high-speed cinephotography perform well at high illuminances and short exposure durations (e.g. exposure durations of about $\frac{1}{10000}$ second).
(d) Aerial films give a satisfactory performance under the conditions of exposure found in aerial photography (e.g. exposure durations of $\frac{1}{2000}$ to $\frac{1}{200}$ second).
(e) Colour films and printing papers give satisfactory results when exposed within the duration limits recommended and published by the manufacturers.

Basic theory of reciprocity failure

8.6 Photographers concerned with sensitometry need to be aware of reciprocity failure and its practical effects, but in most cases it is not essential to understand why it occurs. Nevertheless a basic explanation may be of value.

The theory of the cause of reciprocity failure is associated with the rate at which the latent photographic image is formed and how the electrons freed by light action during exposure are either trapped or displaced at the sensitivity centres on the silver halide grains (Gurney–Mott theory). When a photo-electron is trapped at a sensitivity centre a silver atom is formed. A single atom of silver is unstable on its own and has a very short life, but two or more silver atoms together have much greater stability. Thus the initial formation of a satisfactory latent image depends upon sufficient photo-electrons being trapped at a sensitivity centre in order to form a group of at least two silver atoms. With the trapping of more photo-electrons during normal exposure, the group of silver atoms can then build up to produce a full developable latent image. The basic theory and effects of reciprocity failure can be loosely summarized as follows:

(a) *Low-illuminance effect.* Under conditions of low illuminance the rate of electron release is too low, and on some sensitivity centres the second photo-electron may not be trapped within the lifetime of a single silver atom. This prevents latent-image nucleation and growth. Therefore with a low-illuminance, long-duration exposure the latent image is more unstable and less effectual than it would be after the same exposure to a relatively higher level of illuminance.

(b) *High-illuminance effect.* Under conditions of high illuminance the rate of electron release throughout the silver halide grains is very rapid, resulting in a multiplicity of small sub-developable latent-image specks. So only a proportion of the photo-electrons are utilized to form a developable latent image. Thus an exposure of high illuminance and short duration produces a less efficient latent image than the same exposure at a relatively lower illuminance level.

(c) *Optimum electron release rate.* The optimum rate of electron release, and hence rate of supply of light energy, depends on the properties of the particular photographic emulsion. This means that there is a small range of illuminances and exposure durations that result in the greatest efficiency of photochemical energy conversion. This optimum rate provides the maximum emulsion speed (line B on Figure 8.1).

A very good description of latent image formation and reciprocity failure is given in the book *Basic Photo Science*, and the mechanism and effects are fully explained in *The Theory of the Photographic Process* (see Appendix G).

Intermittency effect

8.7   Intermittency effect is a consequence of reciprocity failure. The same exposure given to an emulsion as a series of intermittent exposures instead of a continuous exposure will often give results of a different density and contrast. For example, a hundred separate exposures of $1/100$ second may not give the same result as a single exposure of 1 second. The photochemical effect may be greater or less than that of the same luminous energy delivered in a single exposure. The result depends on whether the latent image is increased or reduced (or unchanged) during the dark intervals between exposures. This, in turn, depends on several factors: the type of emulsion, the frequency of exposures, the dark intervals between exposures, and the level of illuminance. Intermittency effect is not evident if the frequency of exposure exceeds a certain level. Therefore in an experimental situation the effects may be avoided by establishing the frequency above which no effects are found, and restricting operation to that region. Because of the effects of intermittency, such

exposure methods are only used in sensitometric procedures demanding absolute neutrality of the exposure-modulating device (as in a time-scale sensitometer). In practical photography the possible effect on the resultant image should be borne in mind whenever an intermittent exposure is given. For example, in colour photography a series of intermittent exposures made with an electronic flash can give rise to a loss of colour fidelity.

Reciprocity failure in practice

8.8   Some examples of reciprocity failure that may be encountered in practice are given below and should be related to the reciprocity failure diagram (Figure 8.1). The examples refer to exposures made with an average general-purpose emulsion under non-average conditions.

(a) *High-speed electronic flash.* Exposures of a duration less than about $1/1000$ second may need more exposure and longer development time to obtain the desired speed and contrast. For example, automatic computer-controlled electronic flash equipment will give very short exposure durations, commonly within the range $1/1000$ to $1/50\,000$ second.

(b) *Photomacrography.* A considerable lens-to-film camera extension may necessitate a long exposure, because of the decrease in effective lens aperture (increase in *f*-number). In addition the calculated exposure may need to be further increased, and contrast can also be affected, because of reciprocity failure. In some cases it is more useful to increase the aperture (reduce the *f*-number) to correct for low-illuminance effects, than to lengthen the exposure time.

(c) *High-density optical filters.* If a filter on a camera has a high exposure factor, necessitating a long exposure, the exposure duration will have to be increased more than the filter factor indicates. However, if exposure can be adjusted by suitably increasing illuminance instead of duration (by using a larger lens aperture and/or a higher lighting level), the filter exposure factor indication will be correct.

(d) *Colour photography.* The effects of reciprocity failure are more directly apparent in colour than in black-and-white photography, because they show as variations (which may be unacceptable) in the reproduction of colours (see Chapter 11).

(e) *Large-scale enlargements.* These need more exposure than the degree of enlargement indicates, and a higher contrast is also achieved (provided that stray light is absent). For example, using a basic 10 seconds exposure, if the degree of enlargement indicates a five-fold increase the actual exposure to obtain a good print may necessitate an eight- to ten-fold increase. With colour printing paper, both the speed and contrast of each of the three basic photographic emulsions may be affected to a different degree and thus produce 'cross colour casts' (see also paragraphs 11.31 and 11.119). To prevent these effects, the exposure may be increased by using a greater lens aperture rather than by increasing the exposure time.

8.9 In most applications of general black-and-white photography, the effects of reciprocity failure are insignificant, provided that the image illuminance is suitable for an exposure duration of between $\frac{1}{1000}$ and $\frac{1}{10}$ second. The effects, however, must be understood, and corrections made to exposure and development if conditions of exposure are not within the acceptable range of the photographic material in use. In colour photography reciprocity failure effects are particularly noticeable; therefore the exposure duration must be within the limits recommended by the material manufacturer, otherwise satisfactory colour fidelity will not be obtained (see also paragraphs 11.31 and 11.119).

8.10 *Sensitometry and reciprocity failure*. When carrying out sensitometric tests, the possibility of reciprocity failure must be considered. Under test conditions the value of illuminance and of exposure duration should be similar to those the material will receive in actual use. Thus, if a film is to receive an exposure duration of $\frac{1}{250}$ second in practice, it should receive an exposure duration of a similar order of magnitude on the sensitometer. If it does not, the findings of speed and contrast may be misleading for practical use. This action is often impracticable but it emphasizes the point made earlier, that sensitometric tests must be made as far as possible under practical conditions. Sensitometric comparisons of similar types of emulsions

and tests not made under such conditions will be of value, but the results cannot be considered as being precise. (For the practical application of this, see paragraph 2.11.)

Self-assessment questions

8.11 If you want to test your learning, write out answers to the following:

(a) Explain the reciprocity law as it relates to photographic exposure.
(b) Under what conditions does reciprocity failure occur?
(c) Describe the two main effects that reciprocity failure will have on an average photographic emulsion when it is exposed to: (1) a very high level of illuminance; (2) a very low level of illuminance.

Study the reciprocity failure diagram (Figure 8.1) and answer the following questions:

(d) What is the optimum condition of exposure for this hypothetical emulsion?
(e) If light conditions indicate a change in exposure duration from $\frac{1}{10}$ second to 100 seconds, what corrections for reciprocity failure will be necessary?
(f) If a sensitometer gave an exposure duration of $\frac{1}{10}$ second and a sensitometric test of a film produced a $\overline{G}$ contrast of 0.8, what might the $\overline{G}$ be if the film were then exposed in a camera using a shutter speed of $\frac{1}{5000}$ second, and then processed?

Finally:

(g) On a piece of squared graph paper draw a characteristic curve for a medium-contrast film that has been exposed and processed under average conditions. Then draw another curve to illustrate the effect on the same film of high-illuminance reciprocity failure. On the graph, list the effects you have illustrated.

9

Transmission density

9.1 During the printing process, light passing through a black-and-white silver negative is partly absorbed and partly diffused (scattered) by the grains that form the image, and part of the light passes through directly (undeviated). For contact printing, the photographic material receiving the transmitted light is in contact with the negative, and thus receives both diffuse and direct transmitted light. However, for projection printing, the photographic material is at a distance from the negative and thus receives (for the most part) the direct transmitted light only. Because of this, the printing effect of a negative that is contact printed may differ from that of a negative that is projection printed. Therefore, depending on the printing method used, different values of transmission density may apply to the same negative. If you wish to refresh your memory on this, refer to Figure 2.7 and its associated paragraphs. Note that the effect is more particular to silver images. The dye images of colour photographic materials and chromogenically developed black-and-white films will also cause transmitted light to scatter, but not to any significant extent.

Types of transmission density

9.2 There are basically three different types of transmission density, each appropriate to the optical transmission system used in the printing process and to the optical arrangement of the densitometer when densities are being measured. See Figure 9.1.

(a) Direct transmission density. (The term 'regular' may be used instead of 'direct', and the term 'specular' is often met in photographic literature.)
(b) Diffuse transmission density.
(c) Doubly diffuse transmission density.

DIRECT TRANSMISSION

A

LIGHT RECEPTOR

DIRECT LIGHT INCIDENT
ONLY DIRECTLY TRANSMITTED LIGHT RECEIVED

DIFFUSE TRANSMISSION (1)

B

LIGHT RECEPTOR

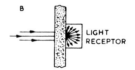

DIRECT LIGHT INCIDENT
ALL TRANSMITTED LIGHT RECEIVED

DIFFUSE TRANSMISSION (2)

C

LIGHT RECEPTOR

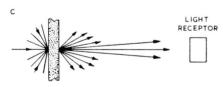

DIFFUSE LIGHT INCIDENT
ONLY DIRECTLY TRANSMITTED LIGHT RECEIVED

DOUBLY DIFFUSE TRANSMISSION

D

LIGHT RECEPTOR

DIFFUSE LIGHT INCIDENT·
ALL TRANSMITTED LIGHT RECEIVED

Fig. 9.1 Types of transmission density and conditions of light transmission. The diagrams can represent part of a silver image in a printing mode or when being measured on a densitometer. The light receptor in contact printing is the printing paper, in enlarging it is the lens, and in densitometry it is the photosensor or measuring device. The light received, and thus the effective density of the image, varies according to the amount of scattered light that falls on the receptor. The less light received, the greater the effective density.

9.3 *Direct transmission density* is applicable when the illumination incident on the negative is direct and the receptor receives only direct transmitted light. This type of transmission occurs when the light source is collimated (made direct) by an optical condenser, and when the receptor (which may be, for example, a densitometer measuring device or an enlarger lens) is at a distance from the negative. Under these conditions only the substantially direct transmitted light is received.

9.4 *Diffuse transmission density* is applicable under two conditions of transmission:

(a) When using direct incident light and receiving all the transmitted light, the light receptor (measuring instrument or photographic material) must be in contact with the emulsion side of the negative.
(b) When using diffuse incident light and receiving only the direct transmitted light, the light receptor (measuring instrument or enlarger lens) must be at a distance from the negative.

The numerical value of diffuse transmission density is the same, whichever of the above conditions is used, owing to the principle of 'the reversibility of optical paths'. This may not be immediately apparent from Figure 9.1 B and C, but it is correct.

9.5 *Doubly diffuse transmission density* is applicable when using diffuse incident light and receiving all the transmitted light. The light receptor must be in contact with the emulsion side of the negative.

9.6 *Difference in value between types of density.* The difference in value between diffuse density and doubly diffuse density is small, but a direct transmission density value is always higher than that of either type of diffuse density. Because of this, a change in optical conditions (for example, a change from a 'diffuser' to a 'compact-source condenser' enlarger) will give a significant increase in the contrast of a print made from a silver-image negative, as explained later.

9.7 *Type of transmission density used in measurement.* Diffuse transmission density can be specified and measured accurately because the measuring instrument is, in effect, in contact with the negative. Direct transmission density can be specified and determined only with respect to the particular optical equipment in use, as its value depends on the solid angle of the beam of light incident on the

receptor: in other words, on the area and distance of the measuring instrument or the enlarger lens from the negative. Because of this, densities of negatives are normally measured and expressed as diffuse transmission densities. Thus, unless otherwise specified, any quoted density may be taken as being a diffuse density. The agreed standard of diffuse density is described in the relevant ISO, British and American standards publications, which are ISO 5, BS 1384, and ANSI PH 2.19.

Transmission density in practice

9.8 Most practical applications do not involve completely direct transmission nor completely diffuse transmission, but a mixture of the two. Nevertheless one type is usually predominant.

(a) *Condenser enlarger with a compact light source* (Figure 9.1A). Direct transmission density is applicable to a condenser enlarger with a compact light source, because light incident on the negative is direct and only direct light reaches the lens and passes through it to form the image.
(b) *Still or cine projector* (Figure 9.1A). Direct transmission density is also applicable to a still or cine projector, because light incident on the image is direct and only direct light reaches the projector lens.
(c) *Contact printing frame using a compact light source* (Figure 9.1B). Diffuse transmission density is applicable to these conditions. The incident light is direct and all the transmitted light is received by the printing paper.
(d) *Electronic contact printer* (Figure 9.1B). Diffuse transmission density is applicable here. The incident light, which originates from one small exposing spot, is direct, and all the transmitted light is received by the material in contact with the negative.
(e) *Diffuser enlarger* (Figure 9.1C). Diffuse transmission density is also applicable to a diffuser enlarger, because the incident light is diffuse and only direct light reaches the lens and passes through it to form the image.
(f) *Contact printer with a diffuse light source* (Figure 9.1D). Doubly diffuse density is applicable to a contact printer or a contact printing frame, which uses a diffuse light source. This is because the incident light is diffuse and all the transmitted light is received by the photographic material in contact with the negative.

The Callier effect and coefficient

9.9   When printing in a practical situation we use not one density, but a range of densities, so we need to consider the different effects of printing a range of densities under direct transmission conditions and under diffuse transmission conditions. This comparison can be made by printing the same black-and-white silver negative first in a compact-source condenser enlarger and then in a diffuser enlarger.

9.10   Consider a silver negative (or step wedge) with a diffuse transmission density range of approximately 0.05 to 0.95 in a condenser enlarger that has a compact light source (Figure 9.2A). Light incident on the negative is direct. Light passes through the lowest densities of the negative with very little diffusion and may be considered as being still direct when it reaches the lens. On the other hand, direct light passing through the middle and higher densities is partly diffused by the granular structure of the photographic image, and most of this diffuse light does not reach the lens. The loss of light from these densities is in addition to the light absorbed during its passage through the negative. Therefore middle and higher densities have effectively a greater density, which accentuates the contrast of the projected image. This effect is greater in the shadow areas (as explained in paragraph 9.12).

9.11   Consider the same negative in a diffuser enlarger, for example the same enlarger with a diffusing screen inserted between the light source and negative (Figure 9.2B). Because of the diffusing screen, the light incident and passing through all parts of the negative is already fully diffuse and is therefore not diffused further by the middle and higher densities of the negative. The only effective factor is the light absorbed by the negative itself. Thus an image from the same negative has less contrast when projected in a diffuser enlarger than when projected in a true condenser enlarger.

9.12   The increase of contrast due to light diffusion when the image of a negative (or positive) is projected in a compact-source condenser enlarger was first investigated by André Callier in 1909, and is called the Callier effect. The ratio of direct

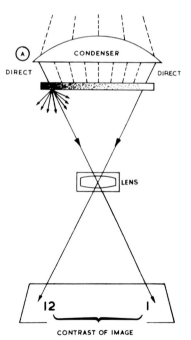
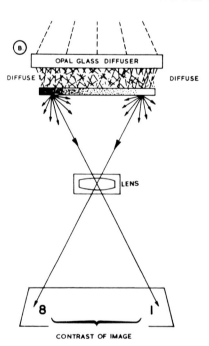

Fig. 9.2 Effect of direct and diffuse transmission in projection printing. (A) In a true condenser enlarger with a compact light source, direct transmission conditions exist. Very low-density areas of the negative allow almost all the light to pass through directly without scattering. Denser areas not only absorb light but also scatter light away from the lens. The contrast of the projected image is thus increased. (B) In a diffuser enlarger diffuse transmission conditions exist. The light passing through all the densities of the negative is already fully scattered in all directions, so the contrast of the projected image depends only on absorption by the densities, and contrast is not increased.

transmission density to diffuse transmission density (e.g. as measured on a densitometer) is known as the Callier coefficient, Callier factor, or Q factor:

$$\text{Callier coefficient} = \frac{\text{direct transmission density}}{\text{diffuse transmission density}}$$

A direct transmission density value is always greater than a diffuse transmission density value, so the numerical value of the Callier coefficient is always greater than 1.0. Its value varies with the amount of light diffusion caused by the granular structure of the negative. There are three inter-related factors that cause diffusion of the light passing through the negative, namely:

(a) *Granular structure.* A fine-grain negative causes less diffusion than a coarse-grain negative, and its densities therefore have a numerically lower Callier coefficient. A hypothetical non-scattering material, for instance a dye negative density, would not cause any significant diffusion. Its Callier coefficient would therefore be 1.0. In practice, dye images do scatter light, and the Callier coefficient is greater than 1.0 but usually less than that of a silver image.

(b) *Gamma (and $\bar{G}$ contrast).* An increase in the development time of the negative gives a higher Callier coefficient, because of the increase in granularity and grain clumping that occurs, together with higher contrast.

(c) *Density level.* Clear film does not cause light to diffuse and thus its Callier coefficient is 1.0. As the level of transmission density increases from zero, the relative amount of diffusion, and thus the Callier coefficient, increases rapidly to a maximum at a density of approximately 0.3 (giving 50 per cent transmittance), this being the density at which the area covered by silver grains is about equal to the area left uncovered. As density increases beyond 0.3 the numerical value gradually decreases, often to a constant level.

Figure 9.3 illustrates the effect of these factors and shows also the distribution of contrast increase from shadows to highlights in the projected image (when using a compact-source condenser enlarger) of typical black-and-white aerial-photography and general-purpose silver negatives. Notice that for aerial negatives, where the minimum density is 0.4 above fog, the Callier effect is more linear than it is for general-purpose negatives.

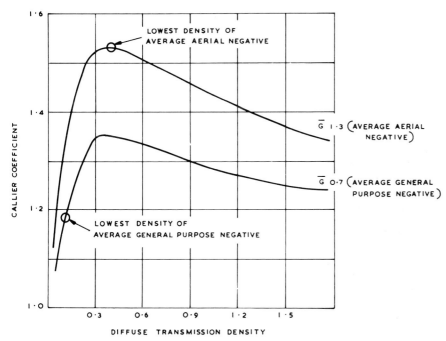

Fig. 9.3 The variation of Callier effect with increasing density and G, for typical black-and-white silver negatives. In conditions where direct transmission density is applicable, its value equals diffuse density multiplied by the Callier coefficient.

The curves thus show that under such conditions effective density, and hence the projected image contrast, increases rapidly in the lower densities, reaches a peak, and then gradually decreases.

9.13   *Characteristic curves for direct and diffuse transmission densities.*   Some densitometers that normally measure a specified standard diffuse density can be adapted so that they can also measure a typical direct transmission density. A sensitometric strip measured on such a densitometer to give both direct transmission density readings and diffuse transmission density readings will, when these values are plotted, give results indicating the different gammas, and therefore the different negative contrasts produced. This is shown in Figure 9.4. The effect is greater with high-speed coarse-grain films than it is with slower fine-grain films.

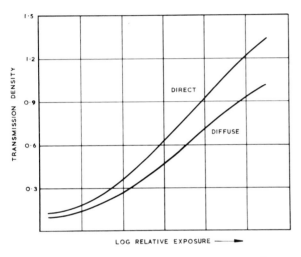

Fig. 9.4 The effect on the characteristic curve of direct and diffuse density as measured on a densitometer. The curves show that the effective density range is increased when measured in direct transmission density conditions. Therefore the image contrast is increased when a negative is printed using direct illumination in an enlarger.

9.14   *Summary.*   Direct illumination in an enlarger, or in any other optical instrument where negative, lens, and printing material are separated, increases the effective image contrast of a typical negative; the increase is greatest in the areas with a density of 0.3 or so. This variation in contrast may be used to produce a print of the desired quality. However, bear in mind that in practical conditions any flare light present in the system also affects the contrast (see paragraph 7.13).

9.15   *Using the Callier effect for contrast control.*   In most cases, using the Callier effect is secondary to other means of obtaining different contrasts, such

as selecting the right grade of printing paper, or using a controlled flashing technique (see paragraphs 5.18 and 5.19), but in certain conditions it can be of value. The method depends on making the illumination either more direct or more diffuse, and the result is more satisfactory when printing silver images than it is when printing the dye images of colour or chromogenically developed materials (see paragraph 9.1).

Many enlargers incorporate a condenser illumination system, and some use an optical light guide. With these a means of reducing contrast is to fit a diffusing screen between the light source and the negative. This provides a large-area diffuse light source. Contrast increase may be obtained if a smaller area light source (smaller lamp) can be fitted, or if a screen with a small aperture in it can be fitted near the existing lamp to reduce its effective size. This makes the light incident on the negative more direct. The possibility of such modification depends of course on the construction

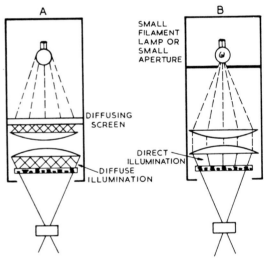

Fig. 9.5 Modifying the illumination system of a typical enlarger.
(A) Using a diffusing screen to obtain diffuse conditions and thus reduce image contrast.
(B) Reducing the light source area to obtain more direct illumination and thus increase image contrast. A stepped sensitometric strip with a density range of 1.0 or so should be printed before and after each modification in order to perceive the effect.

and type of enlarger. Figure 9.5 shows the general system. With a true condenser enlarger, contrast tends to be further increased as the lens aperture is reduced in size, because stopping down the lens makes the image light even more direct (Figure 9.1A).

9.16 *Direct and diffuse illumination in sensitometric testing.* Since transmission density has a variable effect dependent on the optical system used in printing, the conditions of producing and measuring densities in a sensitometric test should be similar to the conditions under which the material will be exposed or illuminated in actual use. This may sometimes be impracticable because of the mixture of direct and diffuse elements involved in exposure, printing, etc. Therefore, any sensitometric test not made under the conditions that will apply in practice must be supplemented by tests under actual conditions on the equipment itself (see also Figure 9.4).

Self-assessment questions

9.17 If you want to test your learning, write out answers to the following questions:

(a) Draw diagrams to illustrate how the three different types of transmission occur.

(b) State, for a measured image area on a negative, which of the three types of transmission density will give the highest numerical value, and explain why.

(c) What type of transmission density is most applicable to:

(1) An electronic contact printer?

(2) A condenser enlarger with a compact light source?

(3) A contact printer with a diffuse light source?

(d) Draw a rough diagram showing two characteristic curves of a typical film, one showing direct transmission densities and the other diffuse transmission densities.

(e) Explain the Callier effect, and how the Callier coefficient is found.

(f) Explain how the variation in image contrast due to the Callier effect might be used to advantage when projection printing.

10

Spectral sensitivity

Wedge spectrograms

10.1 The recorded response of a photographic emulsion varies with the different wavelengths of light, and the relative values of the response often need to be known. These different sensitivities can be measured and are normally shown in the form of a wedge spectrogram, as depicted in Figure 10.1, or as a spectral sensitivity curve. These are curves that indicate the relative sensitivity of a photographic emulsion to different wavelengths of light throughout the visible spectrum (approximately 400 nm to 700 nm). Wedge spectrograms and spectral sensitivity curves are mainly used for comparing the spectral sensitivity of different emulsions in order to determine the best emulsion for a specific task. The effective spectral sensitivity curves of a representative colour negative film are shown in Figure 11.14. The manufacturers of photographic materials may include such curves with the sensitometric information they supply for their various films. The characteristics of the exposing light affect the response of a photographic material, of course, so there are usually two different curves applicable, one for standard daylight and the other for tungsten light.

Equipment and simple methods for evaluating and comparing the sensitivity of films to different colours of light.

138

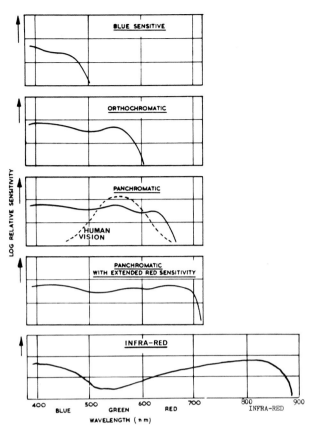

Fig. 10.1 Wedge spectrograms of typical black-and-white film materials exposed to standard daylight. Each solid curve shows the relative sensitivity of the film to different wavelengths of light throughout the applicable spectrum. The dashed curve represents the response of the human eye. Note that the sensitivity of a typical infrared sensitive emulsion extends beyond the visible spectrum up to about 900 nanometres, but in practice a filter that absorbs the visible radiation and transmits only infrared may be used.

Figure 10.1 shows also a dashed curve representing the comparative response of the human eye to different wavelengths of light. Although no particular black-and-white emulsion matches the response of the human eye, the nearest approach is that given by a panchromatic material. However, there is still a considerable difference between visual response and that of a typical panchromatic emulsion. In general-purpose black-and-white photography the result of this difference is often unimportant. On the print, the blues and reds of a subject are recorded as lighter tones, and the greens as slightly darker tones than they appear to our eyes. If a tonal reproduction approaching or matching the response of the human eye is required, colour filters must be used to correct the oversensitivity of the panchromatic emulsion to

particular wavelengths of light. The use of a yellow-green correction filter to record white clouds in a blue sky is an application of this filtration technique.

Figure 10.1 shows wedge spectrograms of five typical black-and-white film emulsions when exposed to standard daylight:

(a) *Blue-sensitive*. Used mainly for copying and duplicating black-and-white originals. (Also used for printing papers.)

(b) *Orthochromatic*. Used for photographic tasks where lack of red sensitivity is unimportant.

(c) *Panchromatic*. Used for the photography of subjects containing all colours. The red sensitivity is limited in order to better match the visual appearance of red objects. Chromogenically developed black-and-white films designed to produce silverless dye-image negatives (see paragraph 4.18) have an overall spectral response similar to that of normal panchromatic film.

(d) *Panchromatic with extended red-sensitivity*. Used mainly for the reduction of atmospheric haze effects in aerial and long-distance photography and for scientific work.

(e) *Infrared-sensitive*. Usually sensitive to all visible wavelengths (but with a reduced sensitivity to green) and extending into the infrared beyond the visible region. In use, infrared emulsions are exposed through a filter that transmits only infrared radiation. Used for aerial photography and scientific recording.

Wedge spectrograms are produced in an instrument called a wedge spectrograph, and spectral sensitivity curves are produced from measurements made following exposure in a spectrosensitometer. These instruments are usually available in film-testing laboratories. They are similar in their operation, but a spectrosensitometer is the more complex instrument and produces more precise data, particularly for the shorter wavelengths. A tolerable measure of the response of an emulsion to different broad regions of the visible spectrum is often sufficient in practice, and can be obtained without the use of special apparatus. This is explained later in paragraphs 10.5 to 10.8.

The wedge spectrograph

10.2   In a wedge spectrograph (Figure 10.2) white light from a standard source, for example standard daylight at 5500 K, passes through a narrow slit. An image of the slit is then dispersed into a continuous spectrum, usually by a diffraction

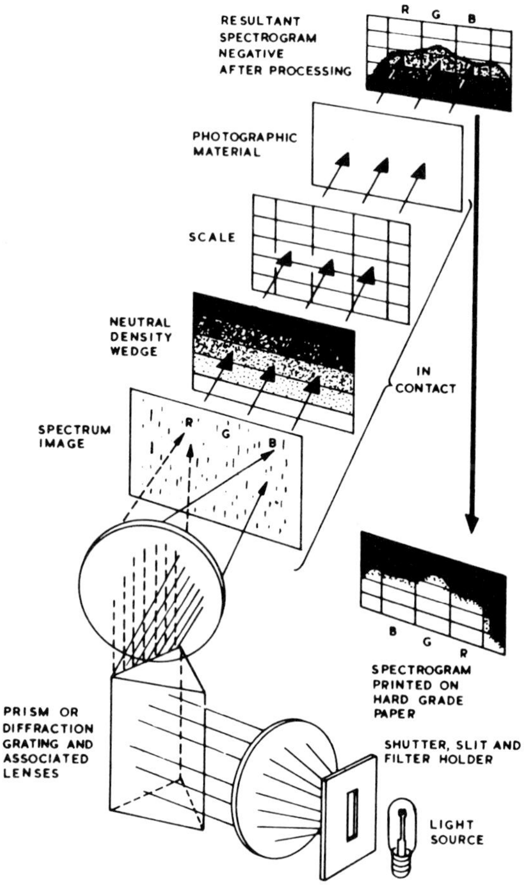

Fig. 10.2 Schematic diagram of a wedge spectrograph and spectrogram. A spectrum comprising the different wavelengths of light is created and arranged so that it falls on a step wedge with the whole range of colours crossing each step. The test material behind the wedge thus receives a full exposure range from each colour. After processing, the relative spectral sensitivity of the material to the type of light used in exposure, is shown by the position of the boundary of the image against the log relative sensitivity scale, at each wavelength.

grating. The grating acts like a glass prism, but gives a better linear separation between wavelengths throughout the spectrum. A neutral-density step wedge (or a continuous wedge) is positioned with its steps of increasing density at right angles to the spectrum display. The spectrum passes through the wedge and exposes the emulsion under test. The emulsion thus receives the colours of the spectrum across from left to right, with the exposure from each colour decreasing from bottom to top. Scales, showing the wavelengths of light on the horizontal axis and log relative sensitivity on the vertical axis, can be superimposed during exposure.

The instrument is enclosed in a light-tight container that has a means of holding the material under test in the exposing position.

10.3   The resultant negative, after processing, is called a wedge spectrogram. The boundary of the developed image above each point along the wavelength axis indicates the relative sensitivity of the emulsion to light of that wavelength. The negative may then be printed onto a hard grade of paper. The denser parts of the spectrogram appear light on the print and the least dense parts appear dark on the print. The hard grade paper emphasizes the gradient between light and dark. A line of equal density (the locus) is drawn on the print for some chosen density of the negative; this curve indicates the spectral sensitivity distribution at the chosen density. Lines drawn for other densities may show slightly different curve shapes; this is because the contrast produced by different wavelengths of light varies slightly, being generally greater for the longer wavelengths. (See paragraph 2.88 and Figure 10.3.)

10.4   *Ultraviolet cut-off.* Some wedge spectrograms show a fairly sharp cut-off in spectral sensitivity just below 350 nm. This is due to the ultraviolet absorption by the glass optical components in the exposing instrument. Thus a wedge spectrogram often indicates a lower sensitivity to the shorter wavelengths than the material may actually have. For general photography this is not important as the glass of a camera lens will also absorb the shorter wavelengths. In fact, all photographic emulsions are sensitive to wavelengths much shorter than those of visible light. In some cases, ultraviolet absorbers are coated in the supercoat on top of the emulsion in order to cut off the sensitivity at approximately 410 nm.

Simple evaluation of colour sensitivity

10.5   A tolerable evaluation of the response of a black-and-white film to different wavelengths of light can be obtained (without the use of special apparatus) by several different methods, three of which we can now consider.

10.6   *Colour sensitivity comparison using filters.* Tri-colour blue, green and red optical filters (see paragraph 11.20) are used to filter the exposing light, either in a sensitometer or in a camera used to photograph a scale of neutral greys. The system

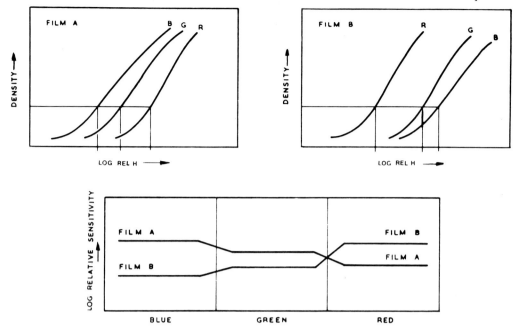

Fig. 10.3 Simple comparative evaluation of the colour sensitivity of black-and-white films. Pieces of film are exposed in turn through tricolour blue, green and red filters. Other than this, exposure and processing conditions are identical. The densities are measured and plotted, and the log exposure shift of a mid-range density gives the ratio of respective colour sensitivities. The results can be shown in the form of a simple spectrogram (lower diagram).

is similar to that used for finding filter exposure factors and is particularly useful for comparison of the response to the three main bands of the visible spectrum (blue, green and red) of different types of film. The procedure is as follows:

(a) Ensure that the exposing light is of the colour quality required, say daylight or simulated daylight.
(b) Fit the first filter.
(c) Expose one piece of each type of film through the filter, keeping the time of exposure constant.
(d) Repeat (b) and (c) for each of the other two filters.
(e) Process all the pieces of film simultaneously using identical conditions.
(f) Make a quick assessment by viewing the results side-by-side on an illuminated viewing table.
(g) Read the resulting densities, and plot the characteristic curves or part characteristic curves (Figure 10.3).
(h) Measure the log exposure shift of the same mid-range density (say 1.0) on each curve to find the ratio of respective colour sensitivities.
(i) Comparison can be made numerically or in the form of a crude spectrogram graph with the shift values plotted against wavelength or colour, as shown in Figure 10.3.

10.7 *Comparison using a step wedge that includes colour patches.* Some photographic step wedges can be obtained complete with small tricolour, blue, green and red filters incorporated near the wedge. The density produced behind each small filter may be used to obtain a simple comparison of the colour response of different emulsions, in a similar manner to that described in paragraph 10.6. This type of step wedge may also be used in deciding whether a particular emulsion can be classified as blue-sensitive, orthochromatic or panchromatic.

10.8 *Comparison using a colour rendition chart.* Another effective, and more informative, comparison of colour sensitivity can be made by photographing a special chart consisting of an array of coloured patches, on two or more different films, and comparing the results by eye. Although the negatives may be viewed directly it is often better to make prints for comparison, as this is how the effect is seen in practice. Exposure of the films can be made under various lighting conditions (tungsten, daylight, electronic flash, etc.) as necessary.

Specially made colour charts can be obtained and should preferably be used, because the paints and dyes that form the colour patches are simulations of natural colours. Most colour rendition charts incorporate a reference scale of neutral greys. Because the tonal differences produced by these are unaffected by the colour sensitivity of the emulsion or by the type of the exposing light, the tones produced by the colours on the chart can be compared directly with the neutral greys. Paragraphs 11.81 and 11.82 describe a typical colour rendition chart and how it can be used.

The effect of various colour filters can also be observed if the chart is photographed first with and then without a filter in place. Again, a practical comparison of the effects is more easily obtained if the negatives are printed.

Self-assessment questions

10.9   Write out answers to the following:

(a)   Describe a wedge spectrogram and a wedge spectograph.
(b)   Make a rough diagram to show the basic difference between the wedge spectrograms of a blue-sensitive emulsion, an orthochromatic emulsion and a panchromatic emulsion.
(c)   Given a step wedge containing small tricolour blue, green and red filter patches, how would you compare the colour sensitivities of two different emulsions?
(d)   Explain how a colour rendition chart could be used to compare the spectral sensitivities of two different films. Then list other useful information that could be obtained from the same comparison.

11

The sensitometry of colour photography

11.1 Now that we have an understanding of the sensitometry of black-and-white photographic materials and processes, we can consider the slightly more complex sensitometry used for colour photography. But first we should briefly consider some of the words used to describe colour and also how colour photography works. If you wish to refresh your memory on light and colour, and how it is specified in photography and sensitometry, refer to Chapter 1, paragraph 1.14 onwards.

The perception of colour plays an important part in our daily lives. Awake, or even in our dreams, it helps us to identify objects and designs. Colour thus has a definite property, and particularly in colour photography it provides information that is just as important as the shapes and sizes of objects on the image.

Colour terminology

11.2 In everyday speech we use many different words to describe a colour. For example, a green can be described as bright, dull, light, pale, vivid. These words are somewhat vague in their meaning, so when considering the reproduction of colours we often need a better way of describing the variables that occur. In general, colours can vary in three respects, which can be described as hue, saturation, and lightness.

(a) *Hue* (or in common usage simply *colour*) is the main variable, being the feature we first notice. It describes the basic appearance of the light we see, for example red, green, yellow, blue.
(b) *Saturation* (sometimes loosely described as *chroma* or *chromacity*) denotes the vividness of the colour. Vivid colours are said to be saturated, pale colours to be desaturated or unsaturated.
(c) *Lightness* (often described as *brightness* or *colour luminance*) denotes the extent to which coloured objects appear to reflect or transmit more or less light. For example, a grey scale or a step wedge shows no hue or saturation but does show a full range of lightness.

In colour photography, lightness and saturation are interrelated in that it is difficult to change one without also changing the other.

Outline of the colour photography process

11.3 Unlike a typical black-and-white photograph, which consists of one black silver image, a colour photograph consists essentially of three superimposed layers of *yellow*, *magenta* and *cyan* dye images. When these are viewed in white light, the dye images act as light filters and produce the colours we see by absorbing or subtracting suitable quantities of *blue*, *green* and *red* light from the white light. Thus in the finished colour photograph we have a fair approximation of the *blue*, *green* and *red* colours and mixtures of colours of the original scene. The majority of present-day colour processes use this 'subtractive synthesis' to present the coloured images to our eyes (see also paragraph 11.11).

11.4 In its basic form, the unexposed colour film consists essentially of three separate layers of light-sensitive emulsion coated one on top of the other on a base. Colour films may contain several more coated layers designed to improve the characteristics of the film, but the principle of operation and use is the same. Each emulsion layer effectively responds to approximately one-third of the visible spectrum: one to *blue* light, one to *green* light and one to *red* light. Because the green- and red-sensitive layers of some colour films are also sensitive to blue light, a yellow filter layer is used above them and below the blue-sensitive layer in order to absorb blue light. The yellow colouring of this filter is removed during processing (Figure 11.1). The emulsions are carefully 'balanced' in manufacture for speed and characteristics, so that, even though they are on top of each other, each layer will receive the appropriate exposure and also respond similarly to processing. Because of its construction, this emulsion assembly is called a multilayer colour film. Each layer is extremely thin and the complete multilayer assembly is only about ¹⁄₅₀ mm thick.

11.5   *Exposure.* Colour materials can, strictly, only be made to produce optimum results when they are correctly exposed to the particular type of light for which they were balanced. For example, 'daylight' films respond correctly to daylight at about 5500 K (182 mireds); 'tungsten' films respond correctly to tungsten light at about 3200 K (312 mireds). The fidelity of colour reproduction therefore depends to a great extent on using the type of film that suits the light used for exposure, or changing the light to suit the film. During exposure the layers of the colour material record separate images of the blue, green and red content of the original scene. Methods of obtaining correct exposure when using colour materials are considered later in this chapter.

11.6   *Processing.* Processing methods for films depend on whether they are classed as substantive or non-substantive. In the former the colour-forming substances, called colour couplers, are incorporated in the emulsion; in the latter they are incorporated in the processing solutions. At present there is only one type of non-substantive film (see paragraph 11.12) all other colour materials are of the substantive type, so we can briefly consider these now.

11.7   If the photographic material is to be a colour negative, it is developed to produce black silver images that correspond in density to the amount of exposure in each layer; at the same time, yellow, magenta and cyan dyes are formed in the respective blue-, green- and red-sensitive layers. The amount of dye formed is proportional to the amount of developed silver, and the colours of the

dyes are complementary to the colours of the original subject photographed (Figure 11.1). All the black silver and any undeveloped emulsion grains are then bleached away and fixed, leaving only the dye images, as a negative both in tone and in colour. The dyes are formed by the oxidized developing agent reacting with colour couplers that are incorporated in the original emulsions.

The processing used for prints made from a colour negative on colour printing paper is essentially the same as that used for colour negatives.

11.8   If the photographic material is to be a direct colour positive, it is developed to produce black silver negative images that correspond in density to the amount of exposure in each layer. The original negative images then have to be reversed; so after the initial development, the remaining undeveloped emulsion grains are fogged by a chemical fogging agent (at this stage this has the same effect as exposing the film to white light). The material is then developed in a dye-forming colour developer. This acts on the fogged emulsion only, and, as in the colour negative process, dyes are formed by the oxidized developing agent reacting with the colour couplers in the emulsion. All the developed black silver is then bleached away and fixed, leaving only the dye images as a colour positive.

The processing used for prints made from a positive transparency on colour reversal printing paper is essentially the same as that used for colour reversal film.

11.9   *Colour dye masking.* The colour-absorption properties of the dyes used in colour materials are not ideal for photography. That of the yellow dye layer is fairly satisfactory, but the magenta and cyan layers absorb some light of colours that they should ideally transmit. Furthermore, if the reproduction is a negative it has to be printed, so the same process is repeated and the effect of the dye deficiencies further emphasized in the print. Because of this, almost all colour negative materials contain couplers that are themselves coloured. Of these, the coloured couplers that are not used up during development produce a pale orange, low-contrast positive mask. This integral mask counteracts the colour-absorption deficiencies of the magenta and cyan dye images, so that prints of a satisfactory colour quality can be obtained from the negative. The different colour-sensitive layers in the colour printing paper are designed to respond correctly to the effects of the

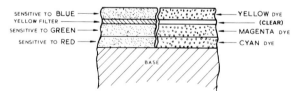

Fig. 11.1 Simplified cross-section of a typical colour film material, showing the colour sensitivities of the three separate light-sensitive layers and the colours of the dyes in the exposed and processed film. Each layer responds to one different primary colour and the appropriate complementary colours are formed during processing. Some colour film materials do not contain a yellow filter layer, and the light-sensitive layers may also be coated in a different sequence.

pale orange mask. The function and sensitometric effect of integral colour masking is explained later, in Appendix D.

The pale orange colour of the integral mask may appear to be equal all over the negative, but in fact, as it forms a positive mask, the colour is only found in areas where the coloured couplers have not been used up during development. Areas such as the unexposed rebates of the negative or the less exposed areas of the image show the greatest coloration. Any areas of the negative that have been fully developed contain no visible masking colour.

Because of this coloration, integral dye masking is unsuitable for colour reversal materials such as transparencies, which are meant to be viewed directly. To counteract the effect of dye deficiencies in such materials, inter-image effects are used.

11.10 *Inter-image and adjacency effects during processing.* Because the three emulsion layers of a colour material are close to each other, developer and the by-products of development can diffuse from one layer into another. Thus development of one colour image can influence the development of an adjacent colour image. These inter-image effects during processing can be used to advantage. The design of both negative and reversal colour material is arranged so that adjacency effects improve image structure (see paragraph 2.103) and inter-image effects improve colour reproduction, contrast, and the balance between all three image layers. The function and sensitometry of inter-image effects are explained in Appendix D.

Both integral colour masking and the formation and manipulation of inter-image and development effects provide an elegant means of correcting the effects of dye deficiencies in photographic colour materials. When we consider that these, and a host of other elements that contribute to the quality of colour photography, are packed into several

light-sensitive emulsion layers, the whole not more than $\frac{1}{50}$ mm thick, we can pay tribute to the art and science of the research workers and emulsion makers.

11.11 *Formation of colours and tones.* After processing, when the finished colour photograph is viewed either as a print or a positive transparency, the yellow, magenta and cyan dyes reproduce the subject colours by selectively absorbing parts of the white viewing light, as shown in Figure 11.2. Different colours are produced by the superimposed dye images of various concentrations. For example:

Magenta and *cyan* together subtract green and red respectively and leave *blue*.
Yellow and *cyan* together subtract blue and red respectively and leave *green*.
Yellow and *magenta* together subtract blue and green respectively and leave *red*.

White is seen where there are no dye images, *grey* where there are suitable quantities of all dyes, and *black* where there are heavy concentrations of all the dyes. Many hues of differing saturation and lightness of colour can be seen as they are produced by various mixtures of the dyes.

11.12 *Processing non-substantive colour films.* Non-substantive colour reversal films, such as Kodachrome, do not have colour couplers incorporated in the emulsions and therefore need a different processing method. The colours are added during processing, using a separate dye-forming solution for each emulsion layer. This is a complicated procedure, and can only be carried out in laboratories that have special continuous-processing machines. The system has an advantage in that it enables precise sensitometric control to be applied throughout all the stages of processing, and thus consistently high-quality results can be obtained.

11.13 *General characteristics of colour materials.* Compared with the general characteristics of black-and-white materials, colour materials have less all-round tolerance. Because they are made up of several different types of photographic emulsion and because comparatively unstable and imperfect dyes are used, colour materials have less tolerance in exposure, in processing, and to adverse storage conditions before and after exposure. They are also visibly more susceptible to reciprocity failure effects, and their keeping qualities after processing

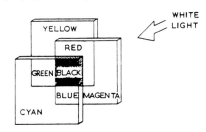

Fig. 11.2 The formation of visible colours by the subtractive colour system. The effect on our vision of single or superimposed dyed emulsion layers can be seen by holding yellow, magenta and cyan colour filters in front of a white light.

are lower. Manufacturers publish recommendations on the treatment and storage of colour materials and these should of course be adopted (see paragraph 6.5 onwards, and paragraph 11.83).

Filters in colour photography

11.14 If the colour quality of the light to be used in exposing colour film, or in printing it, is not correct for the type of material in use, the light has to be modified by using colour filters. Therefore we need to know something about colour filters and how they are used in colour photography and sensitometry.

Filters are positioned in the exposing light beam, and act by either absorbing or rejecting part of the incident light and allowing the remainder to pass through to the photographic material. Colour films are balanced in manufacture to give optimum results when they are exposed to a particular type of light. With other light sources, they can only give optimum colour results when a filter is used to correct the colour quality of the exposing light. Colour filters are used when printing colour negatives, in order to balance the characteristics of the negative and printing light to those of the colour printing paper. They are also used when measuring colour densities on a densitometer. The main types of colour filters can be generally classified according to their intended use in colour photography, as follows.

11.15 *Light balancing filters (Figure 11.3.1).* Light balancing filters are used to raise or lower the colour temperature of the exposing light in order to match it to the colour balance of the film. Their effect is to absorb gradually increasing proportions of the spectrum, and they are typically used to balance the effect of small variations in the colour temperature of a light source. Light balancing filters are available in a series of bluish filters to raise the colour temperature, and a reddish-yellow series to lower the colour temperature. Each filter in a series may be designated by its mired shift value (see paragraph 1.23) or by the maker's identification.

Example. A Wratten 82A filter looks bluish; it converts light at 3000 K (332 mireds) to 3200 K (312 mireds) and thus has an effective −20 mired shift value (312 − 332 = −20 mireds).

11.16 *Colour conversion filters (Figure 11.3.2).* Colour conversion filters are similar to light balancing filters, but somewhat stronger in their effect. They are available in two series, deep bluish to raise the colour temperature and reddish-orange to lower the colour temperature. Such filters are used to convert the colour temperature (mired value) of the exposing light, and thus permit the use of a colour film with a light source for which the film is not balanced. A typical conversion is from daylight to tungsten light or vice versa. Depending on their general colour, the filters either raise or lower the colour temperature of the light by absorbing gradually increasing proportions of the spectrum. In a series of colour conversion filters, each may be designated by its mired or decamired shift value (see paragraph 1.23), but because these filters are designed in manufacture to produce a specific conversion, they are usually described simply by the maker's identification.

Example. A Wratten 85B filter looks reddish-orange and is specifically intended for use when exposing tungsten film in daylight. It converts daylight at 5500 K (182 mireds) to 3200 K (312 mireds) and thus has an effective +130 mired shift value (312 − 182 = +130 mireds).

Both colour conversion and light balancing filters are sometimes classed as 'photometric' filters. They are similar in their effect to the colour filters used in a sensitometer to change the colour temperature of the exposing light (see paragraph 2.8).

11.17 *Colour compensating filters (Figure 11.3.3).* Colour compensating filters differ from conversion and balancing filters in that they are designed to transmit specific regions of the spectrum. They are typically used to compensate for slight colour-balance variations in colour materials due to batch differences, age, etc., or to modify the colour quality of the exposing light. Colour compensating filters are often used to correct or prevent an undesirable overall colour cast in a film or to compensate for possible reciprocity failure effects. They are available in blue, green, red, yellow, magenta and cyan in a range of densities, and may be designated by the letters CC followed by a number which is the density of the filter to light of the complementary colour multiplied by 100, and a letter identifying the hue of the filter. The higher the density value of a filter, the greater is its effect.

Example. CC30Y is a yellow filter with a density of 0.30 to blue light.

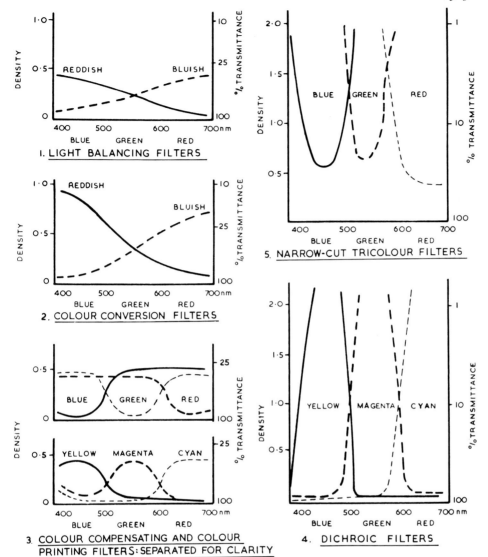

Fig. 11.3 Curves showing the general effect of colour filters used in colour photography and sensitometry. The height of the curve at any wavelength indicates the relative amount of light that the filter absorbs or rejects, and the amount it transmits. In general, blue, green and red filters each attenuate *two* of the three main spectral regions; yellow, magenta and cyan filters each attenuate *one* of the spectral regions. The proportion of incident light that a filter stops or transmits depends on its colour density. Dichroic filters have a general effect similar to that of a dye-based filter.

11.18 *Colour printing filters (Figure 11.3.3).* Colour printing filters may be used in printing in order to match the colour negative and exposing light to the characteristics of the printing paper. They are similar in their effect to colour compensating filters, and as they are usually made of inexpensive dyed acetate (instead of gelatin or polyester sheet) they give better light transmission but have lower optical qualities. This means that they cannot be positioned in the image-forming light but can be conveniently used in a combination filter pack with other colour printing filters and may thus be used for very fine adjustment of colour balance. They are available in yellow, magenta, cyan and red, in a series of densities. Colour printing filters may be designated by the letters CP followed by a number which is the density of the filter to light of the complementary colour multiplied by 100, and a letter identifying the colour of the filter. The higher the density value of a filter, the greater its effect.

Example. CP05M is a magenta filter with a density of 0.05 to green light.

You will find paragraph 11.11 and Figure 11.2 useful if you wish to work out the general effect of different coloured CC and CP filters. Your findings can be checked by reference to Table 11.1.

11.19 *Dichroic filters (Figure 11.3.4).* Many colour enlargers use dichroic glass filters (sometimes called interference filters). These are more efficient in their action than dye-based filters. Dichroic filters are so named because when looked at they show one colour by transmitted light and the complementary colour by reflected light. Their spectral properties depend not on absorption as do dyed filters, but on the reflection of unwanted light, part of the spectrum being transmitted and the remainder reflected. They are made by surface coating a piece of glass with several very thin layers of light-refracting material which creates interference effects on the incident light. Various coatings can be made in order to produce filters with any desired transmission characteristic. Unlike dyed filters, dichroic filters do not fade with use and they can also withstand heat.

Dichroic filters are more expensive than dyed printing filters but they have several advantages, all leading to higher efficiency. By comparison, transmission of wanted light and rejection of unwanted light are high, and they also give a sharper cut-off effect along the spectrum from transmission to reflection. In some colour enlargers, yellow, magenta and cyan dichroic filters are kept at right angles to the light beam, and can be gradually moved across it by moving calibrated controls. The amount of insertion into the light beam controls the effect that they have on the colour quality of the exposing light, so one dichroic filter can produce the same effect as a whole range of dyed filters. Furthermore, because of the gradual insertion, there are no abrupt changes in filter values and thus very fine adjustments can be made. Both the light that passes by the filter and the light that passes through it are thoroughly mixed together (integrated) before entering the negative. Dichroic filters may also be used in colour densitometers and other optical instruments. They are often used for infrared rejection because they are more efficient in this than heat-absorbing filters.

11.20 *Narrow-cut tricolour filters (Figure 11.3.5).* Tricolour filters are special blue, green and red filters that may be used in the 'tricolour' printing of

colour negatives. They are designed to transmit one region only (approximately one-third) of the visible spectrum without significantly overlapping the adjacent regions. Similar but somewhat denser tricolour filters with a narrower cutting effect are also used in colour densitometers, and we shall consider these later.

11.21 *Colour filter curves.* Curves illustrating the effect of colour filters are published by filter manufacturers. Each curve is a plot of the filter density (or sometimes its transmittance or its absorption) against the wavelengths of light. Simplified curves for hypothetical filters of the types we have considered show the differences between the effects of the filters (Figure 11.3). The height of the curve at each wavelength indicates the relative amount of light that the filter absorbs and the relative amount that it transmits. The proportion of incident light that a filter stops or transmits depends on its colour density.

We can see from Table 11.1 that yellow, magenta and cyan filters each attenuate one of the three main spectral regions, and that blue, green and red filters each attenuate two of the spectral regions. A blue filter can be made up by using a magenta and a cyan filter together, and a green filter by a yellow and a cyan filter. Similarly, a red filter can be made by using a yellow and a magenta filter together.

Table 11.1 The general effect of colour filters.

Filter colour	Absorbs/rejects	Transmits
Blue	Green and red	Blue
Green	Red and blue	Green
Red	Blue and green	Red
Yellow	Blue	Green and red = yellow
Magenta	Green	Red and blue = magenta
Cyan	Red	Blue and green = cyan

11.22 *Choice of filters.* Colour filters used to control the quality of exposing light permit a great deal of latitude in the spectral characteristics of the original light source. However, because of the dye and the support that holds it, dye-based filters are not ideal in their photographic effect. For example, a filter cannot abruptly isolate a particular region of the spectrum and have no effect on other regions. The degree of unwanted effect is usually of little significance in practical colour photography, and when the correct filters are used results of a satisfactory colour quality can be obtained.

Manufacturers publish recommendations on the choice of filters for any combination of film and light source, and list the colour temperature conversion or mired shift values as necessary. They also supply information on the use of colour filters, and list the exposure increases that may be needed when filters are used. Manufacturers' instructions should be used as a guide to obtaining optimum results.

11.23 *Basic rules of colour filtration.* The basic rules when using colour filters apply to all aspects of colour photography and conform to the following principle. Using a filter of a particular colour will:

(a) *Reduce* the amount of the same colour in a colour negative material.
(b) *Increase* the amount of the same colour in a colour reversal material.

Colour filters work subtractively and are used when it is necessary to modify the colour of the exposing light. For example, a yellow filter reduces the blue content of white light. If the blue content is reduced, an exposed and processed colour negative material produces less dye in the (blue-sensitive) yellow-forming emulsion layer (see Figure 11.1). Similarly, if a magenta filter is used less magenta dye is produced, and with a cyan filter less cyan dye.

With colour reversal materials the effect of filtration is exactly the opposite. For example, a yellow filter reduces the blue content of white light, and an exposed and processed colour reversal material produces more dye in the (blue-sensitive) yellow-forming emulsion layer. Similarly, magenta and cyan filters cause the production of more magenta and cyan dye respectively. These principles of filtration lead to the basic rules which apply when filters are used to modify the colour of the exposing light. The rules apply to all aspects of colour photography and are used particularly at the printing stage. They are:

(a) To correct a colour cast in negative materials – add a filter of the same colour as the cast, or preferably remove a filter of a complementary colour to the cast.
(b) To correct a colour cast in reversal materials – add a filter of a complementary colour to the cast, or preferably remove a filter of the same colour as the cast.

The practical application of these basic rules is considered later.

Colour sensitometry principles

11.24 Compared with black-and-white photography the effects of exposure and processing in colour photography are more critical and decisive, and the process itself is less flexible. We can also see errors in colour more easily than errors in tone, so extra care is needed. An understanding of sensitometry is therefore invaluable in colour photography and particularly for colour printing and duplicating.

The sensitometry generally applied to colour materials follows the same basic principles as black-and-white sensitometry, except that the characteristic curves are produced separately for each of the three dye images. The general system of finding the sensitometric characteristics of a colour material is by exposure through a neutral grey step wedge in a sensitometer, colour processing the exposed material and measuring the results on a colour densitometer. The density values of each of the three different dye images are found by taking three readings, in turn, of each step of the sensitometric strip, through special narrow-cut (narrow-transmission) filters coloured red, green and blue (see Figure 11.3). *Red* light through the *red* filter is used to measure the densities of the *cyan* image, *green* light the densities of the *magenta* image, and *blue* light the densities of the *yellow* image. The three separate characteristic curves can then be plotted and viewed on the same graph, and in an ideal situation all three curves will coincide. This general system of measurement is called 'integral colour densitometry'. If, on the other hand, the density of one individual dye image is to be measured without the slight overlapping effects of the other images, this is called 'analytical densitometry' (See paragraphs 11.34 and 11.35, and Appendix B.)

11.25 *Spectral response of colour materials.* All (unmasked) conventional colour materials that have been properly exposed and processed should be able to reproduce a scale of greys, such as the sensitometer step wedge, as a similar scale of greys without any colour being directly discernible by the viewer. For example, consider a colour reversal material exposed in a sensitometer through a neutral grey step wedge that has been illuminated by a light of the correct colour temperature, and then correctly processed. The result, when viewed under suitable lighting conditions, will be a grey stepped image with no visible evidence of colour. If this sensitometric strip is measured using a colour densitometer that has a sensitivity and colour response similar to those of the viewer's eyes, the three resultant characteristic curves will be almost identical and combine to appear as one curve on a sensitometric graph (Figure 11.4).

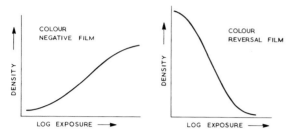

Fig. 11.4 Characteristic curves showing the effect of correct exposure and processing on hypothetical (unmasked) colour materials. The sensitometric strips are read through red, green and blue filters. Thus the effective densities of the cyan, magenta and yellow image layers are measured and can be plotted on one graph as individual characteristic curves. Under ideal conditions throughout, the three curves will coincide and indicate that all the factors in the process are in balance.

A satisfactory reproduction of the original greys indicates that the correct amounts of cyan, magenta and yellow dye layers have been formed. This means that the contrasts and speeds of the three layers are in balance. These 'ideal' conditions are extremely difficult to achieve, but a close approximation to the ideal is satisfactory for most aspects of colour photography. In photographic practice, an approach to the ideal is necessary for reversal film because it provides the end product. On the other hand, a negative film is only a means to an end and deviation from the ideal can often be corrected during printing.

The characteristic curves for a colour negative material slope in the same direction as the familiar black-and-white negative, but the curves of a reversal material slope in the opposite direction. With colour reversal material, the end product of the original low-exposure values is high densities, and of the high-exposure values, low densities. Also, colour negative film curves slope less steeply than those of reversal films. This is because the colour negative has still to be printed, and the colour printing material will produce an appropriate higher contrast. On the other hand, the processed reversal film is an end product, ready for viewing.

Sensitometric exposure, processing and measuring

11.26   As in black-and-white sensitometry, the exposure, processing and measuring of colour materials should be carried out under conditions similar to those to be used in practice. However, in colour work there are additional factors that can cause variations in the result, so the requirements for testing and using colour materials and processes are more stringent than for black-and-white materials.

11.27   All the functions and requirements for the sensitometer, densitometer and processing that we have previously considered for black-and-white sensitometry (Chapter 2) are necessary. However, some requirements and standards of precision are more important in colour sensitometry than in black-and-white. We can consider these now.

11.28   When reading the following paragraphs it is important to bear in mind that what happens in sensitometry also happens when we use the material in photographic practice. The exposure, processing and associated sensitometry of regular colour materials are further considered in paragraphs 11.85 to 11.125.

11.29   *Exposure in the sensitometer.* The exposing light of the sensitometer must have a colour quality that is equivalent to the light for which the material under test was designed and balanced (see paragraph 11.5). This can be achieved by using a stablized power supply and suitable photometric filters. Exposure to a light of a different colour quality will cause one layer of the emulsion to respond more than the others and thus cause a colour cast in the result (Figure 11.5). For example, if the colour temperature of the light is too high (has too much blue content) for the film, the colour cast will be yellow on a negative film and

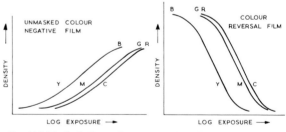

Fig. 11.5 Typical effects of exposure to light for which the colour material is not balanced. For example, if 'tungsten' film is exposed to daylight, the blue-sensitive layer will respond more than the others and the effect will be a colour cast. This shows on the graph as a lateral displacement of the characteristic curves. The cast will be yellow on a negative and blue on a reversal film. B, G and R refer to the original sensitivities of the emulsion layers and the measuring filters in the densitometer, and Y, M and C to the dyes in the layers after processing.

blue on a reversal film. This will show on the sensitometric graph as a lateral displacement of the characteristic curves. In practice this effect could be prevented by adjusting the colour temperature of the exposing light, and we shall consider this in more detail later.

11.30 *Attenuation of exposing light.* If the overall illuminance on the test material is more than is required to obtain correct exposure in the sensitometer, special neutral-density filters may be fitted in the path of the exposing light. These filters should not scatter light and must also be completely non-selective. In other words, they must subtract equal amounts of light from all parts of the spectrum and should therefore be calibrated *in situ* (see Appendix B).

11.31 *Reciprocity failure effects.* The sensitometer shutter speed should correspond closely to that to be used in practice, and must be well within the limits laid down by the manufacturer of the colour material under test. Duration of exposure outside these limits will produce reciprocity failure effects, which may be different for each layer of the emulsion. This will cause changes in both the relative speeds of the layers and in the contrasts they produce. Changes in speed will show as colour casts, changes in contrast as cross colour casts (often called colour imbalance or mismatch). For example, one colour may predominate in the highlights and a different colour predominate in the shadows. This effect shows on the sensitometric graph as characteristic curves of differing slope, which may cross each other (Figure 11.6). Because of the effects of reciprocity failure, some sensitometers use an electronic flash (with a typical short duration) when materials that are in practice to be exposed to electronic flash are being tested.

However, for simple comparative sensitometry, a duration of $\frac{1}{50}$ second is considered to be satisfactory for most types of colour film. For slower materials, such as duplicating and internegative films and printing paper, an exposure duration of a few seconds may be used.

In photographic practice, the effect of slight reciprocity failure may be minimized by using a colour compensating filter on the camera lens, but the effect of gross reciprocity failure cannot be corrected. The exposure given must be within the reciprocity limits for the material. The effect of reciprocity failure can also be very evident on colour printing paper. Therefore, when using an enlarger, changes in printing exposure are best made by keeping the duration constant, within limits, and varying the lens aperture (see Table 11.5). The effect and minimization of reciprocity failure in regular colour materials are considered in paragraph 11.119.

11.32 *Sensitometer step wedge.* (See also paragraphs 2.20 and 2.21, and Appendix B.) As with exposure-attenuating filters, each step of the wedge must be completely neutral so that only the illuminance of the exposing light is varied, not the colour quality. Any light-scattering effect is nullified by contact with the test material. Photographic silver wedges are therefore suitable for most purposes, provided that they have been processed in a non-staining developer. For more exacting work, special neutral-density wedges using carbon or plastic are often used.

11.33 *Processing.* The preparation of solutions and the processing of colour materials must be carried out strictly in accordance with the manufacturer's instructions. The only exception to this is when the purpose of the test is to investigate the effects of different processing conditions. Because of the several layers of photographic emulsion and the need for correct dye densities in each layer, colour processing requires even more care and a higher standard of control than black-and-white work. Correct processing time, temperature and agitation are particularly important. For the majority of colour processes the best practicable method is to use an efficient colour processing machine, as even slight changes in, say, agitation will affect each layer to a different extent. The quality of solutions can be checked by processing a manufacturer's standard control strip of known characteristics (see paragraphs 6.20 onwards). In addition, before processing colour materials, the

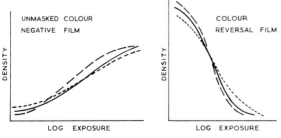

Fig. 11.6 Typical effects of reciprocity failure on colour materials. If the shutter speed is outside the limits recommended by the film manufacturer, the speed and contrast relationship between the three image layers will be changed. This causes colour casts, which may show on the graphs as crossed curves.

effects of possible latent image regression due to delay between exposure and processing must be borne in mind (see paragraphs 6.5, 6.6 and 11.120).

11.34   *Colour densities.* Before we consider the factors involved in measuring colour densities we need to remember that the yellow, magenta and cyan dyes produced in a colour photograph are not ideal. They overlap each other in their effect so that each dye, although it has a major subtracting effect in approximately one-third of the visible spectrum, also absorbs a small amount of light in other parts of the spectrum. Because of this, the measuring of colour densities can be classified as either analytical or integral.

11.35   *Analytical density* refers to the density of individual and separated dye layers: in other words, the density of one of the dye images only, without the overlapping effect of the other dyes. Analytical densities are more the concern of the photographic material manufacturer or the research worker, and are further described in Appendix D, so we need not consider them at present. The photographer is particularly concerned with *integral density*, which is the effective density of all three layers together: in other words, the actual effect of the dye layers when they are viewed or when they are printed. Integral density readings are used when testing and comparing colour materials and for colour process monitoring (process quality control). They are also used in printing, for comparing the dye densities of negatives that are to be printed with the densities of a standard negative for which printing conditions are known.

11.36   *The colour densitometer.* Densitometers used for colour density measurement, by transmission or reflection, are basically the same as those used for black-and-white densitometry (see Chapter 2), but with the addition of special red, green and blue colour filters that can be introduced one at a time in front of the photoreceptor, to isolate a part of the illuminating spectrum. This enables measurements to be made of each of the three dye images in the colour material. Most colour densitometers are constructed so that they can also be used for black-and-white densitometry. Because of the colour measurement and the density of the filters used, the light source must have a stable yet high output in all parts of the spectrum, and the light receptor must have an appropriate sensitivity. The

filters themselves should be protected from infrared and ultraviolet radiation, and must be stable and resistant to the effects of light and heat. An infrared-rejection filter is usually incorporated in the light path so that the filter in use and the receptor, are not affected by infrared radiation.

Measurements made on a colour densitometer must relate to the practical use of the material being measured. Therefore the spectral and optical conditions of measuring should be similar to the spectral and optical conditions that will be met when the material being measured is either viewed or printed. For example, when a colour negative material measured on a densitometer is later to be printed, the spectral and optical characteristics of the densitometer (a combination of densitometer light, optical elements, filters and the spectral response of the receptor) should ideally match those of the printer and the photographic material that will receive the printing light. This ideal condition is obviously not possible to achieve in normal practice, as the characteristics of individual printing conditions will vary. However, the overall response of the densitometer should simulate as far as possible the response of the printing material or (for colour reversal transparencies) the response of the viewer's eye. To achieve this, the densitometer colour filters are designed so that their spectral transmittance characteristics suit the characteristics of the densitometer light and the spectral response of the receptor. Thus when the correct filters are introduced into the desitometer, it will be suitable for measuring either colour material intended for direct viewing or colour negative material that is to be printed. Special filter sets are recommended by manufacturers for use with their colour materials and to suit particular situations. Filters suitable for general use are narrow-cut (narrow-transmission) filters that can isolate a fairly limited band of the visible spectrum. Examples are the Kodak Wratten 92, 93 and 94 filters which are used in some transmission densitometers (see paragraphs 2.40 onwards). They can be used for comparative sensitometry, process monitoring, and evaluating colour negatives for printing.

11.37   *Status densitometry.* Older densitometers used for measuring colour materials give results that are satisfactory for general use. However, when using the material manufacturer's recommended filter sets, variations in the characteristics of the light source, optical configuration and densitometer receptor mean that readings can vary between instruments. Because of this, many modern densitometers are designed to match the spectral characteristics of the direct or reflected light source and of the optical components with the characteristics of the photoelectric receptor, so that the response of any such densitometer will conform to an established standard. When the appropriate colour filters are incorporated into the densitometer, the desired standard of 'status densitometry' can be achieved. Thus, if properly used, all such densitometers will give almost identical results wherever they are located. For example, *Status A densitometry and filters* applies to an unmasked colour material that is intended for direct viewing and for which transmission or reflection density measurements are required; it includes colour reversal and infrared false-colour film as well as colour printing papers. *Status M densitometry and filters* applies to any colour material that is to be printed, and includes masked colour negatives.

Status densitometry may also be used for measuring black-and-white materials, and for this situation it is classified as Status V densitometry (conforming to a standard visual diffuse density). Characteristic curves published by material manufacturers often denote the relevant status densitometry used in compiling the curves.

Sensitometric performance of colour materials

11.38 The characteristic curves of colour materials are interpreted in a similar manner to those of black-and-white materials. In an ideal situation the three curves should coincide in the final presentation, but in practice this can seldom be achieved. There is usually a slight lateral displacement of one or more curves and a slight difference in slope, particularly at the extreme shoulder of the curves. Thus the characteristic curves of colour materials can show the relative speeds of the three emulsions, minimum and maximum densities, dye density range, overall image contrast, and image contrast comparison. Deviation from the ideal presentation indicates a lack of colour balance in the material. A lateral displacement indicates an overall colour cast, and a different slope indicates one colour predominant in the highlights and another colour in the shadows (colour imbalance or mismatch). With negative film, the integral colour-dye mask causes a vertical relative displacement of the characteristic curves. This is corrected

during printing by a corresponding lateral displacement of the printing paper curves (explained later). As an ideal final presentation is seldom achieved, a close approximation is considered to be satisfactory for most applications of colour photography.

Contrast of colour materials

11.39 We know that the speed and contrast response of most black-and-white films can be manipulated and controlled over a fairly wide range without loss of quality, by adjustment of development time, and the effects can be shown as a family of characteristic curves. Colour films do not respond to such changes without loss of quality, and should be considered as producing a fixed contrast if optimum results are required. This means that the processing times and procedures laid down by the manufacturer should not be changed other than in exceptional circumstances (see paragraphs 11.46, and 11.121 to 11.123).

Speeds of colour materials

11.40 The speed number or exposure index for a colour film is an indication of its sensitivity to light and can therefore be used in exposure calculations. As in black-and-white sensitometry, speed numbers are calculated from the reciprocal of the exposure in lux seconds required to produce particular densities. These can be shown on the characteristic curve, or taken down to the log exposure axis as points from which the speed number or exposure index is calculated. The positioning of a speed point differs according to the purpose for which the material is intended to be used. For example, different speed points are used for colour reversal and colour negative films.

Methods of evaluating the speeds of colour materials change from time to time as new materials and processes are introduced, but the changes are usually academic rather than practical. An outline of the current methods of speed determination for still photography is given below, and more specific information can be obtained from the relevant ISO, British and American standards leaflets, which are generally in full agreement and go into detail defining all the factors involved. Currently these are: for colour reversal films, ISO 2240, BS 1380 Part 2 and ANSI PH 2.21; for colour negative films, ISO 5800, BS 1380 Part 3 and ANSI PH 2.27.

11.41   Since a colour reversal film produces a result very different from that of a black-and-white negative, it is not practicable to use a similar speed system, based on a minimum density. A colour reversal film has a restricted exposure latitude, so the correct placing on the characteristic curve of both minimum and maximum densities is important. The speed is thus based on the exposures required to produce both maximum and minimum useful densities. A single characteristic curve is used which shows visual density usually very close to that of the green-sensitive layer. The speed point is given by the mean of the log exposures required to produce two specified densities appropriate to an average colour reversal transparency (Figure 11.7). In the present standard the specified

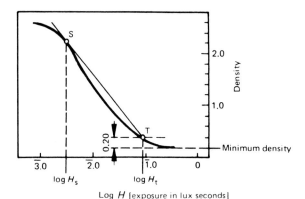

Fig. 11.7 The standard method for determining the speed of colour reversal film for still photography. For explanation see text. (Diagram courtesy ISO/BSI.)

densities are 0.2 above the minimum density and a point either at the start of the curve shoulder where the tangent of a line drawn from D 0.2 meets the curve, or 2.0 above the minimum density, whichever is lower. The log exposures required to produce the two specified densities (S and T in Figure 11.7) are added together and the result divided by 2 to obtain the speed point value. The reciprocal of the exposure at the speed point multiplied by a constant of 10 is the arithmetic speed number or 'exposure index'.

11.42   For colour negative films, the speed system is similar to that used for black-and-white negative films except that the speed points are D 0.15 above the minimum density of each layer of the negative material. Only the speed points of two curves are used, that of the green-sensitive layer and that of the slowest layer. The log exposures required to produce these two speed points are added together

and the result divided by 2 to obtain the mean speed point value of log exposure. The reciprocal of the corresponding exposure is multiplied by the square root of 2 (approximately 1.4) to obtain the arithmetic speed or 'exposure index' (Figure 11.8).

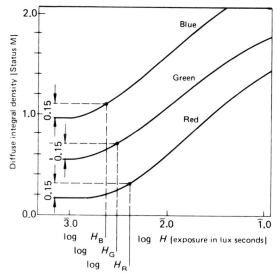

Fig. 11.8 The standard method for determining the speed of colour negative film for still photography. For explanation see text. (Diagram courtesy ISO/BSI.)

11.43   *Speed determination in practice.* The speed determination methods for both types of colour film may appear at first reading to be complicated. However, on the characteristic curve graph the exposure value used to obtain the speed number is simply a point midway between the other two on the log exposure axis. The reciprocal of the speed-point exposure value can therefore be determined directly from the characteristic curve in the same manner as for black-and-white speed systems (see paragraph 4.15). The relevant standards leaflets provide tables enabling the film speed to be found directly from the characteristic curve; the tables also round off the figures to the nearest one-third *f*-stop, for use on exposure meters. Thus no calculation is required.

The actual determination of film speeds, for example in ISO units, is more the concern of film manufacturers. For most purposes a simple comparison of an unknown colour film with a known colour film of the same type will suffice, as long as a suitable density level is used for the comparison. An appropriate density level for colour reversal film is a middle-scale density of about 1.0, and for masked colour negatives a density of 0.8 or so measured through the red filter of the densitometer. Paragraph 2.113 gives practical details of speed comparison.

11.44 *Speed of colour paper and special-purpose films.* At present there is no universally agreed method of expressing a standard speed for colour printing materials, nor is there any real need for one. However, if a comparison between different colour papers is required, a middle density point on each curve can be dropped perpendicularly to the log exposure axis and the difference measured. The speed (exposure factor) figures stamped on boxes of colour printing paper, together with the printing 'filtration adjustment' figures, are simply used for calculating any alteration in exposure that may be needed when changing from one batch of the same type of colour paper to another (see paragraph 11.62).

Most special-purpose colour materials, such as duplicating film, inter-negative film, print film, etc, do not have a specified exposure index because their conditions of use are so varied.

11.45 Unlike the black-and-white films used in aerial photography, colour films (including infrared false-colour films) do not at present have a specific speed standard. The speed numbers or exposure indexes allocated by manufacturers are usually based on data obtained from experimental flight tests, using the material in a camera under typical conditions of exposure and using specified conditions of processing.

11.46 *Varying effective film speeds.* For optimum results, colour materials should be exposed and processed according to the manufacturer's instructions. If exceptional circumstances demand it, most colour reversal materials can be exposed using a higher or lower speed value than indicated, provided that the first development is increased or decreased accordingly. This action will cause some deterioration in colour quality and changes in contrast, but the results will be more acceptable than if processing compensation had not been used. The treatment is not usually recommended for negative colour films, which in any case have a greater exposure latitude than reversal materials. Manufacturers supply information on modified processing techniques for their colour materials. Nevertheless, it is suggested that you should carry out your own practical sensitometric tests on the effects of modified exposure and development in preparation for such eventualities. (See also paragraphs 11.79 to 11.82, and 11.121 to 11.123.)

Sensitometric test exposures and trial development should be carried out on a piece of the same film material before modified processing is used on important films. Typical compensation times for colour reversal films are:

Camera exposure	First development time
1 stop under	130%
Correct	100%
1 stop over	70%

There are also 'developer additives' available which can be used when processing most types of colour negative and reversal films. Their effect is to allow an increase in development time to be given in order to obtain an increase in speed, but to achieve this without changing contrast or decreasing the D_{max} of reversal films. At present these particular additives are made by manufacturers independent of the film makers. As with the straightforward modification of processing times, the effects of such additives should be tested before being used in practice.

Colour reversal films

11.47 Colour reversal films are designed to produce positive colour transparencies. A correctly exposed and processed colour reversal film should

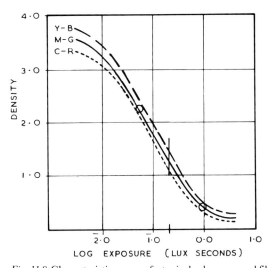

Fig. 11.9 Characteristic curves of a typical colour reversal film showing (as circles) two specified densities from which the speed point, midway between them, is derived. B, G and R refer to the original sensitivities of the emulsion layers and the measuring filters in the densitometer, and Y, M and C to the dyes in the layers after processing. For the purpose of illustration the curves have been separated.

reproduce the neutral tones (greys) of the original scene as neutral tones without a visible colour cast, and any flesh tones in the photograph should also be satisfactory.

Figure 11.9 shows the characteristic curves of a typical colour reversal film. The curves have been separated a little for clarity, but in practice there may be less lateral displacement and also slight differences in slope between the curves. As long as the differences are small, the result will be acceptably neutral. The circles indicate approximately the densities used for speed point determination; the short vertical line indicates the speed point, which is midway in a horizontal direction between the two.

Being an end product in itself, a colour reversal film has characteristic curves that are steeper than those of a colour negative; they have a higher D_{max}, and the minimum density is usually lower. In practical use, the result is a transparency with good colour saturation, with bright highlights and a long tonal range, suitable for direct viewing or projection. The lack of curve matching and of colour balance in the extreme shoulder region (as on Figure 11.9) is not as important as it would be in the low densities. In practice, the lack of colour balance in high densities is not particularly noticeable. The exposure requirements for regular colour reversal films are considered in paragraphs 11.99 to 11.101.

Colour reversal materials intended for film duplicating are designed to produce a gamma of approximately 1.0, which is lower than that of normal 'camera' films. By this means, the contrast of the duplicate is kept similar to that of the original. Duplicating films also have a longer straight-line region than camera films, in order to minimize colour tone distortion.

11.48   *Curve displacement effects and corrections.* Characteristic curve displacement of colour reversal films may be caused by bad storage before or after exposure, an exposing light of the wrong colour quality, or incorrect processing. Differences in speed and a wrong colour balance, shown by lateral displacement of a characteristic curve without change in slope, can be prevented or corrected by using a suitable colour compensating (CC) filter on the camera lens (Figure 11.10).

The lateral (horizontal) displacement in log exposure units is a measure of the filter density required for correction. For example, if the blue-sensitive emulsion curve is displaced 0.3 log exposure units to the left of the other two curves,

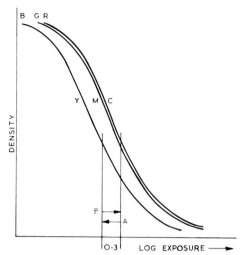

Fig. 11.10 An example of colour correction by using a colour compensating filter on the camera lens. The laterally displaced green- and red-sensitive emulsion curves can be moved across to the blue-sensitive emulsion curve by using a CC30Y filter and doubling the exposure, as shown by arrow A. Alternatively, if the exposure time is not changed, the blue-sensitive emulsion curve will be moved across to the other two curves, as shown by arrow B.

the result will be a blue (magenta + cyan) colour cast. In practice, correction could be made by using a yellow colour compensating filter of density 0.3 (described as CC30Y) on the camera lens and increasing the exposure by a factor of 2. In effect, the green- and red-sensitive emulsion curves will be moved 0.3 log exposure units horizontally to the left to meet the blue-sensitive emulsion curve (arrow A in Figure 11.10). Satisfactory balance would also be obtained if exposure was not increased by a factor of 2, but there would be an overall increase in image density. In this case, the effect is shown by the blue-sensitive emulsion curve moving 0.3 log exposure units to the right to meet the other two curves (arrow B in Figure 11.10).

11.49   *Adding filters and increasing exposure.* The effect of using a filter is always to move the appropriate characteristic curve or curves to the right, since by adding a filter we are reducing the illuminance reaching the material. This applies to all photographic materials, whether they are black-and-white or colour, negative or positive. Characteristic curves are moved to the left along the log exposure axis by increasing the illuminance or the duration of exposure, and to the right by decreasing the exposure.

As we can deduce from Figure 11.3, when used with colour materials the complementary coloured filters (yellow, magenta or cyan) will in effect move one curve, and the primary coloured filters (blue, green or red) will move two curves.

11.50 *Colour and detail reproduction in long-distance photography.* When colour reversal films (and colour negative films) are used for aerial or similar long-distance landscape photography, the effect of atmospheric haze has to be considered. Haze between the camera and subject scatters light and causes a degradation and lowering of contrast in the image, particularly in the shadow areas (see paragraphs 7.5 to 7.11). Haze scatters blue light more than red, so it affects the blue-sensitive emulsion layer more than the green or red layers; in high-altitude aerial photography it shows as a strong bluish cast on a reversal film. The effect can be reduced by using an appropriate yellow 'haze-cutting' filter on the camera lens. Fortunately, for this type of photography the fidelity of colour reproduction is usually not as important as it is, for example, in scientific or medical photography, or in portraiture, where familiar hues such as skin tones must be accurate or at least acceptable.

In most aerial photography the image luminance range is relatively short, so the requirement is usually for a fairly high-contrast process in order to obtain increased colour differences and information content, rather than colour fidelity. Colour films made specifically for aerial photography are designed to produce a higher contrast than general-purpose colour films. The increase also helps to minimize the contrast-reducing effect of atmospheric haze (see Chapter 7). An additional factor is that the colour contrast between different hues may depict differences in detail information on the ground better than the greys of a black-and-white photograph. This particularly applies to objects and detail that may be visible only because of differences in colour and would record on a black-and-white film as almost the same tone of grey.

It might be thought, because of the three superimposed images of a colour film, that the ability to properly record and resolve fine detail may be impaired. This possibility, along with others, was investigated in the United States several years ago. After extensive tests, carried out in the laboratory and under practical flying conditions, it was found that the colour films tested were able to provide precision and accuracy 'approaching or surpassing' that of black-and-white films having similar sensitometric characteristics. These findings have been confirmed by more recent tests (see also paragraph 2.105).

11.51 *Infrared false-colour reversal films.* Colour reversal (and colour negative) films can be made with emulsions that are sensitized to regions of the electromagnetic spectrum other than, or in conjunction with, the normal blue, green and red regions. Furthermore, the emulsion layers of a colour film may also be constructed so that the resulting colours, when viewed, are different from those of the subject photographed. An example of this type of material is infrared false-colour reversal film, often used in aerial and technical photography.

Infrared false-colour reversal films have similar characteristic curves to ordinary colour reversal films, except that the individual curves may be more separated and usually have a higher contrast. They differ from conventional colour films in that the three basic emulsion layers, instead of being sensitive to blue, green and red, are made sensitive to green, red and infrared (up to approximately 900 nm) respectively. A yellow filter is used on the camera to absorb the blue light. During processing, the green-sensitive layer is developed to a yellow dye image, the red-sensitive layer to a magenta dye image, and the infrared to a cyan dye image. The resultant transparency shows the difference between strong infrared-reflecting objects and other objects, as a visible colour difference. Greens and reds on the original object appear as blues and greens respectively on the transparency, and infrared radiation appears as red. Other hues of differing saturation are produced by various mixtures of the dyes.

11.52 *Processing colour reversal films to a negative.* If circumstances demand it, a colour reversal material can be processed to produce a colour negative and prints made from the negative. There will of course be no integral masking, and colour reproduction will probably suffer.

Colour negative films

11.53 Colour negative films are basically designed to produce a negative image, in tone and colour, of the original scene. After correct exposure and processing the colours are complementary to those of the original subject and the image contrast is suitable for printing onto colour printing paper or print film.

Most colour negatives incorporate a pale orange dye mask (see paragraph 11.9); it is this that causes the three curves to be displaced vertically on the

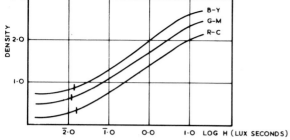

Fig. 11.11 Characteristic curves of a typical masked colour negative film, showing the speed points from which film speed is derived. B, G and R refer to the original sensitivities of the emulsion layers and the measuring filters used in the densitometer, and Y, M and C to the dyes in the layers after processing. The vertical displacement of the curves is caused by the integral colour mask.

sensitometric graph (see Figure 11.11). The difference in density between the layers shown by the vertical displacement is fully corrected during printing by the characteristics of the printing paper. The function of the pale orange mask is to compensate for inherent deficiencies in the dye images, so that prints of a satisfactory quality can subsequently be obtained. Colour correction is further controlled by inter-image effects between the different layers during colour development (see paragraph 11.9 and Appendix D). These effects are used together with the integral colour mask in order to obtain improved colour reproduction.

Unmasked colour negative materials are sometimes used for particular tasks. For example, some colour negative films made for use in aerial photography are made without integral colour masking. This type of film is usually of relatively high contrast and capable of giving a strong colour saturation and good hue separation. For these conditions, the normal requirements for colour fidelity are often less important and colour masking may not be necessary. Although the images of objects are recorded in colours complementary to their natural colours, such negatives can also be used for direct photographic interpretation.

Figure 11.11 shows the characteristic curves of a typical masked colour negative film. B, G and R refer to the original sensitivities of the emulsion layers and the measuring filters used in the densitometer, and Y, M and C to the dyes in the layers after processing. The short vertical lines indicate the speed point positions for this particular film. Compared with colour reversal materials, the colour negative characteristic curves have a lower slope (lower contrast). This, as in black-and-white processes, is so that the density range of the

negative will match the log exposure range of the colour printing paper. A lower slope means that a colour negative material will have more exposure latitude than a colour reversal material; in addition, some compensation for slight exposure variation can be made during printing. Because of this, the use of filters on the camera for correcting the effect of characteristic curve displacement may be less necessary when negative films are used.

In practice, the minimum and maximum luminances of an average subject image should ideally be contained on the straight-line region towards the toe end of the colour negative curves, or at least within the region where the curve slopes match each other. The exposure requirements for regular colour negative films are considered in paragraphs 11.107 to 11.110.

11.54   Curve displacement effects and corrections. Characteristic curve displacement of colour negative films may be caused by bad storage of the film before or after exposure, an exposing light of the wrong colour quality, or incorrect processing. Differences in speed and a wrong colour balance, shown by lateral displacement of a characteristic curve without change in slope, may be prevented or corrected by using a suitable colour compensating (CC) filter on the camera lens (Figure 11.12).

The lateral (horizontal) displacement in log exposure units is a measure of the filter density needed for correction. For example, if the red-sensitive emulsion curve is displaced 0.3 log exposure units to the right of the other two curves, correction would be made by using a red colour compensating filter of density 0.3 (described as CC30R) on the camera lens and increasing the exposure by a factor of 2. In effect the red-sensitive emulsion curve will be moved 0.3 log exposure units horizontally to the left to coincide with the other two curves and thus achieve correct colour balance (dashed line on Figure 11.12).

If, in the same situation, a colour negative had already been made and could not be re-made, partial correction only would be obtained by using a cyan filter of density 0.2 (described as CP20C) during printing (Figure 11.13). The density of the filter would be equal to the vertical interval between the characteristic curves. In effect, the red-sensitive emulsion curve would be moved vertically upward (dashed line on Figure 11.13). Correction would only be effective over the region where the curve slopes match each other. If the original image luminance range exceeds the region where the curves match, there will be a loss of

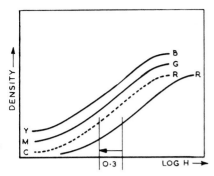

Fig. 11.12 An example of colour correction by using a filter on the camera. The laterally displaced red-sensitive emulsion curve can be moved across to the proper position by using a CC30R filter and doubling the exposure, as shown by the arrow.

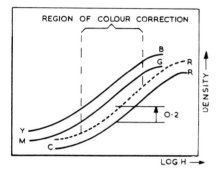

Fig. 11.13 An example of partial colour correction by using a filter on the printer. The laterally displaced red-sensitive emulsion curve can be moved upward so that most of the curve is parallel and in position by using a CP20C filter, as shown by the arrow.

colour quality in the highlights or shadows, or both.

'Universal' colour negative films designed for use by amateur photographers have a suppressed spectral response to blue and red light. These special sensitizing characteristics minimize the detrimental effect of different light sources, and the use of colour compensating or conversion filters is therefore considered to be unnecessary for this particular type of material.

11.55 *Matching colour printing paper to colour negative.* At one time, in any colour negative-positive process, one manufacturer's negative material was probably best printed on colour paper made by the same manufacturer. This was because the characteristics of the colour paper were designed in manufacture to suit the dyes and masking formed in the negative. This matching of the inherent characteristics is known as 'keying'. Nowadays however, high-quality colour materials are so formulated that acceptable results can usually be

obtained even when the negative and printing materials are of different manufacture.

Colour printing paper

11.56 Colour printing papers are designed to produce a positive colour reproduction of the original subject. There are several different types of colour printing material available, all based on the subtractive system of colour reproduction. For example, positive prints on paper or film can be made directly from colour negatives, or from positive transparencies by using direct colour reversal materials. First let us consider colour paper designed for making prints, by contact or enlargement, from colour negatives.

11.57 *Emulsion structure.* Most types of colour printing paper are coated with the red-sensitive cyan-forming emulsion layer on top, and the blue-sensitive yellow-forming layer at the bottom; they have no yellow filter layer. This particular arrangement produces the best image definition at the printing stage and also when the finished print is viewed. During printing the optical image is diffused slightly by passage through the emulsions; the blue-sensitive yellow-forming layer is usually the most turbid. The yellow image contributes least of all to overall definition and, having the visibly darker cyan image on top and the lighter yellow image at the bottom, improves the visual sharpness of the finished print.

The order of coating and the omission of a yellow filter layer are feasible because the emulsion layers of a colour printing paper are sensitized to narrower and more separated bands of the spectrum than are 'camera' film emulsions (Figure 11.14). This is because the paper does not have to respond to light from such a wide range of different natural colours. Also by this means, the overlapping effect of the dye images in the colour negative (see paragraphs 11.9 and 11.34) are further minimized in printing. The speeds of the three different layers are also adjusted in manufacture, so that their response is suitable when printing colour negatives that have integral dye masking.

11.58 *Paper grade.* In black-and-white printing, different grades of paper are needed so that the different contrasts (density ranges) of various black-and-white negatives can be accommodated. Colour negative materials should be exposed to a limited subject luminance range and processed under standard conditions. Therefore variation in the contrast of colour negatives is restricted and the vast majority can be printed on one grade of colour paper. Furthermore, unlike silver images, the dye images of a colour negative do not scatter light to any significant extent, so in printing there is less difference in the contrast produced by different types of enlarger (see Chapter 9). Some manufacturers provide different grades of colour paper to suit colour negatives that have been exposed to a subject of other than average contrast. Flashing techniques can also be used to extend the exposure range of a colour printing paper and thus reduce the contrast of the result (see paragraphs 5.18 and 5.19).

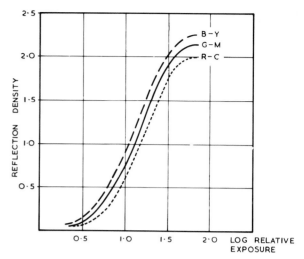

Fig. 11.15 Characteristic curves of a typical colour printing paper filtered in exposure to give a near neutral image. B, G and R refer to the original sensitivities of the emulsion layers and the measuring filters used in the densitometer, and Y, M and C to the dyes in the layers after processing. For clarity of illustration the curves have been separated.

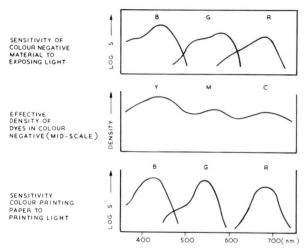

SENSITIVITY OF COLOUR NEGATIVE MATERIAL TO EXPOSING LIGHT

EFFECTIVE DENSITY OF DYES IN COLOUR NEGATIVE (MID-SCALE)

SENSITIVITY COLOUR PRINTING PAPER TO PRINTING LIGHT

Fig. 11.14 Diagrammatic representation of a colour negative–positive process, showing the interrelation of negative dyes and printing paper sensitivities. *Top:* the sensitivity curves of emulsion layers in the negative material. *Centre:* the general printing effect of dyes formed in the layers of the negative when exposed to an approximately neutral subject. *Bottom:* the sensitivity curves of the printing paper are related to the response of the colour negative, and cover narrower bands of the spectrum in order to give maximum separation of colours. The gap between green and red sensitivities indicates that an appropriate safelight may be used with discretion during printing.

The curves do not represent the response of any particular colour material. They can be related to the representative colour tone reproduction diagram of Figure 11.17.

11.59 *Typical colour printing paper.* Figure 11.15 shows the characteristic curves of a typical colour printing paper that has been exposed to a printing light source suitably filtered to produce a neutral grey image. For the purpose of illustration the curves have been separated a little. Since a sensitometer will seldom have the same spectral characteristics as the actual printer that is to be

used, sensitometric tests are most often carried out using the actual equipment, with a step wedge in the printing position. In the diagram, B, G and R refer to the original sensitivities of the emulsion layers and the measuring filters used in the densitometer, and Y, M and C to the dyes in the layers after processing. The general shape, position and extent of the paper characteristic curves are similar to those of black-and-white paper, but with a somewhat higher D_{max} of about 2.3 or so and a low D_{min} with nearly equal densities to give bright highlights without a colour cast. The shape and contrast of the three curves are fairly equal. As with colour reversal films, there may be some lack of coincidence in the extreme shoulder of the curves, but in practical work a slight loss of colour balance in this area is not noticeable. Reflection density measurement is more sensitive in this part than is visual assessment.

11.60 *Colour balance corrections in printing.* A wrong colour balance overall, indicated by the lateral shift of a characteristic curve without change in shape, can be prevented or corrected by adjusting the colour quality of the exposing light. In practice, colour printing materials are exposed using printers or enlargers in which the spectral quality of the tungsten light can be easily adjusted to suit the requirements of a particular colour negative or colour paper. There are two methods available. One, the white-light (or subtractive) method, consists of inserting dichroic glass or colour printing filters of various densities between the light source and the negative, and giving a single exposure. The other involves giving three separate and varying exposures in succession or simultaneously, through red, green and blue 'narrow-cut' filters of constant density, and is described as the tricolour method. The white-light method is the one most commonly used in manual printing. For instance, a low response to blue light could be corrected either by adding magenta and cyan filters to the printer or by taking away yellow filters that may already be there. In all cases, the combination of filters used should be the simplest possible. On most colour enlargers this is easily achieved by 'dialling in' the appropriate dichroic filters (see paragraph 11.19).

11.61 *Excluding ultraviolet and infrared from the printing light.* Most colour printing materials have some unwanted residual sensitivity, in all emulsion layers, to far-blue and ultraviolet radiation, and, in the red-sensitive layer, to near-infrared radiation. So, in addition to the printing filters, ultraviolet and infrared absorbing or rejecting filters are normally fitted or incorporated in the colour printer. Enlarger heads made specifically for colour printing equipment are designed and constructed so that any ultraviolet and infrared radiation is removed from the exposing light.

11.62 *Balance of colour printing paper.* Colour printing papers are designed to produce good prints from the maker's own and most other colour negative materials under average printing conditions. The characteristics of the three different emulsions in the paper are matched to the transmission characteristics of the dyes in an average colour negative.

In order to offset the printing effect of the pale orange dye mask of the negative, printing paper is made with a blue-sensitive layer that is relatively fast and a red-sensitive layer that is relatively slow when exposed to unfiltered printing light (Figure 11.16). The balance of the colour printing paper is also designed to suit the quality of the filtered light that will be used in printing. The other important balance-affecting factors (contrast, characteristic curve shape, D_{min} and D_{max}) are reasonably equal (see paragraph 11.59).

Like other photographic material, different batches of printing paper vary slightly in speed and colour balance. When a different batch is brought into use, compensatory changes may be required in the printing exposure and filtration, to restore the

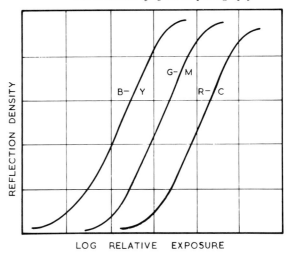

Fig. 11.16 Characteristic curves of a typical colour paper for printing masked colour negatives, showing the result of exposure to unfiltered printing light. B, G and R refer to the original sensitivities of the emulsion layers and the measuring filters used in the densitometer, and Y, M and C to the dyes in the layers after processing. The increased speed of the blue- and green-sensitive layers is designed in manufacture to suit the printing equipment and to offset the printing effect of the pale-orange integral mask of a colour negative.

correct balance between paper, negative and printing light. To facilitate this, manufacturers test each batch of colour paper by comparing it with a known standard batch, and any speed and colour-balance differences are expressed in terms of exposure-adjustment factors and filter-adjustment values. These figures are stamped on the label of each box of colour paper of that batch, and usually show the changes recommended for both white-light and tricolour printing methods. The data thus indicate the adjustments to the printing exposure and filtration that should be needed to compensate for changes in speed and colour balance of each batch of printing paper. Further slight adjustment may be required to obtain a satisfactory colour print, if the old and new batches of unexposed paper have been stored under different conditions, of if there are any slight discrepancies in filter calibration etc.

11.63 *Colour reversal printing paper.* Colour reversal papers made for direct colour printing from positive transparencies are manufactured so that they have the required colour sensitivity, contrast and speed to match the printing characteristics of a typical positive colour transparency. These features include a relatively low curve gradient of approximately 1.0 so that satisfactory prints can be produced from colour transparencies, which always have a greater contrast than colour negatives.

Matching colour paper and negative for printing

11.64   Colour printing paper is designed in manufacture to give a satisfactory response to the exposure effects of an average colour negative under average printing conditions. In practical use, however, there will be variations in the printing characteristics of negatives and different printing conditions, so the effects of these need to be balanced to give a printing exposure that matches the response of the colour printing paper. This can be done, and satisfactory prints obtained, by inserting suitable colour printing filters into the path of the printing light and giving the correct overall exposure (see paragraphs 11.54 and 11.60).

So that correct filtration can be selected and used, the various negatives to be printed are evaluated with regard to general density and colour balance, in order to determine their respective printing characteristics. Because of the integral mask, which prevents a satisfactory visual assessment, this can only be done properly by making trial prints or by using measuring instruments (explained later). The evaluation is more easily made if the negative contains a suitable area that can be measured.

11.65   To facilitate the evaluation of colour negatives for printing, it is a good practice to include in the original scene (outside the picture area or on a separate frame) a grey card lit in the same manner as the original subject. The image of this will provide a suitable middle-tone reference area that can be used for measuring and determining the printing characteristics of the negatives. Such neutral grey cards, giving an 18 per cent reflectance, are available from Kodak.

11.66   Correctly exposed and processed colour prints should reproduce the neutral tones (greys) of the original scene as neutral tones without a visible colour cast, and any flesh tones in the photograph should also be satisfactory. As the processing of colour material is a more or less fixed factor, this standard can only be obtained in printing by controlling the exposure, so that the proper balance between the exposing light and the colour sensitivity of the paper is achieved. The two factors used to achieve this standard are the amount of exposure, which controls the overall density of the

print, and filtration, which controls the colour balance of the result. We can show the effect of these two factors by means of a quadrant diagram.

Tone reproduction diagram for the colour negative–positive process

11.67   The negative–positive process and the matching of masked colour negative and colour printing paper (or print film) can be illustrated by a representative colour tone reproduction quadrant diagram as in Figure 11.17. The diagram gives a graphical representation of the effects of the process on colour tone reproduction, starting from the subject, through exposure and processing of the film, to printing the negative and viewing the final result. It brings together on one graph the fundamental principles of colour sensitometry. Therefore it can be used to relate the effects of exposure and processing, and to predict or show the effects of the variations that occur in a typical colour photographic process.

In practical use, many variables can affect the reproduction of the resultant print, such as the flare effect of the camera and lens, and the optical characteristics of the printer or enlarger. So, for simplicity, Figure 11.17 shows in diagrammatic form the characteristic curves of a masked colour negative that has been correctly exposed, and the simple contact-printing of the negative onto a colour printing paper. It may be convenient to think of the original subject primarily as a step wedge that also includes a representative colour transparency containing a selection of various colours and tones. The diagram follows the same sequence we used previously for black-and-white tone reproduction diagrams.

11.68   Figure 11.17 represents a good reproduction with no colour casts, indicating that the influencing factors of negative characteristics, printing light and paper characteristics are in balance. We can see that in an ideal colour negative–positive process, each separate image of the negative controls only the exposure of, and hence the colour density of, its associated layer of the paper emulsion. The yellow image of the negative controls the exposure of the blue-sensitive layer of the paper, and thus also the density of the yellow image on the final print. The magenta image of the negative controls the magenta image of the print, and the negative cyan image controls the print cyan image. The principle of colour tone

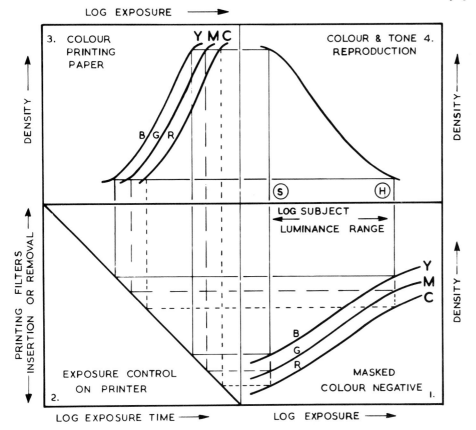

Fig. 11.17 A representative colour tone reproduction diagram for a colour negative–positive process showing, in quadrant 4, good reproduction with no colour casts. S denotes shadow areas and H highlights. B, G and R refer to the original sensitivities of the emulsion layers, and Y, M and C to the dyes in the layers after processing. The exposure relationships between each negative characteristic curve and its associated print curve can be seen. The effect on colour and tone reproduction of variations in the overall printing exposure can be shown by moving the diagonal line in quadrant 2 horizontally to the left or right. The effect of inserting or removing different printing filters can be shown by moving the same line vertically up or down. Any difference in the vertical distance between the colour negative characteristic curves indicates changes in the density and colour balance of the negative. The effects of these can be shown in the reproduction quadrant, as can the effect of any camera or printing filters that may be used to correct such effects. The response to overall exposure changes in the camera can also be shown.

reproduction in the colour negative–positive process, and the effects of changing overall exposure, and adding or removing filters on the camera or in the printing equipment can be worked out by using the diagram.

11.69 *Effects of camera exposure changes.* The effect of overall camera exposure variation, a wrong colour balance during exposure, or a colour-compensating filter on the camera, can be shown by moving the appropriate characteristic curve or curves of the colour negative in a horizontal direction (see paragraph 11.54 and Figure 11.12), and then carrying lines through in each direction to meet in the reproduction quadrant.

11.70 *Effect of printing exposure changes.* The effect of overall printing exposure increases or decreases, which will affect all three of the printing paper emulsions, can be shown by moving the diagonal line in quadrant 2 horizontally to the right or left respectively, and by carrying lines through to the print curves and then into the reproduction quadrant to meet corresponding lines drawn up from the subject luminance range axis. This can best be done by using the straight edge of a piece of thin card, or better still a piece of lightly fogged film, to represent the diagonal line. The effect on the printing paper of removing or inserting yellow, magenta or cyan printing filters can be shown in the same manner, by moving the diagonal line vertically up or down respectively and applying the effect to the relevant blue, green or red curve. Note that this produces the same effect as moving the relevant negative characteristic curve vertically or the relevant print curve horizontally. For example, removal or insertion of a yellow filter adjusts the response of the blue-sensitive emulsion of the print.

In principle, the insertion of a yellow, magenta or cyan filter causes one print emulsion layer to produce less density. The insertion of two different filters causes two emulsion layers to produce less density. For example, a yellow filter plus a magenta filter adjusts the exposure of both blue- and green-sensitive emulsion layers. The opposite occurs if filters already there are removed. We can see that in practice there is no reason for using more than two different colour filters at the same time. If filters of all three colours are inserted, all the colour negative curves are lifted vertically and an unnecessary neutral density is added to the negative. This does nothing useful, but necessitates an increase in the overall printing exposure and should therefore be avoided.

If a working model of the diagram can be constructed, the effect of variations in the process can be more easily demonstrated.

Example. Figure 11.17 shows the situation when the negative characteristics, printing light and paper characteristics are in balance. If, say, a yellow filter is inserted in the printer, the blue-sensitive layer of the print receives less exposure, produces less yellow dye and thus causes a blue cast (magenta + cyan) on the finished print. This effect can be shown by moving the diagonal line in quadrant 2 vertically downward, and carrying lines from the blue-sensitive emulsion curve of the negative through to the blue-sensitive emulsion curve of the paper and into the reproduction quadrant to meet lines drawn up from the subject luminance range axis. The effect of any other camera or printer filter, or combination of different filters, can be shown in a similar way. Try this out yourself. Reference to Figures 11.2, 11.3, 11.5, 11.12 and 11.13 may help when working out your own examples.

Application of sensitometry to practical colour printing

11.71   The basic principles of colour sensitometry apply to all aspects of photographic colour printing and duplicating. Practical procedures, however, can take many forms, depending on the nature of the work and what materials and equipment are to be used. Because of this, and as we are concerned mainly with the association of sensitometry and colour tone reproduction, we can consider only in general the principles and practices involved. The manufacturers of colour printing and duplicating materials and related equipment provide detailed working procedures that are particular to their products, and these should be followed. Nevertheless, whatever practical procedures are used, the same basic principles of colour sensitometry apply and a working knowledge of the factors and effects involved is invaluable when colour printing.

11.72   Figure 11.17 depicts a situation in which a typical colour negative has been printed. The variable factors that can affect the result are in balance and thus the end product is a print with optimum colour quality. To achieve this in practice, and to continue to achieve it, we can first set up the printer or enlarger and find the correct exposure and filtration for an average colour negative. This setting-up procedure is best carried out by printing a standard 'master' negative specially made for the purpose. It should represent the average of the normal negatives that are to be printed and should also include a neutral grey middle-tone 'reference' area (see paragraph 11.65) and a suitable flesh tone. The enlarger is set up using the master negative and an excellent print is produced by trial and error (a method of doing this is briefly described in paragraph 11.74). When the optimum print is obtained, a note is made of the relevant printing data, including the exposure, filtration and paper batch used.

Thereafter, when printing other negatives, the only large variant encountered will be changes in the colour densities of the different negatives we wish to print. These changes could be shown on Figure 11.17 as differences in the vertical interval between the characteristic curves of the colour negative. Therefore, if we measure the density to red, green and blue light of the cyan, magenta and yellow dye densities of a reference area, say the neutral grey middle-tone of the master negative, and then the densities of a similar area on the new negative, we will have two different sets of figures. The difference in value between the red, green and blue densities on each negative can then be used to calculate the exposure and filtration required to produce satisfactory prints from the new negative.

In other words, by densitometric evaluation we are able to predict with a fair degree of accuracy the exposure required and the filtration needed for any particular colour negative. The adjustments we can predict and then carry out are to the quantity of light (by adjusting exposure) and to the quality of light (by inserting or removing colour printing filters).

Evaluating and printing colour negatives

11.73 The practical methods used to evaluate colour negatives for printing, and to decide the exposure and filtration required, depend on what equipment is available to carry out the procedure. Visual assessment can give very little information as the integral dye mask also tends to mask any visible evidence of colour quality or balance. Evaluation is therefore best done by using a measuring instrument such as a colour densitometer, but if none is available printing must be done by trial and error. The visual judgment of colour negatives is considered in paragraph 11.108.

11.74 *Evaluating and printing by trial and error.* If no measuring instruments are available when enlarging, and for the initial setting-up of a printing system, assessment is made from test strip prints of the colour negative. An exposure test strip of the same representative area of the negative is first made. This is then viewed in daylight or, better, using a standard viewing light (see paragraphs 7.34 and 11.80) to find the correct basic exposure. The selected step is also viewed to estimate the correct filtration, bearing in mind that a colour cast is corrected by using a filter of the same colour as the cast (see paragraph 11.23) and that exposure decrease will produce a lighter result, and vice versa. Other tests are then made using the chosen filtration and exposure, and these are viewed to find the filtration and exposure for the final print. Print-judging techniques may be used, and simple tables and calculators are available to assist in this procedure and indicate the changes in exposure necessary to match filtration.

When a series of different colour negatives are to be printed, once the correct filtration and exposure have been found for an average negative it is often advantageous to make a contact print of all the negatives. The procedure is to assemble them and the average negative in a contact-printing frame, or taped to a sheet of plate glass, and to make a contact print using the same exposure and filtration as for the average negative. When the contact print is viewed it may be found that many of the other negatives produce good prints without any change in filtration. With experience, the filtration and exposure changes for any unsatisfac-

tory prints can be decided fairly accurately. The contact print can be used later, as a file reference.

The value of this and similar procedures lies in the fact that the sensitometric effects of all the many influencing factors that can affect the response of the photographic material are automatically included in the result. To obtain the desired colour quality the only factors to be considered are filtration and exposure.

11.75 *Colour negative evaluating instruments.* The most efficient methods of evaluating colour negatives for printing involve the use of measuring instruments, either away from the enlarger (off-easel) or by measuring the projected image (on-easel). For off-easel evaluation a colour densitometer can be used to measure the neutral grey or the reference areas of both master and printing negative for comparison. This is called a 'spot' or 'small-area' measurement. For on-easel evaluation, a colour analyser is used. This is in principle similar to a colour densitometer, but because it measures the projected light of the image it should properly be referred to as a photometer. The advantage of on-easel analysis is that measurements are made with the negative in its printing situation, so they include the characteristics of the particular enlarger, its light, filters and magnification, etc. Some colour analysers can be used for off-easel evaluation, and for this they use their own light source; thus in effect they act as a colour densitometer.

The efficacy of both on- and off-easel methods of evaluation depends on the availability of a suitable area for measuring and comparison with the reference area of the master negative (see paragraphs 11.65 and 11.72). If a suitable reference area such as a grey card image or a satisfactory flesh tone is available, it can be used for a spot or small-area measurement. If there is no suitable small area, then a large-area or 'integrated' measurement can be made, usually of the whole picture area. For this the image is 'integrated to grey'. One method is to place a piece of diffusing material between the enlarger lens and the image. The different coloured light is thus scrambled and mixed so that it loses any particular colour; it is integrated to some colour representing an average grey subject of 18 per cent reflectance. This method of colour negative evaluation is based on experimental evidence that the majority of scenes photographed will contain similar proportions of blue, green and red, and therefore these colours will integrate to give a near neutral grey.

By using careful densitometric or photometric evaluation and applying the rules of colour filtering, we can ensure that the vast majority of colour prints will be visually satisfactory. However, the occasional print may require other than normal filtration. For example, a colour negative that has crossed curves (Figure 11.6) will probably require individual filtration in an attempt to improve the results, or a print intended to have a subjective colour impact on the viewer may also need different filtration.

Assessing and printing colour transparencies

11.76 The basic procedures for negative–positive printing apply also to positive–positive printing, where a positive transparency is printed directly onto colour reversal paper or duplicating film. Because colour reversal material is being used, the effects of exposure and filtration are the opposite of that in negative–positive printing. Decreasing the exposure produces a darker result, and colour casts are corrected by using a filter of a colour complementary to the cast (see paragraph 11.23). Since a colour transparency is a positive record, any necessary filtration and its effect can often, with experience, be visually assessed from the image, without the need for analysing instruments. Direct colour reversal print materials designed for printing have a lower contrast than colour negative–positive printing materials, and furthermore the transparencies to be printed should themselves be correctly exposed and processed (see paragraphs 11.100 and 11.101). Because of this, the effect of changes in filtration and exposure are more moderate and the need for them less frequent than is the case with negative–positive printing.

Colour quality: practical requirements

11.77 There is a vast range of colour printing equipment, varying from the relatively simple, designed for the amateur, through to the highly complex automatic equipment used in professional colour printing laboratories. Nevertheless all printing systems, simple or complex, depend on the same basic requirements for obtaining optimum quality results. The first requirement is a stable power supply. Voltage fluctuations in the power supply to colour printing equipment will upset both the colour balance and the exposure conditions. To overcome the disturbing effect on colour quality, it is essential that the supply voltage is stablized. The best method of achieving stability

for colour printing equipment is to use an electronic voltage stabilizer.

The control of colour quality in printing is aided by the use of measuring instruments that evaluate the dye density present in colour negatives or transparencies, and indicate the correct exposure and colour filtration required. To obtain the necessary colour quality by filtration, the light source of the printer or enlarger must itself produce a continuous spectrum and have a high light output. For example, the cold-cathode illumination used in some black-and-white enlargers is unsuitable for colour printing because it does not produce a continuous spectrum. For these reasons, tungsten or (more usually) high-light-output tungsten–halogen lamps are used.

For satisfactory colour printing the particular requirements of a colour enlarger are:

(a) A light source having a continuous spectral emission with constant output and colour quality. This is facilitated by using a tungsten–halogen lamp fed from a voltage-stabilized power supply.
(b) A diffuse illumination system. This is preferable in order to integrate the light and to minimize the effect of scratches and marks on the negative.
(c) A high-quality colour-corrected lens system.
(d) A means of modulating the colour of the exposing light (usually by filtration) and ensuring that the effect is uniformly distributed over the printing area.
(e) An accurate and reliable exposure-timing device, and preferably click-stop lens apertures with illuminated indication.
(f) A means of protecting the negative and components in the light beam from lamp-generated heat and of preventing both infrared and ultraviolet radiation reaching the printing material.

A piece of equipment made for use on an existing enlarger, and incorporating most of the above requirements, is often referred to as a 'colour printing head'.

In some printing systems the evaluation, exposure and filtration are semi-automatic. This usually involves the determination of filtration and exposure by an electronic colour-analysing device, and the mechanical movement of dichroic filters at right angles across the light path in order to obtain the desired colour quality. In white-light printing, cyan, magenta and yellow filters are used. Their movement may be automatic or they may be connected to external controls with calibrated dials to indicate the filtration. The amount of insertion into the light path of each dichroic filter decides the colour quality of the exposing light in much the same manner as the insertion or removal of acetate colour printing filters. Both the light that passes through the dichroic filters and the light that passes by are thoroughly mixed (integrated) before reaching the negative. (Dichroic filters are described in paragraph 11.19.)

In all situations, whatever electronic and mechanical aids are used in printing and however simple or complex the system is, the final decision on print quality can only be made by the human eye. The operator must therefore be in control of the printing system and be able to apply corrections when necessary. This necessitates an understanding and working knowledge of the basic sensitometry involved.

Summary

11.78 The basic principles of sensitometry, exposure and colour control that apply to making colour prints on paper apply also to making positive colour transparencies or duplicate colour transparencies. The only basic difference is that when printing or duplicating onto a direct colour reversal material, the exposure changes and colour corrections are the opposite of those used in negative–positive printing. In each and every case, however, the balance between the original and the material it is being reproduced on must be achieved in order to obtain optimum quality results.

For example, to obtain the best possible results when printing colour negatives, the colour quality and amount of the exposing light, the colour densities of the three negative images, and the response of the three different emulsions of the paper must be in balance. In any particular printing situation two of the three, the negative and the paper, will be reasonably fixed factors and not easily variable. Balance is therefore achieved by modulating both the colour quality and the amount of the exposing light. In tricolour printing this is done by positioning red, green and blue narrow-cut filters separately in the light beam and varying the amount of exposure through each. In white-light printing it is achieved by positioning one or two from a graded set of cyan, magenta and yellow filters together in the light beam and giving one exposure. With both methods, the degree of filtration adjusts the relative amounts of red, green and blue light so that all the factors are brought into balance and the colour paper receives correct exposure for a particular negative.

When a number of negatives are to be printed, the main variation will be in the colour densities of the different negatives. These characteristics can be measured and compared with those of the first or 'master' negative. Filtration and exposure can then be changed to suit the new negative, and thus maintain a colour balance with the printing paper. The effect of correct exposure and processing, and the proof of a correct colour balance, is most easily seen when the neutral tones (greys) of the original scene are reproduced as neutral tones on the print.

Colour photography reproduction systems are changed and simplified for the user, as new products and methods are introduced. Complex systems and processes, designed to produce high-quality results, have been made more practical by the introduction of automatic or semi-automatic systems. The manufacturers of sensitized photographic materials and the makers of colour analysers, printers and processors provide up-to-date information regarding their products and (just as relevant) the associated measuring, printing, duplicating and processing techniques. These cover a variety of methods depending on what equipment and materials are available to carry out the procedure, and of course on the original and what end product is required. Readers wishing to study photographic colour printing and its practical applications in more detail should read books such as *Kodak Handbook for the Professional Photographer* (Volume 3, *Colour Printing*) and *Advanced Photography* by M. J. Langford (see Appendix G).

Objective and subjective comparisons of colour reproductions

11.79 The dyes used in photographic colour materials are unable to match in full all the visible colours of nature: for instance, the subtle hues of a rainbow or the blues of some natural objects. However the degree of mismatch is often unimportant, as the human brain and eye viewing the colour photographs can adapt and accept them as satisfactory reproductions, just as we accept the cruder mix of hues in a colour television picture. Nevertheless, when several slightly different colour photographs of the same scene, all individually acceptable, are viewed together, one can usually be judged as having a better colour quality than the others. Our visual sense is much better at comparing colours than it is at judging and evaluating colours on their own. This applies particularly when the photographs contain familiar hues such as skin tones, or grey areas such as concrete roads. A similar side-by-side comparison is also helpful when the visual definition of photographic images has to be assessed.

The value to the photographer of innovations in emulsion and processing technology may also need to be assessed under practical user conditions. We know that manufacturers are always striving to improve their colour materials with regard to such things as dye quality and stability, fidelity of colour reproduction, speed, exposure latitude and image definition. The introduction of DIR couplers (development-inhibitor-releasing couplers), which react during development to give an enhanced image sharpness and colour rendering. was a good example of such an improvement (see paragraph 2.103 and Appendix D). Another particularly impressive innovation is the emulsion technology introduced by Kodak as 'T-grain (tabular-grain) technology', whereby speed can be increased without a decrease in photographic image definition. This is obtained by using thinner, flatter, tablet-like silver halide crystals, which are positioned to present more surface area to the exposing light. The techniques used in processing exposed colour materials are also subject to regular improvement. The effects of some of these inovations, and their possible value to the user, can be found by comparative sensitometry, others cannot.

11.80   *Practical tests and comparison viewing of colour materials.*   Simple comparative sensitometry is useful for comparing colour materials and processes with regard to measurable or objective aspects, such as speeds and contrasts, but it has its limitations when subjective things such as colour reproduction are concerned. For example, when comparison is made between different colour reversal films, characteristic curves indicate the difference in speed, contrast, latitude, colour balance, etc., and these can be related to the requirements of the task. However, subtle differences in colour reproduction or image sharpness will not be apparent from a study of the curves. In such cases, the best method is to supplement the sensitometric comparison with a practical comparison under working conditions. Bearing in mind that it is the subjective effect on the observer that is often decisive, several different camera exposures should be made on each film of a typical standard subject. After processing, the films or prints can be visually compared side by side using an even 'white' viewing light (usually similar to 'daylight'

at about 5000 K) or on a viewer having a similar colour quality. If intended for projection, the results should be compared side by side using one projector or two similar projectors with matching light sources. Proper comparison can be made only when the conditions of viewing are similar to those that will be used later and when the observer has good colour vision (see paragraphs 2.122, 7.34 and 11.124).

This type of subjective comparison might be used for materials that are to be used on tasks involving optimum colour reproduction, such as the photography of scientific or medical subjects or the sharpness on projection of small-format images. Bear in mind that the contrast of the material, as shown on the characteristic curves, affects the relative visual sharpness of images, so comparison for sharpness can only be properly made when the curves are of a similar gradient.

11.81   *Colour rendition comparison.*   When assessing colour reproduction it is beneficial if a comparison can be made not only between the results of two or more tests, but also with the original subject photographed. This is facilitated by using a standard subject that contains all the necessary colours and can be used repeatedly. A very useful standard subject is a specially manufactured colour rendition chart such as the Macbeth Colour Checker. A typical chart consists of an array of 24 squares showing a wide range of colours and a six-step neutral grey scale (Figure 11.18). The colours include those that are particularly important in photography, such as light and dark skin, blue sky, typical foliage and other colours all of

Dark skin	Light skin	Blue sky	Foliage	Blue flower	Bluish green
Orange	Purplish blue	Moderate red	Purple	Yellow green	Orange yellow
Blue	Green	Red	Yellow	Magenta	Cyan
White	Light grey	Light-medium grey	Medium grey	Dark grey	Black

Fig. 11.18 The arrangement of colours and grey scale on the Macbeth colour rendition chart. The array provides a standard original subject for the evaluation of colour reproduction processes. The chart having been photographed, the images are processed and compared with the original.

which are precise simulations of natural coloured objects. Included also are the additive primary colours (blue, green and red) and their complementary colours (yellow, magenta and cyan). The coloured squares are made so that they will match the colours of natural objects under any lighting conditions.

11.82 *Using a colour rendition chart.* To find the effect of varying factors in a colour photography process, the chart is photographed and the images processed under the required conditions. The results are then compared with the original chart and with each other. Comparisons that can be made are, for example, the colour quality produced by:

(a) Different kinds of colour film or printing paper.
(b) Different exposure or processing conditions.
(c) Materials of different age, or materials stored under different conditions before or after processing.

For any such comparison it is of course essential that any differences found in the results are caused only by the factor being investigated. All other variable factors that can affect the result must be kept under strict control.

Stability of processed colour materials

11.83 Sensitometry is used in testing the long-term keeping qualities of the dye images of processed colour materials. Organic dyes gradually fade as time goes by, and the deterioration is accelerated if the storage and usage conditions are unfavourable. For example, excessive light, heat and moisture, and particularly ultraviolet radiation, have a detrimental effect. Deterioration is further hastened by incorrect processing and by residual processing chemicals that may be contained in the material. To obtain the best possible stability, colour materials must be correctly processed and must be stored where it is dark, cool and dry. For maximum stability they should be stored in deep-freeze conditions.

Manufacturers need to maintain and improve the stability of photographic materials, so they carry out periodic sensitometric tests to check on the keeping qualities of their processed colour material. Both grey and coloured step wedges, and a series of different colours of varying density, are first recorded on the material. The results are measured on a colour densitometer and noted. The materials may then be subjected to accelerated keeping tests, using known and controlled conditions of temperature and humidity in the dark. They are also subjected to other accelerated fading tests, for example by exposure to direct sunlight or to use in high-intensity projectors. Comparative densitometric evaluation is then used to determine the degree of deterioration in colour quality.

Self-assessment questions

11.84 If you want to test your learning, answer the following questions:

(a) Explain 'colour temperature' and how it can be used to specify the colour quality of a light.
(b) Explain the relationship between 'kelvin' and 'mired' values of colour temperature, and why mired values are preferred for use in colour photography.
(c) Name and explain briefly the three subjective terms that should be used to describe the visual characteristics of a colour.
(d) Describe briefly what occurs during the processing of:
  (1) An exposed colour negative film.
  (2) An exposed colour reversal film.
(e) State the reason for the pale orange-coloured masking that is visible in the clearer parts of a colour negative.
(f) Draw three overlapping circles similar to those shown in Figure 1.8, and imagine them as yellow, magenta and cyan light filters. Name the colours that will be seen when the filter pack is held in front of a white light.
(g) Explain how your answer to question (f) relates to the principle of subtractive synthesis in colour photography.
(h) Name the four main types of colour filter used in colour photography.
(i) Draw density/wavelength (spectral absorption) curves to illustrate the basic difference between a filter used on a camera to lower the colour temperature of the exposing light, and one used to compensate for an excess of blue light. Indicate the colour of each filter on the curve.
(j) Explain how dichroic filters are used in colour printing and how they operate. Give three reasons why they are more efficient than dye-based filters.
(k) Describe in outline the method used to find the sensitometric characteristics of a colour film.
(l) Draw both axes of a $D \log H$ graph; then draw a single characteristic curve representing an ideal colour negative film, and another curve representing an ideal colour reversal film.

(m) Using either the diagram drawn for question (l), or Figure 11.4 as a guide, compare the characteristic curve gradient and exposure latitude of typical colour negative and colour reversal films. Explain why they differ.

(n) Draw the three (slightly separated) characteristic curves of a typical colour reversal film and label each curve with the colour sensitivity of the emulsion layer it represents. Opposite each label, name the colour of the dye produced in the layer after exposure and processing.

(o) Repeat the procedure in question (n), for a typical masked colour negative film.

(p) A *D* log *H* graph shows that one of the characteristic curves of a colour reversal film is displaced laterally by an appreciable amount.
  (1) How will this displacement show in the film image?
  (2) List three factors, any of which may have caused this effect.
  (3) Explain how the effect may be prevented or corrected in practice.

(q) If colour films balanced for use in tungsten light are exposed in daylight and then processed, a colour cast will be seen in the result. Draw characteristic curves to show the sensitometric effect for both reversal film and unmasked negative film. Indicate the colour of the cast for each film.

(r) Describe the two exposure conditions that may cause reciprocity failure in colour materials. Draw characteristic curves to show the probable effect of gross reciprocity failure on a typical colour reversal film, and describe the visual effect as seen in the film image.

(s) The speeds of colour reversal and colour negative films are based on different points on their respective characteristic curves. Explain why this is so.

(t) Describe how you would visibly judge and prove the colour quality of a correctly exposed and processed colour reversal transparency. Then draw imaginary characteristic curves for the three emulsion layers of such a film.

(u) Repeat question (t) for a colour print.

(v) Figure 11.9 represents a correctly exposed and processed colour reversal film. Explain the general effect on each of the three characteristic curves if exposure had been made through:
  (1) A complementary coloured filter.
  (2) A primary coloured filter.

(w) Repeat question (v) with reference to:
  (1) Figure 11.11: colour negative film.
  (2) Figure 11.15: colour printing paper.

(x) Name and explain the two variable factors that have to be controlled in colour printing in order to obtain a good print.

(y) Explain the basic rules of colour filtering that apply when correcting a colour cast in the positive printing of:
  (1) Colour negatives.
  (2) Colour transparencies.

(z) Study the colour tone reproduction diagram (Figure 11.17), and describe in outline the photographic process that it represents. Explain briefly how the diagram can be used to predict the effect on the print of:
  (1) A colour-compensating filter on the camera.
  (2) A change in the printing exposure time.
  (3) A change in the printing filtration.

Obtaining high-quality colour transparencies and negatives

11.85 Now that we have a fair understanding of the sensitometry of colour photography, we can apply it to our everyday photographic activities.

In photography, two distinct sets of variables can be manipulated and controlled to produce the required reproduction. The first set is concerned with exposure, the second with processing. In conventional black-and-white photography either or both sets of variables may be used, but in colour photography it is more usual to have a fixed set of processing conditions and to use only the variables of exposure to obtain the required results. The processing procedures used in colour photography have been designed to produce a high percentage of satisfactory images by adherence to fixed processing conditions: time, temperature, agitation, and processing solution activity, using specified processing solutions. Deviation from these fixed processing conditions will produce a deterioration in colour quality.

Correct exposure

11.86 Because processing is a more or less fixed factor, it is primarily the exposure given that determines whether or not we obtain a satisfactory record of the subject photographed. Therefore the correct exposure of colour materials is the most decisive operation in the colour photographic process. Correct camera exposure can be defined as the exposure that will, after processing, produce the most satisfactory colour transparency, or a colour negative that can be used to produce the most satisfactory print.

The exposure latitude of conventional black-and-white films is such that variation from an ideal exposure can still produce satisfactory results. However, the exposure latitude of colour films, and in particular colour reversal films, is much less than that of black-and-white films. Because of this, it is particularly important that an accurate exposure meter and a suitable exposure determination method is used whenever colour photography is undertaken. Other factors are also important; for instance, the effective speed of the film should be known to a fair degree of accuracy. A precise speed value is often given in the data sheet included with each batch of professional colour reversal film, but the nominal film speed marked on the containers of other films and amateur film must be regarded as provisional. Any error in colour balance or in the exposing equipment, meter calibration, shutter speed etc. will also affect the actual exposure.

Tonal distortion in normal black-and-white photography is acceptable and usually necessary to produce a satisfactory print. The range of tones in a subject can be compressed or elongated in the print; as long as this is not too excessive, such distortion, because it is in monochrome, goes unnoticed. A black-and-white print is accepted as a reasonable representation of the original subject; but when a colour photograph is viewed small distortions of colour, particularly those in flesh tones, are conspicuous and often visually disturbing. We are much more critical of variations in colour than in tone. The exposure of colour materials must therefore be such that a reasonable reproduction of the subject colours is obtained on the final photograph. The basic requirement of correct exposure and accurate colour reproduction is of course that the film type used (tungsten or daylight) should be suitable for the colour quality of the exposing light (see paragraph 11.5). In this respect colour reversal films are less tolerant of exposure errors than colour negative films because they are an end product, whereas with negative films some correction for colour distortion can be applied during the printing process.

Manufacturers attempt to ensure that the shape of the characteristic curves of the various emulsion layers of a colour film are similar, so that the reproduction of colour throughout a range of luminances is achieved. However, this is seldom fully obtainable in practice, and there is often a small variation in the shape of the characteristic curves, particularly towards the shoulder, resulting in a distortion of colour if these parts are used. Subject areas in which colour fidelity is important

must be placed, by exposure, on the steeper parts of the characteristic curves where curve shape differences are at a minimum. They must also avoid the shoulder and lower toe region. The useful exposure range of a colour film is thus limited to the region where the three characteristic curves have sufficient gradient and are similar in shape. Because the useful exposure range of a colour film is limited, the exposure latitude is also limited, and any subject to be photographed must present a luminance range that the film can usefully accept. When a subject with a satisfactory luminance range is photographed, the exposure given must be such that the important parts of the luminance range are placed on the appropriate parts of the film characteristic curves. Obtaining correct exposure when using colour films can thus be summarized as:

(a) Ensuring a suitable colour balance between film and exposing light.
(b) Obtaining an acceptable subject luminance range.
(c) Placing the important parts of the subject luminance range on the correct parts of the film characteristic curves.

There are differences between the exposure measuring and determination procedures used for colour reversal films and those used for colour negative films. To obtain the best reproduction, reversal films may require an exposure that is correct to within one-third of a lens stop. Colour negative films have more exposure latitude than this because of their lower characteristic curve gradient and because compensation for small variations in exposure level can also be made when the negatives are printed.

Subject luminance range in colour photography

11.87 Because both reversal and negative colour films have less exposure latitude than conventional black-and-white films, they cannot successfully record both the highlight and shadow detail of subjects that have a long luminance range (a high contrast). The parts of the subject luminance range that are recorded beyond the useful exposure range of a colour reversal film will be reproduced with poor tonal separation. Because of this, the highlight areas on the photograph may also be pale and desaturated and the shadow areas may be dark and show little or no detail. Only part of the characteristic curves of a reversal film can be used successfully. In particular, if the extreme toe region is used there may be insufficient dye present in the image to reproduce any strong highlight colours. A similar situation applies also to colour negative films. Although they have a little more exposure latitude than reversal films, the densities and density range of a colour negative still have to be printed onto the more restricted exposure range of the colour printing paper. Attempts to carry out manual dodging in order to rectify this when a contrast colour negative is printed will often result in a print with visually disturbing smoky-black shadow areas and veiled highlights. When either reversal or negative colour films are to be used for photography, it is therefore necessary to carefully control the subject luminance range whenever important highlight and shadow detail is required in the final photograph.

Restricted subject luminance ranges are acceptable in colour photography, because the final pictorial presentation and visual effect depends mostly on colour differences (colour contrast), rather than on the tonal differences (tonal contrast) necessary in black-and-white photography. Small differences in colour will have a greater visual effect than similar levels of tone difference in monochrome. Also, two areas of a photograph that have a similar density or tone, but differ significantly in colour (e.g. blue and yellow, or red and green) will show a distinct colour contrast.

Because a suitable subject luminance range is an important contributory factor in obtaining high-quality colour photographs, we need to consider it in more detail.

11.88   As we already know, colour films have a significantly shorter useful exposure range than black-and-white films. Since the majority of subjects present a relatively long subject luminance range, before taking a colour photograph it is necessary to measure and if necessary adjust the subject luminance range, so that it suits the useful exposure range of the film. The two main components of subject luminance range are the subject reflectance range and the lighting ratio; either or both of these can be used to control the subject luminance range in order to obtain a satisfactory result. Let us consider a simple example.

11.89   *Subject reflectance range.*   Suppose we wish to take a photograph of a cube, one face of which is white and another almost black (see Figure 11.19); the cube is illuminated by uniform diffuse lighting.

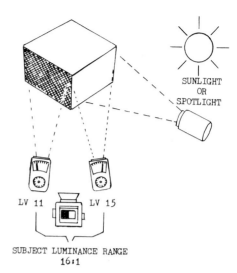

Fig. 11.19 Using an exposure meter to measure the subject luminance range. The meter readings indicate the relative intensity of light reflected from the lightest and darkest parts of the subject. The difference between the two is the subject luminance range, in this case 16:1. (LV = Light value.)

If a light-meter reading is taken, first of the white face and then of the black face, the readings might typically indicate that the white face is reflecting eight times more light towards the camera than the black face. The difference between the two readings is the extent of the subject reflectance range, and in this instance it is eight to one (8:1). The subject reflectance range is thus the difference between the intensities of light reflected towards the camera from the lightest and darkest parts of the subject, when the subject is evenly illuminated.

11.90   *Lighting ratio.*   Now suppose that the uniform diffuse lighting is left as it is, but in addition the white face only of the cube is further illuminated: for example, by a spotlight or with direct light from the sun. The intensity of light falling on this part of the subject is increased; if the white face of the cube is now receiving twice the amount falling on the black face, the lighting ratio is two to one (2:1). The lighting ratio (or lighting contrast) is the difference in intensity between the two extremes of light falling on the subject. It can be measured by taking readings from the subject position using an incident-light meter, with the meter facing each light source in turn. If an incident-light reading is inconvenient, reflected-light readings can be taken from a white (or grey) card positioned near various parts of the subject, with the card in the same plane as that of the subject. The difference between the highest and lowest readings indicates the lighting ratio.

11.91 *Subject luminance range.* The subject luminance range (or subject contrast) is the product of the subject reflectance range and the lighting ratio. It is measured in practice by taking reflected-light readings of the lightest highlight and the darkest shadow, but avoiding specular reflections and strongly coloured areas. The readings taken thus include both the reflectance range of the subject and the lighting ratio that has been applied to the subject.

Consider the situation depicted in Figure 11.19: a reflection measurement of the black face of the cube and another of the white face give readings of LV 11 and LV 15. The difference between successive exposure-meter light values represents the effect of one lens stop in exposure, i.e. a doubling or halving of the intensity of light. Therefore the cube has a subject luminance range of 16:1, which would be calculated as:

11	12	13	14	**15**	Light values indicated on exposure meter.
1	2	4	8	**16**	Relative light difference (16:1).

11.92 *Recommended subject luminance ranges.* As a general guide to obtaining satisfactory results in colour photography, when it is important to retain both highlight and shadow detail, it is recommended that the subject luminance range should not exceed the following values:

(a) To make colour slides that are suitable for projection, 20:1 (a difference of 4¼ light values on the exposure meter).
(b) To make colour transparencies that are to be used for making colour prints, 10:1 (a difference of 3¼ light values on the exposure meter).
(c) To make colour negatives that are to be used for making colour prints, 10:1 (a difference of 3¼ light values on the exposure meter).
(d) To make colour negatives that are to be used for making colour transparencies, 20:1 (a difference of 4¼ light values on the exposure meter).

Remember that one of the effects of camera lens flare is to reduce the contrast of the image falling on the film in the camera, and that the amount of the effect depends not only on the lens itself, but on the extent and proportions of the subject luminance range (see paragraphs 7.5 to 7.7). Film manufacturers are of course aware of this, so the subject luminance range recommendations they give for their colour films normally take into account the contrast-lowering effect of average lens flare. Therefore in the majority of cases, the image illuminance range received on the film will be

shorter than the externally measured subject luminance range.

11.93 *Recommended lighting ratio.* A satisfactory subject luminance range can often be obtained by adjusting the lighting ratio. For subjects in the studio, film manufacturers recommend a lighting ratio of about 3:1 when using reversal and negative colour films to photograph an average subject. By ensuring that this ratio is not exceeded, a satisfactory subject luminance range can usually be achieved.

For subjects outdoors on a clear day, direct light from the sun and reflected light from the sky give a lighting ratio of about 7:1, which in most cases is much too high. An ideal day for colour photography is when the whole sky is covered by a thin layer of cloud; the subject is then illuminated by diffused sunlight and the shadows are soft-edged. Under these conditions the lighting ratio is about the recommended 3:1, enabling you to obtain a satisfactory subject luminance range.

Practical control of subject luminance range

11.94 To control the subject luminance range we can change the lighting ratio and/or the subject reflectance range. For colour photography, a reduction in subject luminance range is more often needed than an increase, so we can now consider some practical examples and methods that may be used to achieve this.

11.95 *Lowering the lighting ratio.* When taking colour photographs it is in most cases easier to reduce the subject luminance range by lowering the lighting ratio than by reducing the reflectance range. In the photographic studio the majority of subjects can be recorded satisfactorily, providing that the lighting ratio is standardized at about 3:1. This ratio is easily obtained by adjusting the relative intensities of the studio lights (see also paragraph 11.90). With the larger subjects usually met outdoors, a high luminance range can also be lowered by controlling the lighting ratio. In these and similar situations, one or more of the following methods may be used outdoors:

(a) If the sun is shining from a clear sky, move the subject into the shade, or wait for a cloud to cover the sun and provide shade. Bear in mind that if the light illuminating a subject is coming from a blue sky, the film may reproduce the subject with a blue cast. Such a cast can be prevented by using the appropriate colour filter over the camera lens.

(b) If possible, carry out photography when the blue sky is covered by a thin cloud layer. This will also minimize the possibility of obtaining an objectionable blue cast due to the effect of light from the blue sky.

(c) Use fill-in flash to illuminate the shadow areas. The flash must have a similar colour quality to that of the daylight.

(d) If the subject is small enough, use a reflector made from stiff white card or colourless polished metal, to increase shadow illumination.

(e) Postpone photography until a different time of day when the lighting is more frontal and any disturbing shadows less evident.

11.96   *Lowering the subject reflectance range.* If it is not convenient to lower the lighting ratio, or if adjusting the lighting ratio has not produced a sufficient reduction in subject contrast, the subject reflection range can be lowered to obtain the required result. For example, with subjects such as silverware, glass or glazed ceramics, where there are many specular reflections, one or more of the following methods can often be used to lower the subject reflectance range:

(a) For specularly reflecting subjects such as metal trophies and cups in the studio, reduce specular reflection effects by building a tent of white translucent material around the object, leaving a small hole for the camera lens.

(b) Spray the subject with an anti-flare matt preparation. This is commercially available in aerosol cans and the spray application can be easily removed after photography.

(c) For large non-metallic subjects, a polarizing filter may be fitted over the camera lens and rotated until unwanted specular reflections are reduced. When photographing metallic objects in the studio, place 'crossed' polarizing filters over the lights as well as the camera lens. Note that a large increase in camera exposure will be required.

(d) Change the camera viewpoint so that troublesome highlights or shadows are no longer included in the picture area or are reduced in size.

11.97   *Lens flare effects in colour photography.* (see also paragraphs 7.5 to 7.7). We know that the general effect of camera lens flare is to reduce image contrast during exposure, so that the illuminance range received on the film in the camera is shorter than the externally measured subject luminance range. We also know that flare light from the lighter areas of the subject can spread into and affect the image shadows more than the highlights.

Because of this, the effects of camera lens flare become particularly significant in colour photography, when subjects contain large areas of high luminance. Common examples are the bright blue sky of a landscape scene, or a brightly lit coloured background in the studio. Owing to the light-scattering effect of camera lens flare, these large areas of colour may cause a coloured fogging effect over the picture area. The main subject may therefore be reproduced together with a disturbing colour cast. A similar effect of contrast reduction but with desaturation of the reproduced colour could be caused by a brightly lit white background. This flare effect from bright highlights is of course another reason for limiting the luminance range of subjects in colour photography.

Correct exposure for colour films

11.98   As we know (paragraphs 11.85 and 11.86), colour processing is in most cases invariable, so the major factor in obtaining excellent results lies in the control of exposure. The method used for practical exposure determination depends initially on what type of light-measuring equipment is available. At present these are, in the main, hand-held exposure meters used separately from the camera, and through-the-lens (TTL) exposure meters built into the camera. When used for measuring exposure, each has its advantages and disadvantages.

The exposure requirements and determination methods used for colour reversal films are somewhat different from those recommended for colour negative films, so let us now consider each in turn.

Exposure requirements for colour reversal films

11.99   The exposure latitude of colour reversal films is limited. This is due to the relatively steep gradient of the film characteristic curves and the fact that the resultant colour transparency is an end product in itself. Furthermore, after first development, each emulsion layer must be left with the right amount of undeveloped emulsion to produce the correct amount of dye in the final image. Therefore, when using colour reversal film, we must ensure that the colour quality of the exposing light is correct for the film, that the recommended subject luminance range is not exceeded, and that the important parts of the subject are recorded on the correct part of the characteristic curves. Correct exposure determination for colour reversal films is thus a fairly precise procedure.

11.100 *Judging a colour transparency for correct exposure.* If a colour reversal film is overexposed, the processed transparency will be too light overall. The effect of overexposure is most noticeable in the lighter parts of a transparency and shows as pale desaturated highlights, lacking in detail. On the other hand, an underexposed transparency will be too dark overall and there will be little or no shadow detail present. Of the two, a slightly darker transparency is always the more visually acceptable.

A correctly exposed colour transparency should contain sufficient dye in the lightest areas to reproduce important highlight detail, and there should also be visible detail in the deepest important shadow. The highlight areas are the most significant part of a transparency when it is viewed, so colour reversal films are more tolerant to slight underexposure than to slight overexposure.

Transparencies that are to be used as originals for photomechanical reproduction, or duplication, should in general be a little darker overall than slide transparencies that are to be projected. This is because it is important that the significant highlight detail is not lost when the transparency is reproduced. Large transparencies intended for display in illuminated boxes should also be made a little darker overall. Such transparencies can be

obtained by giving, say, half a stop less than the optimum exposure for slides intended for projection.

11.101 *Position of highlights and shadows on the characteristic curves.* Figure 11.20 shows the position of the lightest highlight and the darkest shadow of an average subject, on the characteristic curves of a typical colour reversal film. The lightest important coloured highlight should ideally be positioned at a density about 0.4 above D_{min} on the central part of the toe of the characteristic curves, so that sufficient highlight detail and contrast are recorded. A lower density of about 0.2 is just acceptable when it is necessary to use all the available useful exposure range in order to reproduce both important highlight and shadow detail of subjects having a fairly long luminance range. The correct placing of subject highlights on the central part of the toe region is particularly important when the subject contains strongly coloured highlight areas, because there must be sufficient dye present in the transparency to reproduce these strong colours.

The deepest shadow in which detail is required should be positioned at a point on the curves much lower than the maximum density that the film can produce. For the darkest important shadow, a

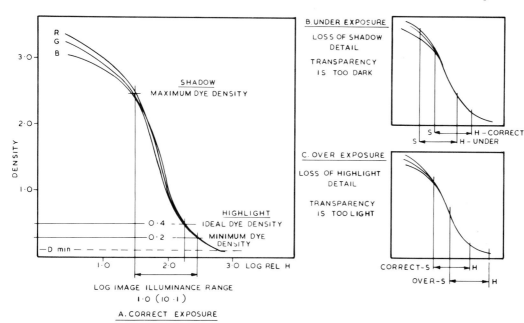

Fig. 11.20 Characteristic curves of a typical colour reversal film showing the positions of ideal and minimum acceptable highlight dye densities and the maximum density for full

satisfactory reproduction of shadow detail. S and H represent shadows and highlights. Diagrams B and C show the effects of under- and overexposure respectively.

density about 2.0 to 2.3 above the minimum (0.2) dye density is usually satisfactory (see also paragraph 11.41). Of the two densities, correct placing of the highlight density on the toe of the curve is most often the more important. These constraints mean that only a portion of the film characteristic curves can be properly used for practical colour photography. We can see from Figure 11.20 that the useful exposure range of a colour reversal film is only about 10:1 (1.0 log). Therefore, if an allowance for a camera lens flare factor of about 2 is taken as an average, the measured difference in luminance between the subject highlights and shadows must not exceed 20:1 (1.3 log). This is particularly important when detail at both extremes of the subject luminance range must be recorded. When a subject has a luminance range of more than 20:1 it is usual to accept a loss of some shadow detail in order to retain significant highlight detail. Ideally, the most visually satisfactory transparency reproduces detail in strongly coloured highlight areas at a density of about 0.4 above D_{min}. Figure 11.20 shows that, for a result with the best detail in both highlights and shadows, the subject luminance range should be reduced to less than 20:1. In this example, with a flare factor of 2, the image illuminance range would therefore be less than 10:1 (1.0 log), and with correct exposure it would be properly accommodated on the film characteristic curves. The lightest important highlight would be positioned on the central part of the toe region, and at the same time shadow detail would be retained.

Diagrams B and C in Figure 11.20 show that increasing or decreasing the camera exposure moves the whole exposure range along the log H axis. This means that, for a given subject luminance range, underexposure of a colour reversal film produces a loss of shadow detail whereas overexposure produces a loss of highlight detail.

11.102 *Measuring for exposure of colour reversal films.* We can see that the determination of correct exposure for colour reversal films is critical because of the need to position the subject shadows and, more importantly, the highlights, on specific parts of the characteristic curves. It is therefore necessary that an exposure-determination method incorporating the following factors be used for colour reversal films:

(a) The exposure must be based upon the subject's lightest highlight in which detail is required, because this will be the most significant part of the transparency when it is finally viewed. (b) A shadow reading must also be taken to check that a subject luminance range of 20:1 (or 4¼ light values on the exposure meter) is not exceeded.

Because of the above factors, the method of exposure determination normally used for black-and-white negative film is unsuitable for all reversal films. Exposure for conventional black-and-white negative film is based upon shadow reproduction, and such films also have a much greater exposure latitude. When using colour reversal films, their limited useful exposure range means that the exposure accuracy may have to be within a third of a lens stop to obtain the best results. There are several methods of determining the required exposure for colour reversal films; those most likely to produce accurate results are based upon a light value (LV) reading taken from a standard white card which simulates a subject highlight. Other methods of exposure determination that may be used for colour films are described in paragraph 11.114.

Whatever method is adopted, the best results can more easily be obtained if a through-the-lens (TTL) meter can be used. Such a meter measures light that falls on the film after it has passed through the camera lens system. Therefore many of the factors (e.g. lens flare) that can affect the actual exposure are automatically taken into account (see also paragraphs 6.42 and 11.115). When a separate (external) exposure meter is used, the effect of many of these factors has to be assessed by the photographer and taken into account before deciding what exposure should be given.

The white-card method with colour reversal films

11.103 Whichever exposure metering system is used, the photographic and sensitometric principles on which any successful exposure-determination method is based depend on particular light measurements of the subject or of its image. Correct exposure for both colour reversal and negative film depends on the proper interpretation and use of these measurements.

Because of the importance of obtaining correct exposure, we need to consider in some detail the practical exposure-determination methods used for both colour reversal and negative films. We shall be dealing with the determination of exposure for colour negative films later, but for the time being we can consider the exposure of colour reversal films using the so-called 'white-card' method.

Although the white-card exposure-determination method is widely used, and can produce a high degree of exposure accuracy, it is not suggested that you should necessarily adopt it for your normal colour photography. However, you should understand the principles of this method, as it gives a practical appreciation of the factors that need to be considered in the production of high-quality results in colour photography.

11.104 The exposure determination for colour reversal film should be based on a highlight exposure meter reading. However, the actual subject highlights can seldom be used, especially if they contain any strong colour, because the difference in colour response between the exposure meter and the colour film may give a misleading result. In addition, any specularly reflecting highlights such as water and polished surfaces must be avoided when taking exposure meter readings. Therefore a white card is used as a substitute subject highlight because it reflects all colours equally, and its matt surface gives no specular reflections. Provided that the card is properly positioned relative to the subject highlight area, so that it behaves like an actual subject highlight when exposure meter readings are taken, a high degree of exposure accuracy is possible. A white card suitable for this exposure-determination method can be made from any piece of stiff matt-white material cut to a size big enough to measure yet small enough to carry. Commercially made test cards suitable for this purpose are available and their use is recommended. Cards made by Kodak have a matt-white side, which may be used when exposing colour reversal films, and a neutral grey reverse side, which may be used when exposing colour negative films. The manufacture of these test cards is carefully controlled to produce neutral surfaces having a standard reflectance, with the white side of the card reflecting five times as much light as the grey side.

Let us now consider the practical application of the white-card exposure-determination method when using a typical exposure meter. Exposure meters that are used to measure reflected light are, of course, most often calibrated to indicate correct exposure when measuring the overall light reflected from a subject having an average tone distribution. However, the luminance level of the white card is about five times higher than that of the integrated light from an average subject. Therefore, when a white-card reading is made, the exposure indication is too low for correct exposure

of the subject and would give an underexposed result. To compensate for this, we need to give about five times more exposure than the white-card reading indicates. This action will position the highlights of a typical subject correctly on the toe of the film characteristic curves (see paragraph 11.101).

In addition to the white-card reading we need to check that the luminance range of the subject is suitable for exposure onto the exposure range of the film, so readings also have to be made of the important highlight and shadow areas. The white-card procedure is suitable for any type of hand-held or through-the-lens exposure meter that can be used to measure reflected light. However, because exposure meters differ in their construction, it is assumed in the following description that a Weston-type meter will be used. The procedure is as follows:

(a)   Take a reflected light reading of the lightest important highlight and the darkest important shadow in which detail is required in the transparency. Where possible, read neutral highlight and shadow areas, as differences between the colour response of the meter and film can be misleading. Avoid reading specular-reflection highlights.
(b)   Calculate and note the subject luminance range (see paragraph 11.91).
(c)   Take a reflected-light reading of the white card. Ensure that the card is positioned so that it receives lighting at the same angle and of the same luminance as the lighting on the subject highlights.
(d)   Find the white-card light-value reading on the meter dial, and position the arrow marker opposite this value.
(e)   Depending on the subject luminance range already found, rotate the meter calculator dial anti-clockwise to position the arrow between 2¼ and 3 light values lower. (Figure 11.22 shows this action.) This increases the indicated exposure by between 5 and 8 times and shows a light value from which correct exposure can be determined.

The exact amount of light-value lowering to obtain the required exposure increase depends on the particular subject luminance range and on an assessment of the subject characteristics. For example, if the subject has a low subject luminance range, say 5:1, a low exposure increase of 5× will be given. If the subject has a high luminance range, say 20:1, a higher exposure increase of 8× will be given. This 8× increase is made so that the subject shadows are recorded at the top of the straighter part of the film characteristic curves, and not above this, on the shoulder. Therefore when a subject has a fairly high luminance range that cannot be lowered, the whole useful part of the film characteristic curves must be utilized in order to include the shadow areas, but less than the ideal dye density will be produced in the highlights. The effects of increasing the indicated exposure over the range 5× to 8× is shown in Figure 11.21 and is a shift of 0.2 log, or the effect of a ¾-stop change in the exposure level.

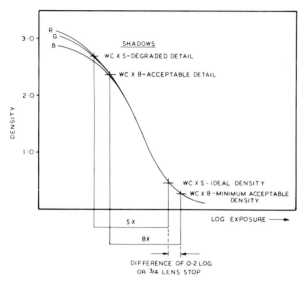

Fig. 11.21 The effect on the density produced in the highlight and shadow areas of a typical colour reversal film, when the indicated white-card exposure is multiplied by 5 and by 8. The full range 5× to 8× gives the effect of a ¾-stop increase in exposure level.

The amount by which the indicated exposure must be multiplied in order to obtain correct exposure depends on several factors, but as a guide the white-card light-value reading is reduced by amounts shown in Table 11.2. The range of 5 to 8 times exposure increase has been determined and established by practical tests. The table gives a 'rule of thumb' guide suitable for most subjects. Other factors may have to be considered before deciding what exposure to give, such as the following.

(a) If the subject has a fairly high contrast, but consists mainly of highlight areas, a low multiplication factor may be used to record maximum detail in these areas, even though there may be some loss of shadow detail.

(b) If the subject consists mainly of prominent shadows and middle-tones, with no important

Table 11.2 Recommended reductions in white-card light-value readings, when photographing subjects of low, medium and high luminance range on colour reversal film. Exposures based on these will position the shadows and highlights of each subject correctly on the film characteristic curves. Changing the exposure over the full range, 5× to 8×, gives the effect of a ¾-stop increase in exposure.

Low (around 5:1)	*Medium (around 10:1)*	*High (around 20:1)*
Reduce white-card reading by 2½ LV. Gives a 5× exposure increase.	Reduce white-card reading by 2½–2¾ LV. Gives a 6–7× exposure increase.	Reduce white-card reading by 3 LV. Gives an 8× exposure increase

highlight areas, a high multiplication factor will have to be used to record detail in the deepest shadow areas.

(c) If the subject luminance range exceeds 20:1 and cannot be lowered, the 8× exposure increase should still be given in order to obtain reasonably satisfactory highlight detail, and accepting that there will be an inevitable loss of shadow detail.

(d) A light 'high-key' effect or a dark, dramatic 'low-key' effect may be required. For a high-key effect a high multiplication factor is used, and for a low-key effect a low multiplication factor is used (see also paragraph 11.100).

11.105   *The white card method in practice.*   From this somewhat detailed description it might be thought that the white-card method of exposure determination is rather complicated and cumbersome to apply in practical colour photography. In practice, however, the measurement and calculation of exposure are as easy as in normal black-and-white photography. Correctly used, the white-card method of exposure determination gives a high percentage of correctly exposed colour transparencies from a wide variety of subjects. As an example, we can consider a typical practical situation.

Suppose that you have to take the wedding photograph shown in plan view in Figure 11.22, with the bride in her white dress and the groom in his dark suit. In order to record the subtle detail and gentle tone gradations in the bride's dress, and at the same time obtain a correct level of exposure for the skin tones and shadows of the scene, the exposure procedure would be:

(a) Take a meter reading of the lightest important highlight. Suppose this is the bride's white dress and gives an LV of 14.

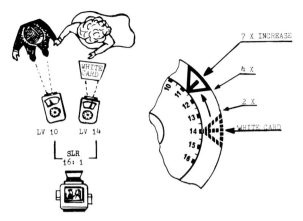

Fig. 11.22 Using the white-card method for colour reversal film. The white-card reading is LV 14 and the subject luminance range is 16:1. This is a medium-to-high subject luminance range, so the exposure indicated by LV 14 must be multiplied by 7 to obtain correct exposure. Move the arrow on the exposure meter calculator dial from LV 14 to LV 11¼, to give a 7× increase, then read the correct exposure off the dial.

(b)   Take a meter reading of the darkest important shadow. Suppose this is the groom's dark suit and gives an LV of 10.
(c)   Calculate the subject luminance range: LV 10 to 14 = 16:1.
(d)   Hold the white card near the bride's dress and take a meter reading. Suppose this indicates an LV of 14.
(e)   Assess the exposure multiplication required. The subject luminance range is 16:1, so the indicated exposure must be multiplied by 7 (see Table 11.2). This is most easily done by turning the meter calculator dial to a position 2¾ LV less than the indicated value.
(f)   Move the exposure meter arrow from LV 14 to LV 11¼ as shown in Figure 11.22, and read off the correct exposure.

In some situations the meter reading of the white card and that of the subject highlight areas may differ slightly, but in most cases this is unimportant. Some examples of situations where differences in these two readings are significant to the calculation of correct exposure are given in the next paragraph.

11.106   *Examples of exposure determination using the white-card method.*   The white-card method provides a well-founded basis for the determination of correct exposure for the majority of subjects you are likely to photograph using colour reversal film. With this method, the most visually significant highlight areas are properly positioned on the film characteristic curves and the subject luminance

range is accommodated. We can now consider the application of the white-card method to a few representative subjects, and some where the luminance range and difference between white-card and highlight readings are significant and must be incorporated into the determination of correct exposure. Table 11.3 lists these subjects and the associated meter readings, together with the white-card reading exposure factors that have been applied to obtain correct exposure. The figures have been determined as typical after practical tests. Figure 11.23 should be used in conjunction with Table 11.3.

Exposure requirements for colour negative films

11.107   Colour negative films have a greater exposure latitude than reversal films, because of their lower characteristic curve gradients, and also because compensation for slight variations in exposure can be made when a negative is printed. However, the allowable tolerance in exposure is less than that applicable to conventional general-purpose black-and-white negative films, and by comparison their useful exposure range is limited. When using a colour negative film we must ensure that the result will be suitable for the characteristics of the printing paper. This means that the recommended subject luminance range should not be exceeded, the colour quality of the exposing light must be suitable for the film, and the subject must be properly recorded on the correct part of the characteristic curves.

Colour negative films have more tolerance to slight overexposure than to slight underexposure, but correct exposure of course always produces the best colour negative for printing. When exposing rolls of colour negative film, the aim should be to ensure that all the resultant negatives have a similar general density. A roll of correctly exposed colour negatives is much easier to print than a roll containing a mixture of correct, slightly underexposed and slightly overexposed negatives.

11.108   *Judging a colour negative for correct exposure.*   Increasing the exposure increases the overall density of a colour negative; decreasing exposure decreases overall density. A correctly exposed colour negative should have a density range similar to that of a correctly exposed conventional black-and-white negative, and should contain sufficient dye in the lightest image areas to retain shadow detail and contrast.

1. Equipment in the studio
The low subject luminance range (SLR) presents no particular exposure complications. The exposure increase factor of 5× for a low SLR subject given in Table 11.2 is therefore used.

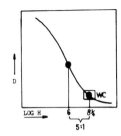

2. Studio portrait
The white-card reading is half an LV higher than the lightest skin tone. However, because the exposure is based on the white-card reading, the lightest skin tone is placed half an LV up the toe of the film characteristic curves. This results in satisfactory colour reproduction of the skin tones. A low exposure factor of 5× for a low-SLR subject is used.

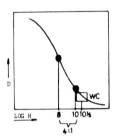

3. Structural exterior (thin cloud)
In daylight conditions when there is an overall thin layer of cloud, the SLR limit of 20:1 presents no particular exposure complications. The exposure increase factor of 8× for a high-SLR subject given in Table 11.2 is therefore used.

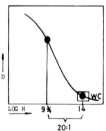

4. Structural exterior (sunny day)
When the sun is not obscured by clouds, the SLR can be very high (64:1 in this example). Increasing the indicated exposure 8× retains highlight detail. However, because of the high SLR, some of the shadow detail may be degraded or lost. This is because the shadows will be underexposed by 1¾ stops (the SLR difference between 20:1 and 64:1).

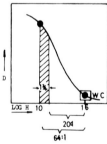

5. Distant landscape
In landscape photography the blue sky is often the most significant highlight. Typically a reading taken from the white card is about 1 LV lower than a blue-sky reading. So if a white-card reading is used as a basis for calculating exposure, the sky is recorded 1 stop overexposed and appears pale and desaturated. Take a meter reading of the sky and increase it 6× to determine the exposure. The low SLR of the rest of the subject usually ensures correct reproduction of all the other tones.

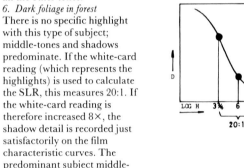

6. Dark foliage in forest
There is no specific highlight with this type of subject; middle-tones and shadows predominate. If the white-card reading (which represents the highlights) is used to calculate the SLR, this measures 20:1. If the white-card reading is therefore increased 8×, the shadow detail is recorded just satisfactorily on the film characteristic curves. The predominant subject middle-tones are then automatically recorded on the correct part of the curves.

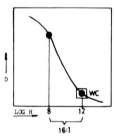

7. Relief-patterned ceramics in studio
Good reproduction of this subject's important highlight areas is required. So although the subject luminance range is medium-to-high, a low exposure factor of 5× is used, even though this may result in some degradation of shadow detail.

Positions of maximum and minimum significant subject tones.

Region where shadow detail will probably be degraded.

Position a white-card density would occupy if included in photograph.

Position of minimum subject tone, and position a white-card density would occupy if included in photograph.

8   12
Meter readings of shadows, highlights and/or white card.

16:1
Subject luminance range.

Fig. 11.23 Examples of exposure determination using the white-card method. The situations illustrated have been simplified for clarity; they do not necessarily show exactly what may happen in a particular situation. Only one characteristic curve has been shown in each; this depicts the average response of the three emulsion layers of a typical colour reversal film.

Table 11.3 Examples of exposure metering, using the white-card method to determine the correct exposure for some representative subjects.

Subject (see Figure 11.23)	Meter readings H	S	SLR	WC	Exposure factor
1. Piece of equipment in the studio	8¼	6	5:1	8¼	5×
2. Studio portrait	10	8	4:1	10½	5×
3. Structural exterior (thin cloud)	14	9¾	20:1	14	8×
4. Structural exterior (sunny day)	16	10	64:1	16	8×
5. Distant landscape	13	10	8:1	12	6×
6. Dark foliage in a forest	6	3¾	5:1	8	8×
7. Relief-patterned ceramics in a studio	12	8	16:1	12	5×

Correct exposure of a colour negative can be visually judged by viewing it through a green filter (e.g. a Kodak Wratten 61). The filtration minimizes the visual effect of the familiar pale orange masking and makes the colour negative appear something like a black-and-white negative. Using the green filter helps the viewer to determine whether adequate shadow detail and correct image contrast have been obtained. A better judgement of correct exposure and image contrast can be made by measuring specific areas of the negative on a colour densitometer, through the red filter. Kodak indicate that the image of their 18 per cent neutral grey test card (which has received the same lighting as the subject), should have a density of 0.65 to 0.85, and the highest density of a normally lit forehead should be about 1.00 to 1.30 for light skin, 0.70 to 1.00 for dark skin. Colour negatives with appropriate densities below these figures may not produce satisfactory prints because of the loss of shadow detail. However, higher densities resulting from about one stop more exposure may still produce satisfactory prints. The correct positioning of highlights and shadows on the characteristic curves of a colour negative film is not quite as critical as it is with a colour reversal film. This is because a negative film is not an end product in itself, and slight adjustments can if necessary be made when the negative image is printed.

11.109 *Measuring for exposure of colour negative films.* The black-and-white concept of exposing for the deepest shadow in which detail is required applies equally well to the exposure of colour negative films (see also paragraph 11.42). The exposure determination system should ensure that the deepest shadows are recorded on the bottom of the straight-line region of the film characteristic curves. The position of the highlights depends on

the image illuminance range and can be at any point on the curves as long as it is not above the upper limit of the straight-line region. Figure 11.24 shows this positioning.

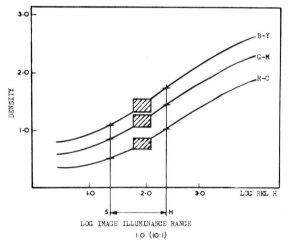

Fig. 11.24 Correct placing of subject shadow and highlight areas (S and H) on the characteristic curves of a typical colour negative film. The approximate position that a Kodak grey test card density would occupy is also shown. The vertical separation of the curves is caused by the pale orange integral dye masking, the effects of which are corrected during printing.

As correct exposure depends on the proper recording of the deepest significant shadow, it might be thought that an external exposure meter reading taken from the subject shadow area would provide a satisfactory basis from which correct exposure could be determined. This exposure should place the darkest important shadow near the bottom of the straight-line part of the characteristic curves. In practice, however, shadow luminances, when transferred by the optical system of the camera to become image illuminances, are often influenced by lens flare effects and light scatter inside the camera. An exposure-estimating system based on a subject shadow reading may therefore give an inaccurate result (see paragraphs 7.5 to 7.7). To avoid any such inaccuracies, the manufacturer's indicated film speed data is usually based on the assumption that correct exposure will occur when a neutral middle-tone of the subject is used as a basis for calculating exposure.

Exposure for colour negative films is often determined by taking a meter reading of the subject highlight and shadow areas and then basing exposure on the mid-point between them. Another method giving similar results utilizes a Kodak neutral grey test card as a key reference area. This method is described in more detail in paragraph 11.111. A neutral grey giving an 18 per cent reflectance is used for measurement because it represents an integration of the tones and colours of an average subject, and thus indicates a similar exposure to that which would be given by the highlight-shadow method. The grey-card method is simple to use and gives a high success rate with colour negative films. It offers the additional advantage that if the card is included in the image (outside the picture area), its reproduced density can be measured on a colour densitometer or analyser as an indication of correct exposure and colour balance. It also provides useful data that can be used to determine the printing exposure and filtration. With both methods, the subject luminance range must of course be checked to ensure that it is suitable for the task in hand (see paragraph 11.92).

As with colour reversal film, whatever method is used, the best results can more easily be obtained with a through-the-lens exposure meter. Such a meter offers several advantages, the main one being that light from the subject is measured after it has passed through the lens system, thus taking into account the effect of lens flare etc. With a separate hand-held exposure meter, the effect of such factors has to be estimated by the photographer. The use of TTL exposure meters for exposing colour films is considered in paragraph 11.115.

11.110 *Exposure latitude of colour negative film.* From Figure 11.24 it appears that colour negative films have a greater exposure latitude than colour reversal films; a slight increase in the illuminance range or exposure level still places the complete exposure range of the subject on the straight-line part of the characteristic curves. However, colour negatives have to be printed. Colour printing paper

has an even more restricted exposure range than colour reversal film, and can only properly accept negatives with a maximum density range of about 0.8 or 0.9.

Most photographic textbooks and manufacturer's literature recommend that a subject luminance range of 10:1 should not be exceeded when exposing colour negative films. This appears from Figure 11.24 to be a very conservative figure. However, the recommendation allows for subsequent printing of the negative onto the restricted exposure range of the printing paper. It also allows for the effects of some possible characteristic-curve displacement which may be caused by variations in camera exposure conditions. The effects of such a displacement can be neutralized during printing by adjusting the enlarger filtration (see paragraphs 11.67 to 11.70). By deliberately keeping the subject luminance range low, there is also an associated increase in exposure latitude. Kodak state that, provided the subject contrast is not excessive (presumably 10:1 or less), up to one stop underexposure and two stops overexposure may be given without loss of colour fidelity.

If the above restricted luminance range is used, some latitude in the colour quality of the light used to illuminate the subject is also permissible, in a difficult situation. This is because the enlarger filtration can be adjusted during printing to obtain the correct colour balance. On the other hand, if the recommended subject luminance range is exceeded, care must be taken to ensure that the colour quality of the exposing light is not too inappropriate for the film in use.

Figure 11.25 shows what would happen if a 'daylight' colour negative film were exposed to light having a lower colour temperature than daylight – say, approaching that of tungsten light. In these circumstances, the blue-sensitive layer of the film would respond less than the others, owing to the lower blue content of the exposing light, and this would be shown in the diagram as a lateral displacement (to the right) of the blue-sensitive emulsion characteristic curve. A subject having an image illuminance range of 10:1 (1.0 log) would still be recorded on the straight-line region of all three curves, and the effects of the curve displacement could therefore be corrected during printing. However, from the diagram, we can also see that with an image illuminance significantly greater than 10:1 the shadows would be positioned on the toe of the blue-sensitive emulsion curve and the highlights on the shoulder of the green- and red-sensitive emulsion curves (dashed lines in

Figure 11.25). Because of differences between the curve gradients and shapes in these areas, the resulting shadow and highlight colour distortions could not be corrected during printing. Thus when a subject luminance range much greater than 10:1 has to be accommodated there can be little latitude in the colour quality of the exposing light. The effects of incorrect colour balance during exposure are also described in paragraphs 11.29 and 11.54.

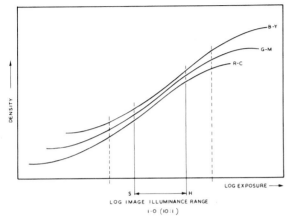

Fig. 11.25 Representative characteristic curves showing the general effect of exposing a 'daylight' colour negative film to light having a lower colour temperature than daylight. A subject presenting an image illuminance range of 10:1 (1.0 log) or less can still be recorded on the straight-line parts of the displaced characteristic curves and the effects of the displacement can be corrected by filtration adjustment during printing. An illuminance range much greater than 10:1 could fall on the toe of the blue-sensitive emulsion curve and on the shoulder of the green- and red-sensitive emulsion curves as shown by the dashed lines. The effects of this could not be corrected during printing because of the differences in curve shape and gradient in the shadows and highlights.

The main point to remember is that, although colour negative films have a greater tolerance to varying exposure conditions than colour reversal films, the resultant negatives still have to be printed. Therefore negatives that have been exposed at different exposure levels, to varying lighting conditions, or to subjects having a wide luminance range, may be difficult to print. It is much more convenient to ensure that the exposure conditions are satisfactory when taking the photographs than it is to attempt correction when printing the negatives. Remember that good prints can only be made from good negatives, so any necessary corrections should be carried out at the camera stage. Failure to do this will always produce problems in printing. At the camera exposing stage, the variables that can affect the

printing quality of a colour negative are measurable or assessable, and corrections can be easily applied. On the other hand, attempting a correction at the printing stage is a more critical procedure and may be ineffective.

The grey-card method with colour negative films

11.111 Exposure determination for colour negative films can be based on the meter reading of a neutral middle-tone area of the subject (see paragraph 11.109). However, it may be difficult to find a suitable neutral middle-tone on many subjects, so exposure is best determined by using a substitute middle-tone. The Kodak neutral grey test card is specially designed to provide such a substitute. The reflection of the matt-surfaced grey card (18 per cent of incident light) provides a standard, representing a subject neutral middle-tone. In addition, any problems of exposure inaccuracy due to camera lens flare effects, and possible differences in colour response between the exposure meter and film, are minimized. The grey card is suitable for use with any type of hand-held or through-the-lens exposure meter that measures reflected light. The procedure used to determine correct exposure for colour negative film is:

(a) Take a reflected-light reading of the lightest important highlight and the darkest important shadow in which detail is required in the final print. As far as possible, read neutral areas and avoid reading specular reflections.
(b) Calculate the subject luminance range (see paragraph 11.91) and check that it is satisfactory and does not exceed the recommended range (see paragraph 11.92).
(c) Take a reflected-light reading of the grey card. Ensure that it is held or positioned near the subject so that it receives the same overall lighting as the subject.
(d) For a typical situation, find the grey-card light-value reading, set the exposure meter dial to the light value indicated, and read off the required exposure.

If the subject has large highlight areas, decrease the exposure (by, say, half a stop); if it has large shadow areas, increase the exposure by a similar amount. Note that for colour negative films, exposure changes for variations in subject luminance range are unnecessary. This is because colour negative films have a relatively greater useful exposure range than colour reversal films, and also because the subject highlights and shadows do not have to be so precisely positioned on the film characteristic curves.

11.112 *Inclusion of grey-card and reference images in the negative or transparency.* An image of the grey card provides a useful reference area when a colour negative is printed. Because it represents an integration of the tones and colours of an average subject, the grey-card area on the negative can be measured using a colour densitometer or colour analyser, in order to establish the exposure and filtration required for printing. It can also be used as a check of exposure level and for a visual assessment of the correct colour balance of test prints. It is therefore recommended that a grey card be included in the image area, but outside the picture area, whenever colour negative film is used. Where this is not possible, an independent exposure should be made of the card on another frame of the same film batch under the same lighting conditions (see also paragraphs 11.65 and 11.72). A grey-card image also provides a useful reference area in colour transparencies that are to be used for making prints or duplicates.

A neutral-reflection grey scale and a set of colour patches are also useful for inclusion when critical colour reproduction is required, especially when copying coloured photographs, paintings or documents. These adjuncts serve as an indication of tone and colour reproduction throughout the complete range of densities. Changes in contrast and colour can then be easily seen by direct comparison of the original and final reproduction (see also paragraphs 11.81 and 11.82).

Using the white and grey cards with special subjects

11.113 From time to time it may be necessary to take colour photographs of some special subjects using reversal or negative colour film. For example, illuminated signs, television or oscilloscope displays, or a colour photograph may be required with the background reproduced as light or as dark as possible. The principles of the white and grey card exposure-determination methods can be applied when photographing these and similar types of subject. Table 11.4 outlines some methods of achieving correct exposure in such situations, when using either type of colour film.

Other methods of determining exposure for colour films

11.114 The methods of determining correct exposure that we have considered up to now are particularly recommended, and give accurate results for the majority of colour tasks when using either reversal or negative colour films. There are, however, other exposure-estimating methods that can produce equally satisfactory results. Most of these have been described in general in Chapter 6, but we can now consider their application to the exposure of colour films. Whatever method is used for estimating exposure, the first priority is that the subject luminance range and the colour quality of the exposing light must be suitable for the task, and for the film to be used.

(a) *Incident-light method.* An incident-light reading is an integrated measurement of the light incident

Table 11.4 Exposure-metering methods for some special subjects using white and grey cards.

Subject	Reading area used and exposure adjustment Colour reversal films	Colour negative films
1 Copying coloured artwork	White card + 2¼ stops	Grey card – as meter reading
2 Subject photographed against the prevailing light (back-lit):		
(a) For detail in the subject.	White card held near to subject + 2¼ stops.	Grey card held near to subject – as meter reading.
(b) For a silhouette effect	Read the background + 2¼ stops.	Read the background + 2 stops.
3 TV or oscilloscope display.	Lightest part of display + 2¼ stops.	Lightest part of display + 2 stops.
4 Coloured illuminated signs or lights at night, sunsets, stained glass windows, fireworks.	Light source + 2¼ stops.	Light source + 2 stops.
5 Photographs in a studio or indoors using lights:	White card + 2¼ stops.	Grey card – as meter reading.
(a) To obtain a dark background	Background reading must be a minimum of 4 LV less than white card reading.	Background reading must be a minimum of 3 LV less than grey card reading.
(b) To obtain a clear or white background.	Background reading must be a minimum of 1 LV more than white card reading.	Background reading must be a minimum of 3 LV more than grey card reading.

on the subject. The type of exposure meter used for this usually has a diffusing screen or plastic hemisphere positioned in front of the meter cell, and a reading is made with the meter pointed at the camera from the subject position. The incident-light diffuser is designed so that the exposure indicated records the highlights of an average subject on the correct part of the film characteristic curves; it gives an exposure indication similar to that given by a reflected-light measurement of a white-card substitute highlight, multiplied by about 8. The incident-light method of exposure determination is therefore often recommended for use with colour reversal films. As with the white-card method, the indicated exposure must be corrected, when necessary, to take into account the effect of different subject luminance ranges or overall light or dark subjects, etc. Several types of electronic flash exposure meter also use the incident method of exposure measurement.

(b) *Average overall reading method (general reading).* When using black-and-white negative film the most commonly used method of exposure determination is based on a general meter reading of the subject, from the camera position. The procedure is simple, and with certain reservations can also be used for colour negative films. The method gives an average overall measurement of all the light reaching the meter from the subject, so it is only suitable for subjects that have a reasonably average luminance distribution. An exposure based on a general reading of such a subject ensures that the subject luminance range is suitably positioned on the film characteristic curves. For subjects with a high or low average luminance, such as those with large light areas or large dark areas and back-lit subjects, the exposure indication is misleading and the photographer must assess the effect and make a correction.

(c) *Natural highlight or shadow method.* A carefully chosen subject highlight may be used as a basis for exposure determination when using colour reversal film, but misleading readings can be given if the measured highlight is strongly coloured or gives specular reflections. The darkest shadow in which detail is required may sometimes be used when exposing colour negative film, and this method is suitable for subjects containing important shadow areas. However, exposure variation can occur when shadows are used for assessing exposure, because of a possible difference in shadow illuminance between subject and camera image. This is due to the effects of camera lens flare, which will affect the illuminance and contrast of shadow areas

much more than the highlight areas (see paragraphs 7.5 to 7.7). In each situation, whether highlights or shadows are measured, an allowance (similar to that used with the white-card method) must be applied to the value found in order to obtain correct exposure. If a natural highlight is measured the indicated exposure has to be increased by an appropriate factor, and if a shadow is measured exposure has to be similarly decreased.

(d) *Exposure tables and calculators.* Colour film manufacturers often include an exposure guide in the data sheet supplied with their films or in their technical literature, in the form of a table or calculator. These are only a very approximate guide; accuracy in exposure depends on the photographer's assessment of the subject and its lighting conditions.

Through-the-lens exposure metering

11.115 The best basis for evaluating exposure is a measurement of the light reaching the film inside the camera. By this means, many of the factors that can affect exposure, such as camera lens flare, lens characteristics, filtration, and any lens extension, are automatically taken into account. A through-the-lens (TTL) meter measures the actual image the film will record and not the external subject luminances, and this leads to greater accuracy in exposure determination. Many camera TTL metering systems are sophisticated devices that can monitor the internal camera image and may also provide a close match between the colour response of the meter and that of the camera film. Some can be used to measure and control the exposure duration of a dedicated flash unit.

A typical modern camera fitted with a TTL meter, if properly used, will give an accurate indication of exposure, and the exposure details (*f*-stop and shutter speed) may be automatically or manually set on the camera. Actual exposure may be given directly by the automatic setting, or in some instances a manual override may be used so that either exposure duration or aperture can be controlled by the decision of the photographer. With the advent of microprocessors, all types of exposure metering and monitoring devices are becoming more versatile, accurate and simple to use.

TTL meters may be designed to measure either the average illuminance of the subject image, or to give an emphasis to the central area (centre-weighted), or main part of the subject. Some meters can be used to measure a selected small area; this facility is particularly useful for measuring a white or grey card, or the key tone areas of the subject as applicable. By following the maker's instructions and applying your sensitometric knowledge, TTL meters can be used for determining the correct exposure for both reversal and negative colour films in almost any photographic situation.

In general, the measurements made by using a TTL system are more precise than those made by a separate exposure meter. However, as with external metering systems, the need to base the exposure of colour films on particular key tone areas of the subject still applies. With a TTL system being an integral part of the camera, the measurement of such key tone areas may present some practical difficulties. However, most of these problems can be minimized for both reversal and negative colour films by basing exposure on a grey-card reading. The card should be positioned correctly, so that its image covers the relevant measuring area of the TTL meter.

Depending on the meter calibration and the mode of measuring used (average luminance, centre-weighted, small area, or whatever), the indicated exposure may need to be adjusted by the photographer to take into account the effect of different subject luminance ranges, and subjects with large highlight or shadow areas (see also paragraphs 6.42 to 6.46).

Factors influencing colour exposure accuracy

11.116 All the exposure-determination systems we have considered will give acceptable results for most types of subject, provided that the exposure meter is calibrated and used as recommended by the meter or camera manufacturer. Of course, no method can provide an infallible answer to the problem of obtaining precisely correct exposure when using colour materials. All exposure-determination methods require an application of sensitometric knowledge to properly assess the effects of many of the variables involved. Thus the actual method of determining exposure, while important, matters less than the photographer's proficiency in using it. Apart from the basic need to use a type of film that suits the colour quality of the exposing light, the following factors can all affect accuracy in exposure and in exposure determination:

(a) Manufacturing variations between batches of film, including indicated and actual film speeds.

(b) Film age and storage conditions before and after exposure.
(c) Exposure meter calibration, colour sensitivity and correct usage.
(d) A difference in light level which may occur (particularly outdoors) between measuring and giving the exposure on the camera.
(e) The light transmittance of the camera lens and any filters used.
(f) Accuracy of camera shutter speeds.
(g) The effective lens aperture and changes caused by lens extension in close-up photography.
(h) Exposure duration effects (reciprocity failure).
(i) Processing variations.
(j) The final viewing conditions and the personal judgement or requirements of the viewer.

Because of these and other variables, the only certain method of obtaining correct exposure when critical colour reproduction is required, is to make a series of exposures at different camera settings. To achieve this the exposure is carefully determined in the normal way, one frame of the film is exposed, and then three or more other frames are shot at, say, half-stop intervals around this, thus bracketing the estimated exposure. When making a series of bracketing exposures, colour reversal films should be exposed to a majority of decreasing exposure levels (e.g. one more than, and two less than the estimated exposure) in order to ensure adequate highlight detail. On the other hand, colour negative films should be exposed to a majority of increasing exposure levels to ensure adequate shadow detail.

When carrying out photography on location, or when unfamiliar light sources are likely to be encountered, a practical exposure test under the actual working conditions is advised if time allows. To minimize the possible effects of some of the listed variables, the test should be carried out at a fixed shutter speed and using fresh film of the same batch number for both test and task.

11.117 The probable effects on exposure of the majority of factors listed in paragraph 11.116 are self-evident and have been considered previously. However, we need to consider further the effect of changes in the exposure level, reciprocity failure, latent-image regression and varying the effective film speed. Because they influence the colour produced, these effects are particularly evident when a final colour reproduction is viewed.

11.118 *Effects of changing the exposure level.* A variation in the exposure level changes the reproduced colour saturation of a colour transparency or negative and also affects the colour balance. Increasing the exposure level of colour reversal film reduces the overall colour saturation in the transparency. Prints made from colour negatives that have received increased exposure may have a reduced colour saturation in the highlight areas. In this respect, a 'correct exposure level' depends very much upon the intended use of the photograph, the final viewing conditions, and the personal preference of the viewer.

If, in sensitometric terms, the positioning of the imaged subject colours on the characteristic curves of a film is not correct, the overall colour balance is also upset. For example, if a series of different exposures are made on colour reversal film, the colour rendering of a grass lawn changes significantly as successive frames are projected or viewed side by side. This is because, to reproduce the green of the grass satisfactorily, the image must be positioned on the appropriate part of the film characteristic curves in order to produce the correct amount of dye. The personal judgement of the viewer may also be affected by areas of high or low colour saturation, which tend to distract attention from the main subject.

This local rendering of increased or decreased saturation of subject colours can sometimes be usefully employed. A common situation is when there is a strongly coloured background object that could upset the composition of a photograph. The reproduction of this strong colour can be diluted on the photograph by over-lighting the particular area of the subject. Similarly, where a strong colour is to be recorded vividly (such as a brightly coloured studio background) the lighting intensity for that particular area should be less than that used for the subject (typically about one light value difference on an exposure meter). Table 11.4 gives exposure recommendations for similar situations.

11.119 *Effects of reciprocity failure.* The exposure of photographic materials occasionally involves exposure durations longer or shorter than those recommended by the manufacturer. Such exposure duration may produce the effects of reciprocity failure – a loss of speed, a consequent change in density, and a change in contrast. These effects may often be ignored in ordinary photographic practice when using black-and-white materials. But colour films and papers are less tolerant of speed and contrast changes, which may be different in each of their several emulsion layers.

The significant results of reciprocity failure in colour materials are:

(a) A loss of overall speed, which causes a change in overall density.
(b) Variation in speed loss between individual emulsion layers, which causes a change in colour balance.
(c) A possible change in individual emulsion contrasts, causing colour casts that differ between highlight and shadow areas.

When a very long or a very short exposure is made, one or more of the emulsion layers tends to be more affected by reciprocity failure than the others. For instance, if the blue-sensitive emulsion layer of a colour reversal film is the most affected by speed loss, the processed transparency shows too much dye density in that layer (underexposure) and this produces a yellow cast. With gross reciprocity failure there can also be an associated change in contrast, as shown by a change in slope of the characteristic curve. The colour cast may then be visually different at each end of the tonal range. This effect is called 'crossed curves' or 'colour mismatch'. Similar reciprocity failure effects can occur in a colour negative–positive system, and may happen to both the negative film and the printing paper. The effects of reciprocity failure on a colour reversal film are illustrated in Figure 11.26. (See also Chapter 8 and paragraph 11.31.)

The manufacturers of colour materials aim to balance the characteristics of the individual emulsion layers of their products so that they give a satisfactory response under the average conditions of exposure for which the material is designed. In situations where reciprocity failure may occur, the subject lighting level and/or the lens aperture should be adjusted so that the exposure duration is

Table 11.5 Exposure duration recommendations for avoiding reciprocity failure in typical colour materials. If durations are kept within the given ranges there should be little or no visual effect on the finished result.

Colour material	Recommended exposure duration
Daylight reversal film	$1/10$–$1/1000$ second
Tungsten reversal film: Slow	1–$1/100$ second
Fast	$1/10$–$1/1000$ second
Daylight negative film	$1/10$–$1/10\,000$ second
Tungsten negative film	10–$1/50$ second
Colour printing paper and print film	30–5 seconds
Duplicating film	5–$1/100$ second
Internegative film	15–$1/10$ second

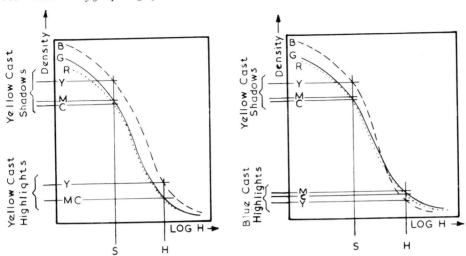

Fig. 11.26 Effect of reciprocity failure on the characteristic curves of a colour reversal film. Left: minor reciprocity failure causes curve displacement and thus a colour cast. Right: gross reciprocity failure shows as crossed curves, indicating a different colour cast at each end of the tonal range (speed loss and contrast change). B, G and R refer to the original sensitivities of the emulsion layers, and Y, M and C to the dyes in the layers after processing.

within a recommended range. Table 11.5 gives typical exposure durations which can be used to avoid or minimize the effects of reciprocity failure. For more specific information concerning the reciprocity characteristics of a particular material, the manufacturer's data should be consulted.

Exposures outside the recommended duration limits may still give satisfactory results if the appropriate colour-compensating filtration is used to correct the effect of speed differences in the emulsion layers. With an already affected negative, some compensation can be made when the negative is printed. Film manufacturer's exposure and filtration recommendations will minimize the effects of reciprocity failure in their colour materials. However, for critical work, a practical test using the particular batch of material to be used for a task is advisable. If exposure durations outside the recommended limits are indicated, either the lens aperture or the lighting level, or both, must be changed to compensate for the loss of overall speed and the effect of any filtration. To obtain correct exposure in these circumstances, the exposure duration should only be adjusted if the change shifts the duration nearer to the acceptable range.

When colour negatives are printed, small amounts of characteristic curve displacement caused by reciprocity failure can be corrected by changing the printing filtration. However, the effects of gross reciprocity failure that has caused crossed characteristic curves cannot be properly corrected. Although not visibly different from a normal negative, such a colour negative may prove impossible to print satisfactorily (see also paragraph 11.31).

11.120   *Effects of latent-image regression.* After exposure and before processing, the latent-image-keeping properties of colour materials are more critical than those of conventional black-and-white materials. The general effect of latent-image regression is a slight fading of the recorded latent images with time. With colour materials, this regressive effect may be different in each emulsion layer. Therefore the recorded response to light of the individual emulsion layers changes if a significant time is allowed to elapse between exposure and processing. This causes minor visible changes in overall density, contrast, and colour balance.

To minimize the effects of latent-image regression when using colour materials, the time interval between exposure and processing should be kept reasonably short (see paragraphs 6.5 and 6.6). In general, the change in all colour materials is most significant within the first hour and up to four hours after exposure. After this time, any change is significantly less. The changes are increased by high temperature and a high relative humidity, so the general rule is: 'in camera or out, keep films cool and dry, and process as soon as possible'. If correct colour reproduction is critical, and films cannot be processed without delay, they should not be kept longer than twenty-four hours after exposure before they are processed. If this is unavoidable, they must be stored in a freezer, if possible at −18°C (0°F) or lower. If the relative humidity is high, the film must be first dried with a desiccant and then sealed in a moistureproof wrapping, before refrigeration. When colour materials are removed from the freezer they must be allowed to warm up to the ambient temperature before processing (see also paragraph 6.5).

Non-professional colour films may if necessary be considered an exception to the above recommendations. The emulsions of these films are adjusted by the manufacturer so that they can be stored at an average room temperature, and will achieve a satisfactory performance after a typical delay has occurred between exposure and processing. Nevertheless the consistency of batches of such film will be improved if they are treated in the same way as professional films.

Colour printing paper must be used so that the interval between exposure and processing is as consistent as possible. Most of the latent-image changes in colour paper occur in the first two hours after exposure. After that time, with some papers, a slight colour cast and a half-stop loss of emulsion speed may occur. Subsequently there may be little change for three days or so, but after this a slow drift to a more visible colour cast may occur. The effects of latent-image regression are most noticeable when several colour prints made from the same negative, and exposed together, are processed after various time intervals. Therefore, after exposing a quantity of prints over a period of time, batch processing is best delayed for an hour or so to allow all the exposed latent images to reach a similar stage of regression.

The same effects may be evident when a delay of several days occurs between individual exposures made at the start and end of a roll of colour transparencies or negatives. This is known as the Christmas tree effect, familiar in processing laboratories, since amateur films may contain pictures of last year's Christmas tree, this year's holidays, and this year's Christmas tree on the same roll of film.

11.121 *Adjusting speed of colour film.* (See also paragraph 11.46.) To obtain the highest-quality results, all colour materials should be exposed and processed according to the manufacturer's instructions. However, if circumstances require it, most colour reversal films can be exposed at higher or lower speed values than that indicated on the film

container, provided that some loss of colour quality is acceptable. This is achieved by modifying the processing conditions. Such treatment is *not* usually suitable for colour negative films, which in any case have a greater exposure latitude than colour reversal films.

The successful rerating of film speed is achieved by increasing or decreasing the first development time of the reversal process. A change in development time increases or decreases the density of the black silver negative image, and thus ultimately affects the dye density of the positive colour transparency. If the film speed is uprated, thus allowing a decrease in exposure, and first development time is increased by the correct amount (less exposure but more development), the processed transparency will have a satisfactory range of dye densities.

When uprating is necessary, select the fastest available colour reversal film rather than try to uprate the speed of a slower film. All the frames on a roll of film must be exposed at the uprated value.

Manufacturers supply particular information on modified processing techniques for their films, when indicated speeds have been uprated or downrated. Typical compensation times for colour reversal films are as follows. If the indicated film speed is uprated by one stop (for example, ISO 200/24° to ISO 400/27°), the first development time is increased by 30 per cent. If the film is downrated by one stop, the first development is decreased by 30 per cent. Some colour processing laboratories offer special processing services for the treatment of colour reversal materials that have received other than normal exposure. If this service is to be used, the films must be clearly labelled as requiring modified processing and must have the ISO, ASA or DIN speed actually used marked on the container.

11.122 *Disadvantages of uprating and downrating colour films.* The main disadvantage of uprating the speed of colour reversal film by increasing the first development time is the consequent loss of colour quality. The most visually disturbing change, as uprating is increased, is that a lower than normal maximum density is produced. This is because the extra development reduces the amount of emulsion grains available for coupling during colour development. Associated effects are undesirable changes in contrast and colour balance. The downrating technique also causes a change in colour balance and contrast, and shows particularly as veiled highlight areas. Of the two, modest uprating produces less visible loss of quality in the colour transparency.

If an attempt is made to uprate colour negative film by extending colour development time, there will be an increase in overall contrast and also changes in the contrast of individual emulsion layers. When such a negative is printed, the increased negative density range may make it impossible to obtain both highlight and shadow detail in the print, even if dodging is attempted (see paragraph 11.87). Furthermore, the crossed characteristic curves caused by contrast changes in individual emulsion layers may produce uncorrectable colour casts when the negative is printed. These casts may show as one colour in the highlight areas and another colour in the shadows. For these reasons the conventional uprating of colour negative films is not recommended.

11.123   *Colour developer additives.* (See also paragraph 11.46.) The undesirable side-effects of uprating both reversal and negative colour films by prolonging development time can be minimized by using special contrast-reducing developer additives. These additives allow increased development time to be given with little detrimental effect to image quality. The additives work by retarding the contrast-increasing action of more than normal development. Thus, when extended development is given, only the normal contrast is reached and at the same time film speed is increased.

When colour reversal films are to be uprated, the additive is mixed with the first developer and extra development time is given to gain an effective speed increase. The effect of the additive counteracts the maximum density loss that would normally occur with this treatment. The uprating of colour negative films calls for a different developer additive. This is mixed with the colour developer and an increased development time is given. An increase in effective film speed results, but with normal negative contrast.

Although the uprating or downrating of colour film speeds will not produce the best results, it is well worth carrying out some sensitometric tests and visual comparisons with and without developer additives to determine just how far your colour films can be 'pushed' should the need arise (see also paragraphs 11.79 to 11.82).

11.124   *Effect of viewing conditions.* The final viewing conditions and intended use can have a profound effect on the apparent quality of reproduction in both transparencies and prints. Strictly speaking, colour prints should be viewed under lighting of standard colour quality and intensity (see paragraphs 7.34 and 11.80); the optimum colour fidelity and tonal range of a print can then be seen. In practice, the majority of colour prints are viewed under very different conditions. Therefore the quality of a print can only be properly verified when the viewing conditions are similar to those that will be used for exhibiting the print. Similarly, the overall density and colour quality of a colour transparency must suit the final viewing conditions. For example, each slide projection system (back-projection and front-projection) has a different light output, and the reflecting quality of projection screens varies. For a precise effect, slides should therefore be made with a density that is correct for each particular projection system, but as this is usually impracticable some sort of compromise is necessary. Compared with slides that are made for normal projection, transparencies intended for illuminated display are usually made somewhat denser overall, because of the high level of the illuminance. Transparencies intended for colour printing or photomechanical reproduction, or to be duplicated, must also be made slightly darker than normal (by giving slightly less exposure), in order to fully retain highlight detail.

Summary of key facts

11.125   From the foregoing descriptions we can extract several key facts that need to be borne in mind when using colour materials. If you follow these recommendations they, together with your sensitometric knowledge, will help you to obtain consistently high-quality results when exposing colour materials.

(a)   *Colour balance.* Ensure that the colour quality of the exposing light is suitable for the type of film used (daylight or tungsten).
(b)   *Subject contrast.* Keep the subject contrast low. Aim for a maximum subject luminance range of 20:1 for reversal colour films, and 10:1 for negative colour films. Arrange for a lighting ratio of approximately 3:1. Use colour contrast rather than great differences in luminance between subject highlight and shadow areas.
(c)   *Exposure.* Correct exposure determination is most important and relies upon intelligent assessment of the subject. Use a reliable and calibrated exposure meter. For *reversal* colour films use the white-card (highlight) method together with a check of the subject luminance range. For *negative*

colour films use the grey-card (middle-tone) method together with a check of the subject luminance range. Other systems of exposure determination are also suitable, provided that the principles of the white- or grey-card method are applied. For critical situations and subjects where exposure accuracy is very important, make a series of bracketed exposures at half-stop intervals: for *reversal* colour film a series of mostly *decreasing* exposures; for *negative* colour film a series of mostly *increasing* exposures.

(d) *Exposure level.* The exposure level affects overall density, colour saturation and colour balance. The correct exposure level for transparencies and prints is decided by the final viewing conditions and intended use.

(e) *Reciprocity failure.* The duration of the exposure may affect the colour balance and film speed of colour materials. The approximate recommended exposure times to minimize the effects of reciprocity failure when using camera films are typically:

Reversal films, daylight: $1/10-1/1000$ second
Reversal films, tungsten: $1/10-1/500$ second
Negative films, daylight: $1/10-1/10000$ second
Negative films, tungsten: $10-1/50$ second

Exposure times outside these durations are permissible provided that the effective film speed is adjusted and that filters (as recommended by the film manufacturer) are used over the camera lens for exceptionally long or short exposure times. Colour printing paper should be exposed within the range $30-5$ seconds.

(f) *Latent-image regression.* Latent-image regression affects the speed and colour balance of all colour materials. Therefore the time allowed to elapse between exposure and processing should be fairly short. Where this is unavoidable, the materials should be stored in a moistureproof container at $-18°C$ ($0°F$) to preserve the quality of the latent images. The basic rule is: in camera or out, keep films cool and dry, and process as soon as possible.

(g) *Film speed adjustments.* The effective speed of colour reversal films can be uprated or downrated by modifying the first development time. This action causes some loss of colour quality. Uprating reversal films generally produces a less visually disturbing side-effect than downrating. The technique should not be used for colour negative films.

(h) *Grey-card reference area.* Inclusion of a grey card in the photograph will provide a reference area for checking exposure level and colour balance.

12

Modulation transfer function

12.1 The basic function of sensitometry and tone reproduction is to enable a measurable comparison to be made between the input and the output of a photographic system and to evaluate what happens in between, so that the complete process can be controlled and modified as required. The overall comparison is between subject contrast and image contrast.

The sensitometric system is satisfactory for the majority of photographic applications, where the characteristic curve accurately describes the con-trast relationship between density and log exposure. However, the contrast shown by a characteristic curve – or more clearly by its derivative, the gradient/log exposure curve – applies only to the reproduction of fairly large images. Within areas of the negative less than about 0.5 mm, contrast between adjacent small images is often less than shown on the characteristic curve, and in general continues to decrease as images get smaller, mainly because of light scatter in the emulsion during exposure (see paragraphs 2.101 to 2.110).

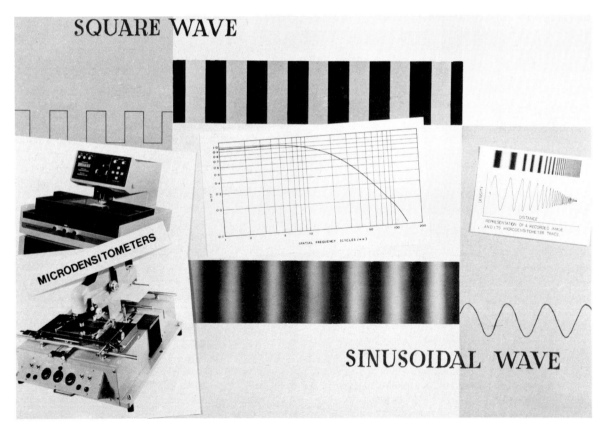

The effect of light scatter within a film emulsion during exposure on the reproduction of image detail, from large to small, can be shown by a modulation transfer function curve.

Such curves are derived from a recording on the film of the variable spacing of a special test object, and its analysis by microdensitometry.

This knowledge is probably sufficient for the practical photographer, knowing that sensitometric curves can still be used as a guide to the contrast of fine detail, but that (with full, active development, which will minimize adjacency effects) contrast may be somewhat lower than indicated on the curve. Figure 2.36 shows the general effect on contrast of close-spaced fine-detail images, but such low-gradient lines can only depict the contrast for one particular size of detail. There is often therefore a need to indicate the contrast of the image relative to that of the subject, for all sizes of image. This decline in image contrast with decreasing image size, caused by a film (or a lens, or any stage in the photographic process) can be investigated and shown as a curve representing the modulation transfer function (usually abbreviated to MTF). MTF curves are often given, for instance, in manufacturers' literature, so we should have an understanding of their meaning and value. The following paragraphs are an introduction to the concept of modulation transfer, sufficient for a basic understanding. If you want to find out more about the subject, there are several books available that explain MTF and the evaluation of photographic imagery in more detail (see paragraph 12.12 and Appendix G).

The concept of modulation transfer

12.2   The concept of modulation transfer is convenient for use in photography because the same method is used for evaluating other communication systems, such as radio and television, and in electronics (see Appendix E). Photography is also a communication system, and like the others it can be evaluated by comparing the output (image density range) with the input (subject log luminance range). The MTF describes the relation of output to input modulation, for example the change in image contrast as the images of fine detail become smaller. It thus gives more information than a simple resolving power value (see paragraph 2.92). Modulation is used as a particular way of expressing image contrast so that the values found can be given as numbers between 0 and 1.0. For example, in terms of maximum and minimum exposure given by each pattern of an MTF test object image, modulation can be expressed by the formula:

$$\text{Modulation} = \frac{\text{Max. exposure} - \text{Min. exposure}}{\text{Max. exposure} + \text{Min. exposure}}$$

or, in terms of the intensity of the image:

$$M = \frac{I_{\max} - I_{\min}}{I_{\max} + I_{\min}}$$

Modulation can only have values between 0 and 1.0.

Production of MTF curves

12.3   An MTF curve can be derived from the results of recording, on the photographic material, an image of a test object such as a chart comprising a set of grid patterns of a range of line frequencies. Alternatively, images may be prepared by contact printing a knife edge (see paragraph 2.108). A scanning microdensitometer is used to measure the processed images, and in each case futher analysis is carried out to obtain the MTF curve.

12.4   A scanning microdensitometer is an instrument that uses the optical system of a microscope to both illuminate and measure extremely small areas of the film under test. It is similar in principle to a transmission densitometer but uses a very small aperture to scan the image. With an automatic recording microdensitometer, the sample of film is moved slowly across the detector head and a recording device produces a trace on paper of the density variations found in small areas (see also Figure 2.35 B). Several types of microdensitometer are made by the Joyce Loebl Company which also makes the Type 2L sensitometer (see paragraph 2.16).

12.5   *MTF test object.*   A typical test object used for the determination of MTFs is a bar chart with sinusoidally varying transmittance over a range of spatial frequencies. Other test objects that may be used are similar charts but with a 'square-wave' variation of transmittance; see the photograph on page 192.

In a typical sinusoidal test object:

(a)   The transmittance of its image varies in a wavelike (sinusoidal) manner, going from a low value, gradually increasing to high and then gradually decreasing back to low.

(b)   The number of times each cycle (or pattern) is repeated in a certain distance is varied. For example, as the spacing of patterns becomes closer, so spatial frequency is increased.

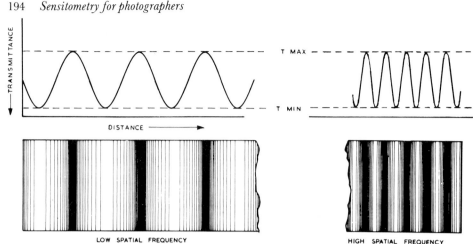

Fig. 12.1 A representation of two of the various sinusoidal transmittance variations of an MTF test object. The test object provides illuminances that vary spatially in a sinusoidal manner, and these are recorded on the material under test at a greatly reduced scale.

An image of the sinusoidal test object is recorded on the photographic material under test at reduced magnification, so that the spatial frequencies in the image range from, say, one cycle (or line) per millimetre to 200 cycles (or lines) per millimetre. Such a test object can best be visualized by means of a schematic diagram (Figure 12.1).

A sinusoidal test object may seem complex in its form, but in fact it is the simplest and best type to use. This is because, unlike other patterns (such as a square-wave pattern of sharp-edged bars with lighter spaces between), it tends to keep its basic form when transferred through a photographic system. It thus produces an image that is also sinusoidal, and this enables the results to be more easily measured and the necessary calculations made.

12.6 *Measuring and plotting for MTF.* After exposure to the test object and controlled development to a known gamma, the modulation of the image by the film is found by using the automatic microdensitometer to traverse the developed image. The trace produced shows the reduction in contrast as

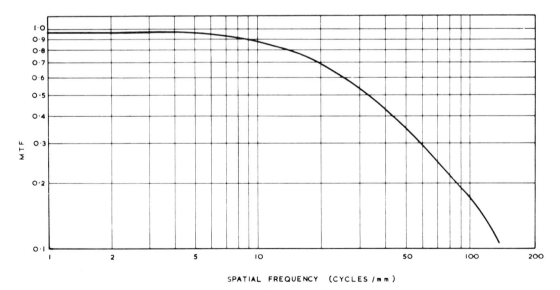

Fig. 12.2 The MTF curve for a typical medium-speed film. The curve shows that the contrast of images in the film decreases as the spacing between them becomes smaller. Such MTF curves are essentially normalized; this means that the modulation transfer for zero frequency is taken as being 1.0.

the spatial frequency of the images increase; so the effective modulation of the image in the film emulsion for a range of spatial frequencies can be calculated.

It is useful to know that, provided low-contrast images are used, giving a density difference in the developed image of 0.7 or less, then that difference closely approximates the modulation of the image.

12.7 *The modulation transfer function curve.* (Figure 12.2.) The MTF curve is constructed from a plot of the comparison between the output and the input modulations (output divided by input), as a function of the spatial frequency. Values can be expressed as fractions between 0 and 1.0, or as a percentage. For example, for 100 per cent (or 1.0) modulation transfer over a range of spatial frequencies, the curve would plot as a horizontal straight line. The graph is often drawn using logarithmic scales, which make it easier to concentrate attention on the important low frequencies.

On some film MTF curves, a modulation greater than unity (more than 100 per cent) may be found at low frequencies. This is due to adjacency effects during development, which cause image edge enhancement (see paragraph 2.103). Photographic MTF curves, which include the effects of processing and adjacency effects, are therefore different from optical MTF curves, which show only the effects of light scatter in the emulsion layer during exposure. The true optical performance of the emulsion is most closely approximated when development effects are minimized by using low-contrast exposures and active development conditions.

12.8 *Published MTF curves.* Strictly speaking, the MTF concept can only be applied to a processed film that has a linear response, so that the output to be measured has a linear relationship to the input exposure variation. This can be obtained by plotting back through the characteristic curve of the test film, so that the measured densities of the film sample can be interpreted in terms of the effective exposure received by the film. However, for many practical purposes, the MTF can be measured by using low-contrast exposures made at the lower useful parts of the film characteristic curve. In fact, this is the major part that is used in practice. Non-linearities are minimized by such procedures, and the MTF curves produced may be accepted as adequately describing the response of the film under the specified conditions of exposure and processing.

Published MTF values and curves, as given for example in manufacturers' literature, generally include the development adjacency effects. This is because such 'photographic' modulation transfer functions can best be related to practical photographic needs, which involve both exposure and development.

Modulation transfer and contrast variation

12.9 The characteristic curve of an emulsion (or of its derivative, a gradient/log exposure graph) shows that different levels of exposure produce different grades of contrast. Therefore the exposure level used will affect the modulation of the developed image. Because the MTF curve shows the modulation of the optical image in the emulsion at any spatial fequency, as a fraction of that of the optical image falling on the emulsion, the MTF is independent of the contrast of the developed image in the absence of adjacency effects. It is also very largely, and in principle wholly, independent of exposure level.

In direct photographic terms, the reduction in contrast ($\Delta D/\Delta \log H$) with increased spatial frequency, as it relates to different exposure levels, can be illustrated by a three-dimensional presentation (Figure 12.3). The three interrelated variables

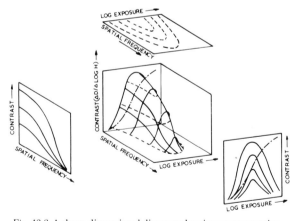

Fig. 12.3 A three-dimensional diagram showing representative emulsion response curves and the relationship between contrast, spatial frequency and log exposure. The conventional characteristic curve of the emulsion is shown as a dashed and dotted curve on the contrast/log exposure graph. *Left:* contrast (gradient)/spatial frequency curves for different levels of log exposure. These curves, when normalized by dividing throughout by the zero frequency value in each case, are found to be identical and represent the MTF of the emulsion. *Top:* spatial frequency/log *H* curves for different contrasts (gradients). *Right:* contrast (gradient)/log *H* curves for different image spatial frequencies.

of contrast, image spatial frequency and log exposure are shown in Figure 12.3 as a three-dimensional representative graph. The surface of such a graph can be sectioned in different planes to show three conventional two-axis graphs. These show the relationship between two of the variables, with the third as a family of curves at various values.

Using MTF curves

12.10   MTF curves are used by photographers, research workers and engineers, when evaluating all or part of a photographic system. One advantage is that the MTFs for a complete system, from subject through lens and film to the final print, can be found by simply multiplying the MTFs of each stage of the process at each value of spatial frequency in succession. This is called 'cascading the functions'. (As an example, $0.8 \times 0.6 = 0.48$, etc.) An MTF curve can then be plotted for the overall performance of the system.

12.11   The practical photographer can use published MTF curves to compare the response of different films when deciding the best film for a specific task. However, because of differences in methods of measurement, comparison should only be made between the films of one manufacturer.

Because, in the strictest sense, MTF cannot be applied to non-linear characteristics, and because this applies to the non-linear response of a processed emulsion, some film manufacturers use a different system to describe the film's response to the images of fine detail. This is based on the method of presentation outlined in paragraph 12.9, and may be depicted as a family of curves relative to the gradient of different parts of the original characteristic curve and showing reduced contrast for a representative selection of spatial frequencies (see also paragraph 2.110). The results are just as satisfactory to the practical photographer as are MTF curves, and comparison can be made between the films of one manufacturer in the same manner.

Like sensitometric curves, modulation (or contrast) transfer curves represent the response to a particular set of conditions, so they should be used only as a guide to what may happen in practice.

12.12   *Further information.*   This chapter is only an introduction to the concept of modulation transfer and the evaluation of photographic imagery. Suggested further reading is contained in *The Manual of Photography* and *Basic Photo Science*. Both these books, published by Focal Press, contain informative and easy-to-read sections on the micro-properties and evaluation of the photographic image. Particular references are contained in the *SPSE Handbook of Photographic Science and Engineering*, *Photographic Considerations for Aerospace*, *Applied Photographic Theory*, and *Introduction to Photographic Theory*. The structure of the developed image is also considered in detail in *The Theory of the Photographic Process*. See Appendix G.

13

Simple sensitometry

13.1 If we have a clear mental picture of the sensitometry of a photographic task, and know the result required, we do not need to use a sensitometer, a densitometer, or curves on graph paper, but simply to think in a logical sensitometric manner: to visualize the effects of exposure and processing on the characteristic curve of the chosen material.

13.2 If we need to assess or compare the performance of photographic materials or processes, this also can be done in an approximate manner without using any measuring instruments other than our eyes. When precise information is not required, simple yet satisfactory sensitometry can be carried out with little more than a step wedge and/or a grey scale.

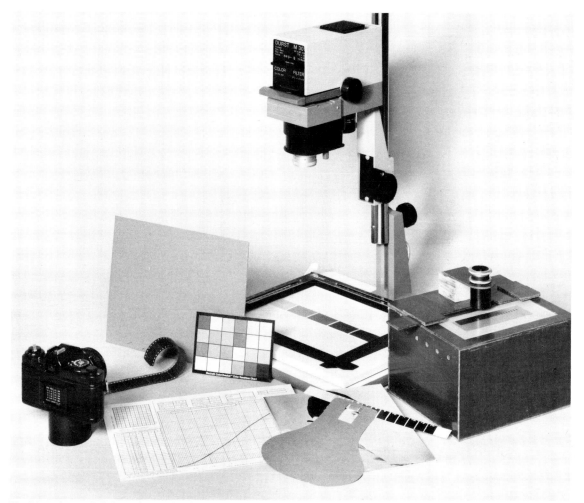

Useful sensitometric information can be obtained without using special sensitometric equipment.

As we know from everyday experience, the human eye is very sensitive to tonal or to colour differences, when they are seen together. In photography we use this ability when comparing negatives or prints produced by different types of material or by various exposure or processing times. On negatives or prints, however, the random tone distribution caused by the pictorial content tends to confuse our comparison, but if a step wedge is exposed on each, differences become much more apparent. This is because the steps on a wedge have large even tones that are set out in a logical order, and are therefore very convenient for viewing side by side. Thus by using a simple step wedge or a grey scale (preferably, but not essentially, one with known increments of density) a comparison or a fair subjective assessment of results can be easily made. For such a comparison, the step wedge or grey scale alone can be the subject, or it can be included with the pictorial content of a photograph.

Simple sensitometry of this kind can be used to compare the effect of most of the variables that occur in both black-and-white and colour photography – for example, the effect on speed and contrast, and on tone or colour rendition, of using different sorts of film or paper, different exposure conditions, or different processing conditions.

13.3   Now let us see how simple sensitometry can be accomplished and how we can get useful information from the results. As we know, sensitometric information is obtained by carrying out five progressive steps, using known and controlled conditions for each one. These steps are exposure, processing, measuring, plotting, and interpreting the results. The steps that call for different procedures, because of lack of special equipment, are exposure and measuring, and the means of achieving them depend on what equipment is available.

First we need a means of exposing the material to a suitable range of luminances. The best and most obvious way to do this is to use a step wedge (or a grey scale), but let us first briefly consider what can be done if a wedge is not available.

Producing a known range of exposures without a step wedge

13.4   A stepped range of exposures can be produced on photographic material without the use of a step wedge, by various methods. The processed results of such a range of exposures is

generally a series of steps having an uneven scale of transmittance or reflectance. In some cases, these may then be used instead of a master wedge for later experiments.

13.5   *Using a camera.*   To obtain a known range of exposures, the consecutive frames of a 35 mm or roll film in a camera are given a series of decreasing exposures to the light reflected from either a matt white or grey card. The different exposures can be obtained most accurately by adjusting first the lens *f*-stops and then, if necessary, the shutter speeds of the camera. By careful planning, a known range of exposures can be obtained in increments of stops (0.30 log) or half-stops (0.15 log). The known range can then be used to plot a sufficiently accurate log exposure scale for constructing a characteristic curve. Figure 13.1 shows an example of this.

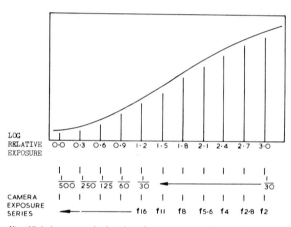

Fig. 13.1 A geometrical series of exposures can be produced on film by using a camera to photograph a matt white or grey card, using different exposure settings. Exposure is decreased in progressive steps by varying first the lens aperture and then the shutter speed. The series of exposures can be plotted as a fairly accurate log exposure scale for constructing a characteristic curve.

Points to bear in mind throughout this procedure are mostly those that apply to more precise sensitometry. For example:

(a)   The tone of the card must be even overall. Kodak sell a 'neutral test card', which is matt white on one side and grey on the other.
(b)   The card should be reasonably parallel to the plane of the film.
(c)   Subject lighting must be even and constant throughout the procedure.
(d)   The lighting needs to be positioned behind the camera and adjusted so that the minimum density

of the film is obtained only at the smallest aperture and the fastest shutter speed planned.

(e) A long focal length lens produces a more even lighting over the image area than a short focal length lens.

(f) A lens hood should be used to minimize any possible flare effects.

(g) The image of the card should fill the frame.

13.6 *Using an enlarger.* Photographic materials to be tested can be given a series of increasing exposures to light projected by an enlarger. The test sample (or two samples side by side) is positioned and suitably masked on the baseboard of the enlarger. The illuminance level is controlled by adjusting the height of the enlarger head and the lens aperture. A range of exposures can be given in a similar manner to that used when a test strip is exposed in printing, by giving a series of increasing time exposures. This time-scale method is satisfactory for a rough assessment of results but may show the effects of reciprocity failure. If the material under test is later to be exposed by illuminance variation (as in a camera), it is better to increase exposure by varying the illuminance, as far as possible, instead of the time of exposure. In this way exposure is being made as in an intensity (illuminance) scale sensitometer.

A suggested method of making a stepped series of exposures involves using a black opaque card with an aperture cut in it to the size of one of the required steps. This is positioned over and in contact with the photographic material, which is then moved along under the card one step at a time between exposures. The material thus receives exposure from the same area of light each time an exposure is made. The series of exposures is obtained by using an appropriate exposure time and adjusting first the lens aperture and then, if necessary, the time of exposure. Figure 13.2 shows an example of this method.

For films, better control of exposure is obtained if a camera inter-lens shutter and a click-stop iris can be fitted onto the enlarger. This will provide the necessary short exposure times, and the camera iris will probably have more *f*-stops than an enlarger lens. It may also provide more equal increments of exposure. The shutter speed can be set to give the necessary short exposure time; as in a camera, exposure is controlled by changing first the *f*-stop and then, if necessary the shutter speeds (see Figures 13.1 and 13.2). By careful planning, a known range of exposures can be obtained with increments of stops (0.30 log) of half-stops (0.15 log). Whichever method is used, the known range can then be plotted to produce a sufficiently accurate log exposure scale for constructing a characteristic curve in the same manner as that used in Figure 13.1. A major difficulty with panchromatic materials is, of course, having to work in total darkness or dim safelight conditions.

Points to bear in mind throughout this procedure are mostly those that apply in more precise sensitometry. For example:

(a) The lighting on the exposed area must be as even as possible. (Paragraph 2.14 refers to checking this.)

(b) The lighting should be of a suitable colour quality for the material under test. Typically a blue colour conversion filter, such as the Kodak Wratten 80A, will convert tungsten enlarging light to approximate standard daylight.

(c) Opal glass, or a neutral-density filter, can be used if it is necessary to reduce the illuminance.

(d) To prevent reflection of the exposing light from the base, the photographic material being tested must be placed in contact with a matt-black surface, such as black paper.

(e) The lighting needs to be adjusted so that the minimum density of the material is obtained only at the smallest lens aperture and shortest time planned.

(f) The material screening aperture must make good contact with the test material to prevent light spread during exposure.

(g) The material should be moved an equal distance between each exposure to obtain evenly spaced steps. This can be aided by using a series of marks or notches alongside the material.

(h) If intended in particular for subsequent use as a step wedge, there must be no gaps between the steps.

(i) The procedure of stopping down to obtain halving of exposure may not strictly apply to a pure condenser enlarger.

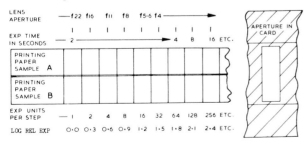

Fig. 13.2 A method of producing a geometrical series of exposures by using an enlarger. The photographic material is moved under the fixed aperture and is progressively exposed by varying first the lens aperture and then the time of exposure.

This method can also be used for determining the exposure range of printing paper (see paragraph 5.15).

13.7 *Processing the results.* Processing should be the same as that used for more precise sensitometry with the aim of obtaining uniform development (see Chapter 6).

13.8 *General remarks on the procedures.* The procedures given above are satisfactory for comparing two or more factors (say two different films), or for exposing two samples of the same film so that the effect of two different processes can be found. This is because the effect of any variation in the exposure will apply equally to both. For a visual side-by-side comparison of the processed results there is no particular need to have a known increment between each exposure.

Making a step wedge

13.9 Other methods of producing a series of exposures involve exposing the material in a series of steps to a light source – for example, by using a small light source at varying distances (intensity-scale sensitometry), or at a set distance and varying the time (time-scale sensitometry). All methods call for experiment before a satisfactory result can be obtained. (See also Appendix B, paragraph 11.)

13.10 *Producing a master step wedge.* The method of using an enlarger, or a small light source at a distance, to produce a range of exposures may be utilized to make a master step wedge for the subsequent testing of other photographic materials. If the majority of the exposures given fall on the straight-line region of the film, and if it is developed to a gamma of 1.0, the density increments between the majority of steps will be similar to the increments between the exposures given. These conditions are not easy to achieve, and if they are not achieved the increments between steps will not be similar to those of the exposure range given. However, if a densitometer is available this first film can be measured and the density values plotted to obtain a characteristic curve. The curve can then be used to find a suitable series of exposures, which will produce fairly equal density increments on a second film of the same type. The series of exposures is found by marking the densities required on the density axis of the plotted characteristic curve, and then tracing back

through the curve and down to the log exposure axis to find the required exposures for the second film. If necessary, the exposure values can be found from a table of antilogarithms. After correct exposure and processing, the wedge on the second film will have approximately equal density increments and can be used as a master step wedge. Figure 13.3 shows an example of this procedure.

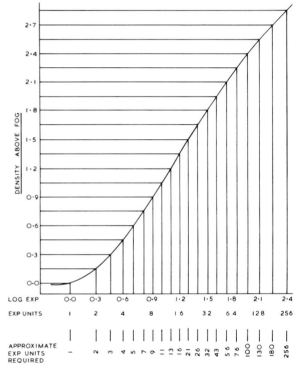

Fig. 13.3 A method of determining correct exposure for making a master step wedge, by using a characteristic curve relevant to the photographic material, its exposure and processing. The required equal density increments are marked on the density axis and the exposures to produce them found by plotting back through the characteristic curve.

The method described above involves the use of a slow, fine-grain, blue-sensitive film to obtain the necessary control of exposure and enable working to be carried out in safelight conditions. A slow-working and non-staining developer should be used in a dish, using vigorous and random agitation to obtain uniform development. This is probably best obtained by brushing the surface of the film immersed in the developer with a soft broad brush. The gamma aimed for should be above rather than below 1.0, and the conditions of exposure and processing must be the same each time the method is used. To obtain a satisfactory master step wedge there will probably be some trial and error involved because of the many variables in the procedure. We can see from Figure 13.3 that to obtain exposures that can be used in practice, there will be a need for rounding off the values obtained. Wedges produced by this method can be used for simple sensitometry, but if required for more precise work the wedge would need to be calibrated.

A similar way of making a step wedge is described in detail in Dr G. L. Wakefield's book *Practical Sensitometry*. It includes an ingenious method of using the movement of a typewriter carriage to produce a series of well-defined and evenly spaced steps.

13.11 *Making an experimental step wedge.* To make a very simple experimental step wedge, take a piece of good-quality thin white paper, such as tracing paper or greaseproof paper, and cut it into strips to the width of the required wedge. Arrange successive strips to overlap each other in steps, and hold them in position at the edges with tape. The idea is that light passes through no layer, one layer, two layers, and so on. Densities are additive, so the exposure through the steps is on a logarithmic scale. For example, if the density of the paper is 0.15 (a good value to select) in theory the log increment between exposures will be about 0.15. In practice this may not be obtained owing to irregularities and inter-reflection between the paper surfaces.

The wedge and its steps can be made to any size, bearing in mind the requirement that, if intended for experimental use, the wedge should ideally be in contact with the test material. The limit of exposure range is controlled, in theory, by the number of paper layers used. To obtain rigidity the wedge can be mounted on a piece of clear glass. It must also be masked completely around the edges, except for the last step, which of course is clear glass.

13.12 *Making a practical step wedge.* A more practical and permanent step wedge than the paper wedge can be made by a similar method. This involves using several pieces of gelatin neutral-density filter, or pieces of evenly fogged fine-grain film of neutral density. Remember that densities are additive in their effect; for example, a density of 1.0 combined with a density of 0.5 gives a density of 1.5.

The wedge can be constructed in a similar manner to the paper wedge, by overlapping the pieces on glass to build up the required step densities. However, if the selection of density values available is suitable, it is more practical to carefully butt-join each piece or to make only a slight overlap of each step. The essential thing is that there must be no clear areas between the steps, otherwise light spread will occur when the wedge is used. If neutral-density filters or suitably fogged pieces of film are not available, it is cheaper in the long term to buy a commercial step wedge or to use one of the methods already described, rather than buying expensive neutral-density filters or attempting to obtain an even fog of varying densities on pieces of film.

13.13 If home-made step wedges are intended to be used for more than a few experiments, the steps must be identified. Paragraph 2.13 gives information on the numbering of steps, and paragraph 6.4 on the preservation and care of wedges. The above methods of making a wedge may be tried and will certainly present the maker with a sense of achievement, but the best and most convenient way to produce a range of exposures is to buy a step wedge.

13.14 *Commercial step wedges and grey scales.* Kodak and other manufacturers supply a selection of step wedges and grey scales that are already nominally calibrated. This means that the full range of densities and the density increment between each step are known to a degree of accuracy that is satisfactory for simple sensitometry. Precisely calibrated wedges are also available from the manufacturers of densitometers. (These are expensive, as they are intended for instrument calibration.) A typical step wedge has a transmission density range of 3.0 and consists of 21 steps with approximate 0.15 increments. A typical grey scale has a reflection density range of 2.0 or so and consists of about 20 tones with approximate 0.10 increments of density. Other grey scales may have 10 tones at approximate 0.20 density increments but with each tone presenting a larger area. Manufactured grey scales are specially made to produce a neutral density, and the reflection density values are often indicated near each step.

Having made or obtained a step wedge or grey scale, we need to know how each can be used for sensitometric testing. We can first consider the use of a reflection grey scale and then that of a transmission step wedge.

Using a grey scale

13.15   A grey scale may be used by including it with or alongside the subject of a photograph, particularly for colour photography. By this means, subsequent evaluation of the scale image will include the effect of all the factors (such as lens flare) that have also affected the image of the subject photographed. The scale may also be used on its own and photographed as the original subject. To be relevant to each situation, the complete scale must be uniformly illuminated and receive the same lighting as the important parts of the actual subject. The image of each step of the scale must also be large enough for later visual or densitometric evaluation. Used in this manner, a grey scale provides a series of conveniently arranged luminances with known relative values. It can thus serve as the input when a photographic system is to be evaluated.

13.16   A grey scale can be used to assess the overall effect of the complete photographic system, from camera to final print. The input and the output (the image of the scale on the final print) are compared visually, side by side. Furthermore, to digress just a little from simple sensitometry: if a densitometer is used, the measured densities of the output can be plotted against the known density values of the input. The relationship between the two can then be shown as a curve on a graph describing the overall tone scale reproduction of the entire photographic process. (See paragraphs 1.3, 7.1 and 11.67.) The output can of course be plotted against an input at any stage in the process, for example at the negative stage.

A grey scale can also be used as a camera subject to test for any variability in shutter speeds, or to determine filter exposure factors (see paragraphs 2.117 and 2.118).

13.17   *Using a grey scale as a simple densitometer.*   Let us get back to simple sensitometry. A calibrated grey scale can be used as a simple comparative reflection densitometer to measure the densities of a black-and-white print or of a produced paper sensitometric strip (grey scale): for example, to determine an approximate paper log exposure range (see paragraphs 5.6 and 5.15). The procedure is to match an unknown density with a known and value-marked density on the calibrated grey scale. This is easily done because our eyes are particularly adept at matching adjacent densities. A suggested method for doing this is shown in Figure 13.4. The procedure is:

(a)   Cut a piece of black or dark grey card to the shape shown.
(b)   Cut a rectangular aperture about the width of a step, near the side of the card.
(c)   Position the sample to be measured under a good, bright viewing light – daylight is best.
(d)   Place one half of the aperture over the area to be measured and hold it in position.
(e)   Place the calibrated grey scale under the card so that it shows alongside the area to be measured.
(f)   Slide the scale to and fro until a known density matches the unknown, and note its value.
(g)   As necessary, estimate between value-marked densities.

Kodak produce a reflection density guide, which can be used as a simple reflection densitometer.

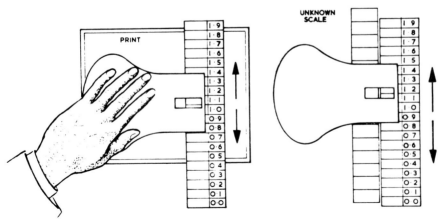

Fig. 13.4 Using a calibrated grey scale as a simple reflection densitometer. The unknown density is held under the aperture in the card and the grey scale is moved to and fro until unknown and known densities match by eye.

This is a rigid card that contains a calibrated grey scale with a series of densities from 0 to 2.0. The densities have punched out apertures that can be positioned over the area to be visually matched and evaluated.

13.18 *Plotting the results of a simple grey-scale measurement.* The density measurements made of a paper sensitometric strip can be used to construct a characteristic curve. If the measured strip was not exposed through a step wedge, but to a series of known exposures, the log relative exposures are plotted as a scale increasing from left to right along the log exposure axis of a graph. The characteristic curve of the paper as processed can then be constructed in the usual manner, measured density being plotted against log relative exposure as shown in Figure 13.5. This situation could relate, for example, to a series of exposures produced directly by varying the light from an enlarger (see paragraph 13.6).

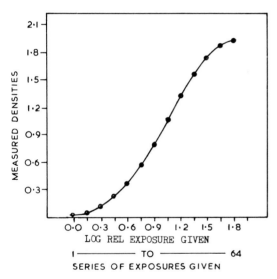

Fig. 13.5 Plotting the results of a paper sensitometric strip measurement. The densities found are plotted against the log relative exposure that produced them. A characteristic curve can then be constructed.

If the measured strip was exposed through a transmission step wedge, by contact or by projection, the densities of the transmission step wedge are plotted along the log exposure axis as a scale increasing from right to left. Thus the log relative exposures that were made through the wedge increase from left to right (see paragraph 2.55). The curve can then be plotted in the usual way as shown in Figure 13.6. If the measured paper strip

was obtained by projection of a step wedge image, the characteristic curve will include the effect of lens flare and any other relevant enlarger characteristics.

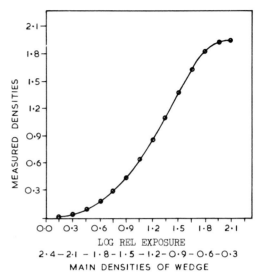

Fig. 13.6 Plotting the result of a paper sensitometric strip measurement. The densities found are plotted against the corresponding densities of the master wedge used in exposure. A characteristic curve can then be constructed.

Making a simple sensitometer

13.19 The prime function of a transmission step wedge is to provide the means of obtaining a wide range of known exposures when light is passed through it onto photographic material. A calibrated step wedge is, as we know, intended to be used in a sensitometer, and the results from it measured on a densitometer. If a sensitometer is not available, we may be able to make one using a suitable light-tight box and components that are to hand. We can also simulate the function of a sensitometer by using the wedge with other equipment such as a suitable large-format camera, a contact printer, a printing frame or an enlarger. In fact, if we are testing a material or a process that in practice will involve the use of the camera, printer or enlarger, using the step wedge with the same equipment will probably produce more useful results then will a proper sensitometer. By using the same equipment, all the factors that can affect the result will be automatically built in to the test. Any results or tone reproduction curves produced will then be characteristic of the system comprising the material and its method of exposure and processing.

A cardinal principle in sensitometry is that to be of value the tests should utilize as far as possible the conditions of exposure and processing that the material will receive in practical use. A good example is the use of a step wedge in an enlarger to find the effective log exposure range of printing paper (see paragraph 5.14).

13.20 When making a simple sensitometer or when adapting existing equipment to be used as one, we need to consult the list of components and their functions as described in paragraph 2.6 and Figure 2.1, and then to comply with it as much as possible. The importance of each component or function is of course related to the type of test intended.

In each case, one of the basic things to bear in mind is that the step wedge and the photographic material to be exposed should, if at all possible, be in intimate contact. If a projected image of a step wedge is used, for example illuminated from behind and photographed by a camera, or projected by an enlarger, the flare effect and other effects will be included with the results.

If you intend to make a simple sensitometer the following list of suggestions may be useful. It is certainly not exhaustive but should help.

(a) *Light sources.* The output from a light source needs to be consistent and must be sufficient to effectively expose the test material through the densest step of the wedge. Some light sources that may be used are:
(1) A domestic 60 or 100 watt lamp.
(2) A slide-projector lamp.
(3) An electronic (xenon) flash.
(4) The illuminated opal glass of a contact printing box.
(5) The projected light from an enlarger.
New tungsten lamps should be aged for an hour or so before use in order to obtain a reasonably unvarying light output when the lamp is used in practice.

(b) *Colour quality of the exposing light.* The colour quality of the light will depend on the colour sensitivity and intended use of the photographic material being tested. It is not of overriding importance in comparative black-and-white sensitometry but is important when testing colour materials. For testing colour materials the colour quality of a light source can be converted by using colour filters. For example, a blue colour conversion filter, such as the Kodak Wratten 80A, can be used to convert tungsten light to approximate standard daylight. If a filter is used it should be positioned close to the shutter or close (but not too close) to the lamp; a small-area filter will then suffice.

(c) *Shutter or exposure-timing device.* The type of shutter used depends on the inherent speed and the intended use of the photographic materials to be tested. It must be positioned sufficiently close (but not too close) to the light source in order to obtain a uniform illuminance over the step wedge.
(1) A between-lens shutter such as a Compur type is probably suitable for the majority of tests.
(2) The shutter should be able to give a fairly repeatable exposure duration.
(3) The shutter should open only after the lamp has reached its peak output.
(4) It may need to be operated remotely, for example by a cable release.
(5) For printing paper and exposures longer than 5 seconds or so, the exposing lamp can be switched on and off, or a swing shutter can be used.
(6) If an electronic flash is used as a light source there is no need for a mechanical shutter.

(d) *Step wedge and test-material holder.* A step wedge suitable for general use has a density range of 3.0 or so with increments between steps of 0.15 density.
(1) The step wedge should be held flat on a piece of strong clear glass.
(2) It must be mounted so that the wedge plane is at right angles to the centre of the light beam.
(3) The wedge can be cut to size to fit the format of the test material and/or to help in obtaining an even exposing light over its area.
(4) If cut to size, the steps must be arranged so that the density difference between adjacent steps is kept to a minimum.
(5) The step wedge needs to be masked so that only light that has passed through the wedge reaches the test material.
(6) It is helpful if the steps are identified by numbers.
(7) There must be a means of holding the test material in intimate contact with the wedge. A printing frame or hinged lid may be suitable for this.
(8) The backing plate of the test material holder must have a matt-black surface to prevent reflections during exposure.
The step wedge must be kept clean and scratch-free, and the sample to be tested must be handled with care both before and after exposure (see paragraph 6.4).

(e) *Uniform light on the step wedge.* Illuminance varies inversely as the square of the distance between the light source (if it is of small area) and the wedge. In addition, illuminance is reduced as the angle from the light source becomes more oblique towards the ends of the wedge, because a similar amount of light will be spread over a larger area. For example, on a 10 cm wedge at a distance of 50 cm, the variation in illuminance would be about two per cent between the centre and ends of the wedge. If such a distance is impracticable, a distance less than this, down to say three times the diagonal of the wedge, should still be satisfactory for simple sensitometry. Points to bear in mind are:

(1) The wedge may be cut and fitted on the glass to a square or rectangular shape, in order to obtain a smaller diagonal.

(2) Evenness may be improved if an opal diffusing glass is used (in effect as a light source), positioned near the shutter.

(3) On a contact printer, the light distribution should already be fairly uniform over the exposing surface.

(4) The evenness of light distribution can be checked as described in paragraph 2.14.

(f) *Light-tight container.* The container must be light-tight and, if in box form, painted matt black inside, so that only direct light from the shutter aperture reaches the step wedge. Items that might be used in the construction are:

(1) A suitably sized box with a hinged lid (see paragraph 13.21).

(2) A large camera body with bellows.

(3) A contact-printing frame.

(g) *Neutral-density filters.* Optical-quality neutral-density filters or pieces of chemically fogged fine-grain film, fully developed in a non-staining developer, can be used to reduce the intensity of the exposing light for simple sensitometry. Photographic neutral-density filters can be made by developing individual pieces of unexposed film in a dish, in a vigorous developer and using continuous but irregular agitation to obtain an even chemical fog. The development times to obtain specific density values can only be found by trial and error. Development is followed by vigorous agitation in a stop-bath, careful fixing, a good long wash, wetting agent and gentle drying. Note that neutral-density filters made from photographic materials (unlike optical-quality filters) scatter light, and are therefore not suitable for use in direct illumination or in the optical path of any lens-image-forming system.

Using a step wedge as a simple densitometer

13.21 A calibrated step wedge can be used as a simple comparative densitometer in order to measure the transmission densities of a produced black-and-white sensitometric strip. This is done by visually matching each unknown density with a known value density on the calibrated wedge. The human eye is excellent for comparing densities when they are next to each other, particularly when any surrounding distractions are masked out (see also paragraph 13.25). The suggested method for doing this is similar to that described for measuring with a grey scale (see Figure 13.4 and associated paragraphs) except that a different size viewing aperture will be needed. A 20 mm diameter hole should be about right. Two step wedges, known and unknown, could be held by hand side by side behind the aperture and in front of a domestic opal lamp, and a comparison made by sliding one against the other. However, to assist matters a contact printer or some sort of viewing box is needed to rest the wedge and sample on, and to provide a fairly strong viewing light. If a box is to be constructed it could be made of wood, metal, paxolin etc. Electronic/TV/radio shops supply ready-made aluminium and metal boxes in a variety of sizes. Figure 13.7 shows a sketch of a typical simple comparative densitometer, the box and structure of which was made from paxolin sheet.

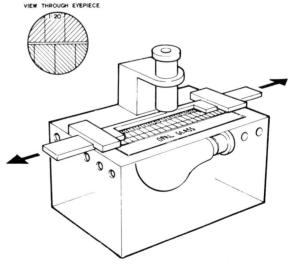

Fig. 13.7 A typical arrangement for a home-made densitometer, using a calibrated step wedge. The unknown density is held on the opal glass top and the calibrated wedge is moved to and fro until known and unknown densities match by eye.

The box contains a 40 watt opal lamp and has a piece of opal glass recessed into the top surface. The lamp is positioned well below the opal glass and should only be switched on when a comparison is being made. The box has ventilation holes along the top and bottom of the sides and ends.

As the areas of density to be measured are likely to be fairly small, comparison is more easily made by using a magnifying viewer. This also helps to concentrate the eye on to the viewing area. It can be hand-held or, better still, positioned above the viewing area. Added refinements are a slide to hold the calibrated wedge and a dimmer to control the intensity of the lamp when viewing the lower densities.

Using an exposure meter as a simple densitometer

13.22   Some highly light-sensitive (photoresistive) exposure meters include a fibre-optic probe or similar device for small-area measurements. Thus they can also be used as a reasonably effective densitometer. The maker's literature should give full instructions on this particular application.

A photoelectric exposure meter that does not have a small-area measuring function (such as the Weston meter) may also be used as the light detector of a simple transmission densitometer. The device will not be able to measure very small areas as a commercial densitometer can, but it should be able to measure, say, the densities of steps on successive 35 mm frames. The construction and arrangement is similar to that for the visual comparator described previously, and involves using either a movable or a variable-intensity light source of high illuminance diffused by a piece of opal glass. To prevent heat damage, the lamp should only be switched on when a measurement is being made; this can be facilitated by a push-button switch. An aperture with an opaque surround, to act as a stage for the sample, should be placed on the opal glass. The cell of the meter is positioned above the aperture and screened so that no light other than that passing through the aperture can enter the photocell. The densitometer is zeroed by adjusting the light source with no sample in place, until a full-scale deflection is shown on the meter scale. The scale can then be calibrated by measuring a set of known densities.

In use, the needle deflection is reduced, and the amount of reduction is a measure of the density of the sample. In general, and if no calibration wedge

or device is available, each change of a full number on the meter scale represents a density of 0.30. Depending on the meter scale size, in-between densities may be estimated to an accuracy of about 0.10. It is emphasized that a simple densitometer made by utilizing a photoelectric exposure meter is only suitable for measuring fairly large areas and areas of moderate density.

13.23   *Other density- and light-measuring devices.* The simple aids to sensitometry and densitometry that we have considered up to now are of value for measuring density and assessing results. However, more refined and elegant light-measuring devices can be made. Photographers with a do-it-yourself aptitude who wish to construct their own equipment can obtain valuable advice from books and manufacturers' literature. Dr G. L. Wakefield, in his book *Exposure Control in Enlarging*, describes in detail the construction of several home-made densitometers for use as integrating enlarging meters. Popular photographic and electronic magazines also publish articles and instructions on constructing printing exposure meters, timers, colour analysers, photometers, and similar aids to sensitometry and better photography.

Plotting the results of transmission-density measurement

13.24   The density measurements made of a produced sensitometric strip can be used to construct a characteristic curve. If the measured strip was not exposed through a master step wedge, but to a series of known exposures, the log relative exposures are plotted as a scale increasing from left

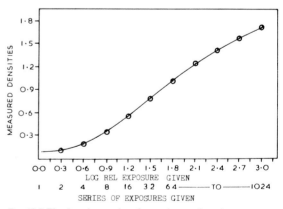

Fig. 13.8 Plotting the results of a sensitometric strip measurement. The densities found are plotted against the log relative exposures that produced them. A characteristic curve can then be constructed.

to right along the log exposure axis of a graph. The characteristic curve of the film as processed can then be constructed in the usual manner. Measured density is plotted against log relative exposure as shown in Figure 13.8. This situation would relate, for example, to a known series of exposures produced directly by varying the light entering a camera (paragraph 13.5) or by varying the light from an enlarger (paragraph 13.6).

If the measured strip was exposed through a master step wedge by contact or by projection, the densities of the master wedge are plotted along the log exposure axis as a scale increasing from right to left. Thus the log relative exposures made through the wedge increase from left to right (see paragraph 2.55). The characteristic curve can then be plotted in the usual way (Figure 13.9). If the measured

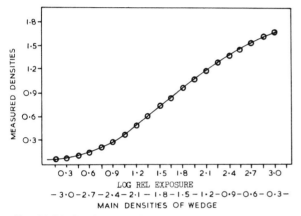

Fig. 13.9 Plotting the result of a sensitometric strip measurement. The densities found are plotted against the corresponding densities of the master step wedge used in exposure. A characteristic curve can then be constructed.

strip was obtained by projection of a master step wedge, the characteristic curve will include the effect of lens flare and any other relevant enlarger characteristics.

Obtaining information from simple sensitometric tests

13.25   When the same range of stepped exposures is given to two or more photographic materials and the increment between exposures is not known, a fair comparison can only be made by viewing the results side by side. If the processed strips are held so that the steps that have received the same exposure are adjacent to each other, a visual judgement can be made with regard to such factors as fog level, speed and contrast. Comparison is best made with the relevant steps adjoining each other,

and it is often convenient to trim each strip so that this can be achieved. Fog levels and very low densities on film strips are often difficult to compare when the viewing light is strong, but if viewed side by side on a piece of matt-white paper, small differences can be more easily seen.

When the range and the increment between the exposures given to the photographic material is known and when the results can be measured to produce values of density, characteristic curves can be constructed. The comparison is then shown graphically, the effects are more obvious and easy to interpret, and they may also be measured.

Whichever method is used, visual side-by-side comparison or constructing curves, assessment and decisions can be made with regard to several factors and situations. For example:

(a)   When different types of material have received the same exposure.
(b)   When the same type of material has received different processing conditions.
(c)   When the same type of material has received different exposure conditions – for example, when finding the exposure effect of light filters.

Simple sensitometry of this sort can be of real practical value in testing materials and for obtaining information when more precise exposure and measuring instruments are not available.

13.26   *Visual comparison of colour materials.* The effect on colour materials of varying factors in storage, exposure and processing can be found by simple sensitometry using visual side by side comparison. For example, the response of different colour photographic materials, or of the same materials used in different exposure or lighting conditions, can be found in a simple and direct manner. All that is needed is a suitable set of natural coloured objects to serve as a standard that can be photographed. The colours of the final images can then be compared with the original colour standard and with each other. Photographic manufacturers supply specially made colour charts that incorporate a grey scale along with a set of coloured patches. Paragraphs 11.81 and 82 describe a typical colour rendition chart and how the chart can be used. (See also paragraph 13.30.)

13.27   *Visual comparison of black-and-white materials.* The same sort of colour chart that is used for comparing colour materials can also be used for comparing the spectral response of black-and-white materials (see paragraph 10.8).

Simple quality control in processing

13.28   Quality control in processing is concerned with establishing conditions that will produce the desired quality of results and then ensuring that subsequent processing has the same effect. It is used for all photographic materials and is of particular importance in the processing of colour material. Process quality control, as described in Chapter 6, includes the use of a densitometer for monitoring the process; if a densitometer is not available, simple quality control tests can be carried out by visual comparison against a known standard. This visual assessment does not provide a precise check of quality but is much better than estimations made by viewing the regular processed results without a comparison being made.

Basic control is established and can be maintained by complying with the maker's recommendations with regard to mixing, storing, using and replenishing processing solutions and by following the recommended processing techniques. However, if quantities of photographic materials are to be processed over a period of time, there is a need to check occasionally that the process is still producing satisfactory results. A slow decline in the quality of regular results is almost impossible to detect, but if a correctly exposed and standard 'control strip', on the same type of material, is processed with each batch of material and compared with an already correctly processed 'reference strip', the results will indicate whether the process is correct or not.

Control strips, whether on film or paper, are basically correctly exposed and stabilized sensitometric strips made under precise conditions from the same batch of photographic material. Manufacturers supply boxes of process control strips, together with one correctly processed reference strip. The reference strip can therefore be used as a comparative standard for the other control strips after they have been processed. The storage and handling of control strips and reference strips is described in paragraphs 6.4 and 6.22.

13.29   *Visual quality-monitoring procedures.* The procedure for visual quality monitoring is to process a control strip along with the normal batch of material or at regular intervals, according to the amount of work being carried out. The control strip is then compared visually side by side with the reference strip. As most control strips contain only a few well-separated densities, comparison is made more easily than if a full step wedge had been used. Preferably both strips are trimmed so that the areas of density can be positioned adjacent to each other, and compared using a standard viewing light. (See also paragraphs 7.34 and 11.80.) For film materials, the viewing light needs to be masked so that light only passes through the control strips. If the results are a fairly close match, the process is probably under control. If the contrast and general overall density or colour are not closely related, then remedial action needs to be taken, and this should be followed by processing another control strip as a check before more material is processed. With colour negative materials the pale orange integral masking makes visual assessment more difficult. For these, a better comparison of contrast and overall density may be obtained by viewing the adjacent steps through a green filter (see paragraph 11.108).

These procedures are only suitable for an *estimation* of acceptable processing. More precise results can only be obtained by using a densitometer and following the procedure for quality control provided by the manufacturer.

13.30   *Home-made. control strips.* If manufactured control strips are not available, home-made strips (in the form of prints or transparencies made of a typical standard subject) can be processed at intervals. These can then be compared with a previously made optimum-quality 'reference strip' of the same subject. A suitable standard subject, particularly for the process monitoring of colour materials, is a human face and a grey scale or a colour chart. (See paragraphs 13.26, 11.81 and 11.82.)

In process control monitoring, the one variable factor being investigated is the effect of processing. Therefore all other factors that can affect the results must be constant. To achieve this, all the control strips and reference strips for a particular type of film or paper must be exposed on the same type of material, using identical conditions throughout. Furthermore, the produced control strips must be properly stored and handled carefully before use (see paragraph 6.22).

Appendix A

Logarithms

1 A logarithm is the power to which a base number must be raised to equal a given number. For everyday practical purposes the base is 10, giving what are called 'common logarithms'; 10 is the first power of 10 and is written as 10^1. Thus for example:

$10 = 10^1$ and the logarithm of 10 is 1.0
$100 = 10^2$ and the logarithm of 100 is 2.0
$1000 = 10^3$ and the logarithm of 1000 is 3.0

and so on. Looking at this list we can see that the logarithm of a number between 10 and 100 is greater than 1 and less than 2, and the logarithm of a number between 100 and 1000 is greater than 2 and less than 3. For example, the logarithm of 20 is almost exactly 1.3 and that of 40 almost exactly 1.6. The logarithm of a number thus consists of two parts, a whole number (called the characteristic) and a decimal part (called the mantissa).

We can see from the above list that the characteristic of 100 is 2 and that of 10 is 1. Therefore, numbers between 10 and down to 1 must have a characteristic of 0, and numbers less than 1 must have a negative characteristic. For convenience the mantissa of a logarithm is always positive, so negative characteristics are indicated by placing the minus sign above the characteristic instead of before it. This emphasizes the fact that only the characteristic is negative. Negative characteristics are thus written as $\bar{1}$, $\bar{2}$, etc., and read or described as 'bar one', 'bar two', etc. For example, the logarithm of 0.2 is $\bar{1}.3$ or 'bar one point three'. If a calculator is used to find the logarithm of 0.2 it will indicate −0.7, which is less convenient than $\bar{1}.3$ but exactly equivalent to it. ($\bar{1}.3$ is $-1.0 + 0.3$, which equals −0.7.)

2 *Finding the logarithm of a number.* The logarithm of a number can be found by using an electronic calculator, or from printed tables of logarithms which can be obtained complete with instructions and examples of use.

The mantissa, the decimal part of the logarithm, is found in the table marked 'logarithms', which

usually give four figures after the decimal point. For sensitometry calculations a two-figure mantissa is usually sufficient. For example, the logarithm of 20 is 1.3010 in four-figure tables, and the logarithm of 60 is 1.7782. These may be rounded off to 1.30 and 1.78 respectively.

The characteristic is not given in the tables and must be found by inspection of the original number. If this number is greater than 1, the characteristic is positive, and is 1 less than the number of figures to the left of the decimal point. Thus the logarithm of 2 = 0.3010; log 20 = 1.3010 and log 200 = 2.3010. If the number whose logarithm is required is less than 1, the characteristic is negative, and is 1 more than the number of zeros to the right immediately following the decimal point. Thus log 0.2 = $\bar{1}.3010$ and log 0.02 = $\bar{2}.3010$.

3 *Finding the antilogarithm.* The number that corresponds to a particular logarithm is called its antilogarithm. It can be found by reversing the procedure used for finding the logarithm; this is most easily carried out by using a table of antilogarithms. The procedure is to find in the table the number corresponding to the mantissa. The characteristic is then used to determine the position of the decimal point. For example, the antilog of 2.4531 is 283.9, and that of $\bar{2}.4531$ is 0.02839.

4 *Multiplication and division.* To multiply two (or more) numbers, add their logarithms and then find the antilogarithm corresponding to the sum. To divide one number by another, subtract their logarithms and then find the corresponding antilogarithm.

5 *Powers, roots and reciprocals.* Logarithms can also be used to obtain powers, roots and reciprocals of numbers. The power of a number is obtained by multiplication of the logarithm by the number representing the power, and the extraction of roots by division by the power of the root. The

209

antilogarithm of the result is the answer required. The reciprocal of a number is obtained by subtracting its logarithm from 0 (see paragraph 4.15).

6   *Logarithmic scales.* Logarithmically marked scales, where equal intervals represent equal ratios, are often required. In sensitometry a logarithmic scale of exposure is used when plotting characteristic curves in order to present the curve in a manageable form. The reasons for this are

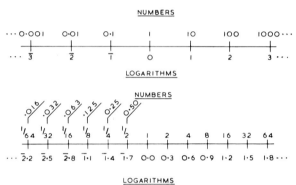

Fig. A.1 The relationship between logarithmically and arithmetically numbered scales.

explained in paragraph 2.53. On such a scale, equal ratios of exposure show as equal distances along the scale. Figure A.1 shows the relation between typical logarithmic and arithmetic scales. (See also Figures 2.13 and 3.7.)

7   *General remarks on logarithms.* If we work out problems by using four-figure logarithm tables and then check the results (say by normal multiplication or by using an electronic calculator), we find that the answers often differ slightly. This is because four-figure logarithms give only three-figure accuracy. However, this is satisfactory for the majority of calculations. As an example, we multiply 3 by 2 using logarithms:

$$\begin{aligned} \text{Log } 3 &= 0.4771 \\ \text{Log } 2 &= \underline{0.3010} \\ \text{Sum} &= 0.7781 \end{aligned}$$

From the tables the antilog of $0.7781 = 5.999$. Since $3 \times 2 = 6$, there is an error of 0.001 ($\frac{1}{1000}$) in the answer given by the four-figure log tables. The theory of logarithms is explained in most mathematics text books and these also give detailed explanations and examples of their use.

Appendix B

Absolute sensitometry and the calibration of sensitometers

1 Comparative (or non-absolute) sensitometry, where the colour quality of the light and the exposure conditions are not precisely known, is adequate for the majority of local sensitometric applications. As long as the exposures given relate to practical conditions and are constant from test to test, direct comparison of the results produced by different films, developers or development times etc. will generally provide the information needed. Absolute sensitometry, on the other hand, is the sort that is carried out by film manufacturers to determine, for example, the absolute speed of a film. This requires an accurate knowledge of the precise exposure received by the test material in terms of illuminance, duration and colour quality. It thus involves the luminous intensity and colour quality of the exposing light, and the duration of exposure given. Since the latter may be easily determined by conventional methods of shutter testing (for example, by measurement using an instrument that can display the duration directly in milliseconds), it is usually the characteristics of the exposing light source that are most in question and require calibration.

The luminous intensity of a light source is measured in candelas, photometric units that relate only to visible radiation (light). However, since photographic exposure is concerned with both visible and non-visible radiation, photometric units may not always be applicable for measuring and calibration purposes, and the use of other measuring units may in some cases be necessary and preferable.

2 *Units of photographic exposure.* Exposure (illuminance × duration), is traditionally expressed in metre-candle-seconds, but this measure has been replaced by the current standard of lux seconds (see paragraph 2.3). These are 'photometric units' related to the visual impression of illuminance. Alternatively, 'radiometric units' may be used so that non-visual radiation can be included, and these units are concerned with the energy received by the test material. For fundamental scientific work, particularly with monochromatic radiation, the exposure may also be expressed in 'quanta per unit area'. The quantum or photon of light is the smallest bit of light, just as an atom is the smallest bit of an element. Light may be regarded as a stream of such photons. The relation between photometric, radiometric and quantum units is given in paragraphs 14 and 15.

3 *Applications and standards of absolute sensitometry.* Before examining the practical calibration of sensitometers we can briefly consider some of the applications of absolute sensitometry and the international standards that apply. Although comparative (or non-absolute) sensitometry may be all that is required for in-house or local purposes, the exchange of sensitometric information between different laboratories (which may be world-wide) requires an acknowledged standard basis for exposure and measurement. Thus the standard determination of film speeds to meet ISO (ASA or DIN) requirements needs absolute sensitometry to be carried out by film manufacturers. Similarly the international maintenance of sensitometric quality control procedures in technical laboratories, particularly those concerned with motion-picture photography, has demanded the use of absolute sensitometry in the processing laboratory.

International standards for sensitometric testing are laid down by the International Standards Organization and published in ISO leaflets. Currently these are ISO 6, 2240 and 5800, which describe the exposure and overall testing standards, techniques and conditions for speed determination, and ISO 2239, 2241 and 2242, which describe the standard light sources to be used for testing particular types of film.

The calibration of sensitometers

4   Paragraphs 2.4 to 2.26 describe the function and operation of a typical sensitometer and the general points that may need attention before carrying out sensitometric testing. When any sensitometric equipment is in use, and particularly for absolute sensitometry, regular maintenance and periodic calibration is necessary to maintain standard and repeatable operating conditions (see paragraphs 6.38 and 6.39). A sensitometer to be used for absolute sensitometry must of course be optically clean, serviceable, and set up correctly in accordance with the maker's instructions (see paragraph 6.4). Particular elements that need to be calibrated are the exposing light source, for colour quality and luminous intensity, and the optical elements in the exposing light beam (such as neutral-density filters and exposure-modulating wedges), for neutrality and density. Similar conditions are applicable if non-visual sources of radiation, such as X-rays, ultraviolet or infrared, are to be used.

5   *Calibration of sensitometer lamps.*   Most conventional sensitometers are fitted with tungsten filament lamps, although some instruments use continuous-output xenon-discharge lamps and others use xenon flash tubes. In each case the colour quality and luminous intensity of the light source must be determined, and the instrument calibrated against a known predetermined set of standards, if absolute sensitometry is to be carried out.

The output characteristics of a lamp used in a sensitometer for the determination of sensitometric values must be precisely known, and must be held constant over a period of time and whenever the lamp is in use. The light must also be uniform over the exposure plane and of an appropriate colour quality and luminous intensity. To approach this requirement, the majority of sensitometers use under-run tungsten-filament lamps that have been calibrated so that their colour quality and luminous intensity are known. Stability of light output and a long operating life are achieved by using a stable DC electrical supply, and applying a voltage significantly less than the rated voltage of the lamp. Differences between the colour quality given by the lamp at this voltage and that required for testing the photographic material can be overcome by using photometric filters in the sensitometer (see also paragraphs 2.7 and 2.8). The usual practice in a sensitometric laboratory, is to use tungsten lamps that have been calibrated against a master or 'standard lamp' which itself has been previously calibrated (e.g. by a standards laboratory) to the highest possible accuracy. This practice is advisable because the output characteristics of lamps in regular use change gradually and therefore need to be recalibrated at intervals, whereas the standard lamp (because it is not in regular use) retains its calibrated characteristics for a considerable time. When used under a particular set of operating conditions, a standard lamp produces light of a specified colour quality and luminous intensity. These conditions are determined by calibrating the lamp; once they are known, the lamp can be used directly in a sensitometer as a 'running lamp', or else as a standard by which other lamps can be calibrated.

6   *Calibration and use of standard lamps.*   The output characteristics of a tungsten lamp change during its operating life, particularly during initial use, so before calibration lamps are first 'aged' by running at their rated voltage for a period of time in order to obtain a reasonably stable performance. The calibration of standard lamps is carried out by establishments such as the National Physical Laboratory in the United Kingdom or the National Bureau of Standards in the United States: these establishments are able to determine the required characteristics of a lamp. Tests are carried out either to determine the voltage required in order to produce a given colour temperature, and then the luminous intensity at that voltage; or to examine and determine the lamp performance at a specified number of applied voltages. Some typical calibration data for a tungsten-filament lamp are shown in Table B.1.

The table shows the variations in luminous intensity and colour temperature that occur as the voltage applied to the lamp is changed. Note that there is a non-linear relationship between voltage and the resultant changes in luminous intensity and colour temperature. Because of this, calibration details as given in the table cannot be used to find the voltage necessary to obtain intermediate values. For example, if a colour temperature of 2854 K were required, the applied voltage to obtain this value could not be found directly from the table. However, the data given there may be used to construct graphs such as Figure B.1, from which intermediate values could be determined.

Figure B.1 also includes applied voltage expressed as a percentage of the rated voltage of the lamp. If a colour-temperature value of 2854 K is required

Table B.1 Calibration details for a typical tungsten-filament lamp intended for sensitometric use as a standard lamp.

Rating	Applied voltage (volts)	Luminous intensity (candelas)	Colour temperature (K)	Current consumption (amps)
115 V 500 W	79.0	359.5	2700	3.612
	89.0	540.0	2825	3.857
	102.0	842.5	2960	4.160
	115.0	1226.0	3090	4.450

it can be seen from the graph that the lamp will be operating well below its rated voltage. This will produce a stable light output and ensure a longer operating life. Graphs such as Figure B.1 can be used for calibration purposes; however, it is usually

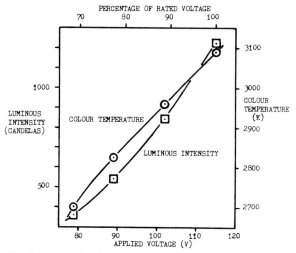

Fig. B.1 Graph showing calibration data for a 115 V tungsten-filament lamp. The non-linear variation of colour temperature and luminous intensity with applied voltage can be clearly seen.

easier to obtain the required information from straight-line graphs. These can be constructed from plots made of the log colour temperature in kelvins against log applied voltage, and also of colour temperature (expressed in mired values) against log luminous intensity. Data plotted in this way can be used to produce straight-line graphs as shown in Figure B.2. (The relation between kelvin and mired values is explained in paragraphs 1.22 and 1.23.)

From the plotted data of Figure B.2, the applied voltage required to produce a stipulated colour temperature may be determined, and then the corresponding luminous intensity found. Thus, for the lamp in question, a colour temperature of 2854 K (equivalent to 350.4 mireds) is obtained at 91.9 volts, giving a luminous intensity of 607 candelas. Note that, as this 'running condition' is

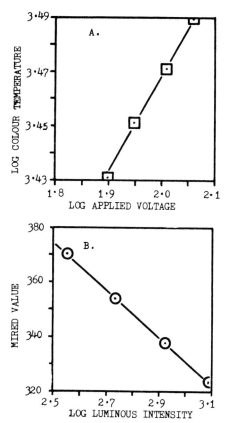

Fig. B.2 Straight-line graphs showing calibration data for a tungsten-filament lamp. Diagram A shows log colour temperature against log voltage; diagram B shows colour temperature in mired values against log luminous intensity. For a sensitometer lamp, the sequence of determining the correct conditions in order to obtain a stipulated colour temperature is to work from A to find the correct voltage, and from B to work out the resulting luminous intensity.

well below the rated voltage of the lamp, it gives a marked increase in lamp life and a low rate of change in light output. A graph of relative lamp life against operating voltage for a typical tungsten lamp is shown in Figure B.3.

7 *Calibration of running lamps.* A calibrated 'standard lamp' may itself be used in a sensitometer. However, if suitable instrumentation is available,

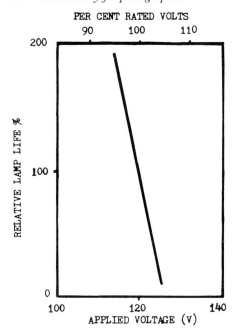

PER CENT RATED VOLTS

Fig. B.3 The variation of tungsten lamp life with voltage. The steepness of the graph line illustrates the benefit gained by under-running sensitometer lamps. It shows that even a small decrease in applied voltage significantly increases the operational life of a lamp.

the characteristics of this standard lamp may be preserved by using it as a master for calibrating other tungsten lamps that are to be in regular use as 'running lamps'. A standard lamp reserved for calibration purposes is used infrequently for short running times, so its output characteristics will not change significantly over a considerable period of time. On the other hand, the characteristics of the running lamp in the sensitometer change with regular use, and it must be recalibrated at intervals.

The operating characteristics of all tungsten lamps change with use. This is because some of the filament evaporates and becomes a brownish discoloured deposit on the glass envelope; also as a consequence of evaporation, the filament becomes thinner. Because of these two conditions, and in order to maintain the required colour quality, it usually becomes necessary to increase the current flow by raising the operating voltage. Thus as the lamp ages and the operating voltage is increased at each calibration, the luminous intensity also increases. The rise in filament temperature causes more and more tungsten to evaporate and deposit on the glass, so the rate of ageing is accelerated until finally the filament becomes so thin that it fails and a replacement lamp is required.

8 *Procedure for calibrating sensitometer running lamps.* Before calibration is carried out, the lamp must be pre-aged by operating at its rated voltage for five hours or so. This is done to avoid the rather rapid changes in performance that take place in the early life of a lamp. Bear in mind that the lamp envelope should not be touched and must be clean, particularly during calibration and use. (See also paragraphs 2.7 and 6.4.)

The calibration of a sensitometer running lamp is initiated by comparing its performance characteristics with those of the standard lamp. Adjustments are then made to both the applied voltage and the distance between the lamp filament and the exposure plane, so that the performance of the running lamp matches that of the standard lamp and thus produces the same exposure conditions. The factors to be equalized are colour quality and illuminance value. Colour quality is matched by adjusting the voltage applied to the running lamp, and illuminance value by adjusting the distance between the lamp filament and the exposure (or wedge) plane. The method used for the calibration of a running lamp depends on what light-measuring instruments are available to carry out the procedure. One of the following methods should be suitable.

Method 1. A suitable calibration can be obtained by using a precision photometer equipped with a measuring probe and incorporating red, green and blue filters, the probe being placed in a central position at the wedge plane of the sensitometer. As the matching of light sources by taking measurements through red, green and blue filters is somewhat similar in principle to that used for analysing colour negatives before printing, a good quality spot-reading colour analyser may also be suitable for this method. A suggested procedure is:
(a) Position and properly align the standard lamp and then adjust the applied voltage (check with an accurate voltmeter) to produce the required colour temperature. Note the red, green and blue arithmetic readings of the photometer, and then remove the standard lamp.
(b) Position and align the running lamp to be calibrated and adjust the voltage until the ratio between the previously noted red and blue readings is re-established. This is the voltage at which the running lamp must be used. (The indication of equality of the ratio between red and blue readings on the photometer shows that at this particular voltage the running lamp is producing light of the same colour quality as the standard lamp.)

(c) Adjust the distance between the lamp and the sensitometer wedge plane until the previously noted green reading is equalized. The illuminance value given by the running lamp is then equal to that of the standard lamp. The running lamp can now be identified with its calibration data, by attaching a label showing its particular operating voltage and working distance.

Method 2. A similar method of calibration can be used if an accurate colour temperature meter and a photometer are available, both being used in a central position at the wedge plane. A suggested procedure is:

(a) With the standard lamp in position, properly aligned and operating under its required conditions, use the colour temperature meter and then the photometer to measure the colour temperature and the illuminance value respectively. Note the two values, and then remove the standard lamp.

(b) With the running lamp to be calibrated in position and aligned, use the colour temperature meter and establish the voltage that will produce a colour temperature value equal to that of the standard lamp. Then, with the lamp at this voltage, and using the photometer, adjust the distance between lamp and wedge plane until the illuminance value is equal to that of the standard lamp. The running lamp can now be identified with its calibration data, by attaching a label showing its particular operating voltage and working distance.

9 *Effects of optical elements in the exposing beam.* Once the sensitometer lamp has been calibrated, any optical elements in the exposing beam also need to be examined, in terms of spectral neutrality and density. The former affects the colour quality while the latter affects the overall level of illuminance received by materials under test. Neutral-density filters and exposure-modulating wedges should be as near ideally neutral as is feasible; that is, their spectral absorption should be as constant as possible throughout the spectral region of interest. The performance characteristics of neutral filters can be measured using a spectrophotometer and plotted as spectral density curves. Curves for typical neutral filters are shown in Figure B.4.

10 *Effect of light scatter by neutral filters.* The direct or specular nature of illumination in most sensitometers reduces the choice of neutral-density filters because of their possible Callier (light-scattering) effect when in the exposing beam. If it is

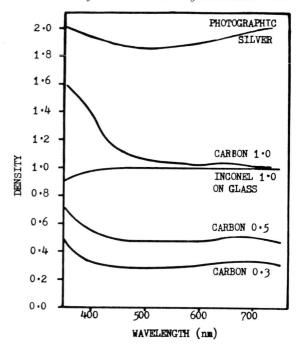

Fig. B.4 Spectral density curves of a number of neutral-density filters of different composition. The curves are marked with their nominal neutral-density values.

not to be held in contact with the test material, the Callier coefficient (or Q value) of the filter should be near unity. On the other hand, exposure-modulating wedges that are in contact with the test material may possess high values of Q without causing problems (see also Figure 9.1 and paragraph 9.12). Such wedges and neutral filters may be composed of dispersions of metallic silver or finely divided carbon in gelatin, or metal (inconel) coated on glass. Table B.2 lists some types of neutral filters with their characteristics and applications.

11 *Illuminance at the exposure plane.* Ideally a sensitometer should have a facility for changing the distance between the light source and the exposure plane over quite a wide range so that the illuminance received by the test material can be correspondingly varied. Provided that the light source is sufficiently compact, the inverse square law can be invoked to enable the illuminance at the exposure plane to be calculated. The illuminance in lux is found by dividing the luminous intensity in candelas by the distance in metres squared. This also provides an absolute scale of illuminance against which all exposure modulators can be calibrated. The use of an absolute scale is not

Table B.2 Characteristics and general applications of typical neutral filters.

Type of absorber	Callier coefficient (green light)	Application and characteristics
Neutral-density filter Kodak Wratten 96; very finely divided carbon + dyes in gelatin.	1.02	Camera use, and sensitometric neutral filters for wavelengths from 400 to 700 nm.
Inconel on glass.	1.01	Neutral filters, limited only by surface reflection.
M-type carbon: larger particles of carbon in gelatin.	1.27	Unsuitable for camera use; used for sensitometric wedges, but not for neutral filters.
Photographic silver	1.41	Unsuitable for camera use; used for wedges, but not for neutral filters.

essential, however, as a correct relative scale can be used for the calibration of exposure modulators.

12   *Calibration of neutral-density filters.* The calibration of neutral-density filters and wedges is commonly carried out using densitometers measuring visual diffuse density with an optical geometry and light quality unlike those of the instruments in which they are to be used. Such calibrations are usually adequate for comparative sensitometry, but something more rigorous is needed for absolute use. One method is to use the optical characteristics of the sensitometer itself.

For the calibration of a neutral-density filter (by Toy's method), a range of exposures may be made on a film using the sensitometer at known relative illuminance levels but at a constant exposure time. A similar range of exposures is then made on the same film but with the neutral filter to be calibrated inserted in the exposing beam in its operating position. If the two exposure samples are processed identically and measured using a densitometer, two curves of density against unmodified log illuminance may be plotted, as shown in Figure B.5.

The horizontal separation of these curves (the separation in log illuminance) is measured at a number of convenient density levels and the mean value is the calibrated density of the neutral filter. This can of course be carried out for a range of such filters, and by this means an entire step wedge can be calibrated. The procedure is rigorous and reproducible, and often yields different results from a direct densitometric calibration. An alternative procedure, particularly suitable for absorbers of low Q value, is to use a high-quality photometer with a measuring probe that can be placed at the exposing plane in the sensitometer. In the case of non-neutrality of the absorber, the photometric method will not generally duplicate the sensi-

tometric calibration unless the photometer has a similar spectral sensitivity distribution to that of the film, or if near-monochromatic radiation has been used.

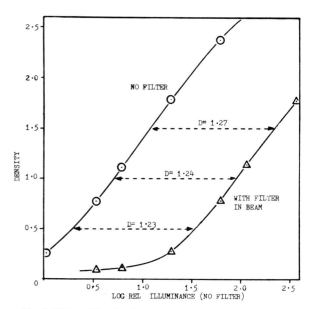

Fig. B.5 The calibration (by Toy's method) of a neutral-density filter to be used in a sensitometer. A piece of film is given a range of exposures in the sensitometer, first without and then with the filter in position. After identical processing, the two results are plotted as shown and the mean of the horizontal separation of the curves indicates the calibrated density of the neutral filter. In this case $D = 1.25$.

13   *Calibration of neutral filters in a spectrosensitometer.* In the case of a spectrosensitometer, which is an instrument designed for exposures to narrow spectral bands throughout the useful spectral region, calibration becomes more awkward. Generally the illuminance (photometric units) in each band is not of great interest but the irradiance (energy units) is. It is customary then to calibrate

each band using a sensor such as a 'thermopile radiometer' (which is calibrated in energy units). Departures from neutrality of any absorber present may mean that a calibration is required for each wavelength band of interest. An alternative, sometimes used, is to replace neutral absorbers by opaque material arranged in grid patterns instead of filters, and with stepped apertures instead of wedges. In each application the device must be effectively out of focus at the film surface. Grids can only therefore be used in diffuse systems, while stepped apertures have to be 'streaked' past the emulsion under test. Examples of such modulators are shown in Figure B.6. However, the exposures given by such moving apertures are time-scale exposures, and as these may not be typical of use, they can be of rather limited value.

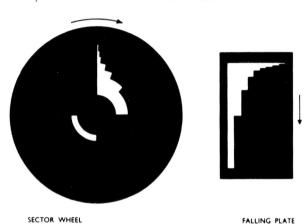

SECTOR WHEEL   FALLING PLATE

Fig. B.6 Time-scale exposure modulators. Movement of the stepped aperture across the film surface gives a range of different exposures. Multiple exposures are often required, but these usually give different sensitometric results when compared to results produced by intensity (illuminance) scale methods using a step wedge, owing in part to possible reciprocity and intermittency effects.

Photometric and energy units of exposure

14 The traditional units of photographic exposure are based on photometry, a system that measures illumination in terms of what the standard human observer sees, by visible radiation. The units are expressed in lux seconds (lux s). Now if a piece of photographic film is exposed by invisible radiation at a wavelength of say, 370 nm (in the near-ultraviolet region), the almost non-existent sensitivity of the eye at that wavelength could not detect the exposure. Thus the exposure in lux s (being a unit of visible light) would effectively be zero. However, as the exposed film is very sensitive to radiation at 370 nm, after

development it will produce a definite image. Thus in photometric terms we might argue that photographs could be taken at zero lux s exposure.

This absurdity serves to illustrate the limitation of an exposure calibration based on photometric units which are related to visible radiation. Clearly, in such cases, the exposure is better measured in terms of the irradiance received by the film instead of illuminance. Exposures may then be expressed in terms of joules per square centimetre or per square metre ($J\,cm^{-2}$ or $J\,m^{-2}$). Other units commonly found in the literature are ergs per square centimetre ($erg\,cm^{-2}$). Although the exposure in photometric units can be related mathematically to that in radiometric units (see paragraph 15), the method is potentially of low accuracy and is somewhat tedious. It is preferable in such cases to calibrate an instrument using radiometric units throughout. If monochromatic or near-monochromatic exposures are made, it is possible also to calculate the exposure rather simply in terms of quanta per unit area. The applicability of the different units of exposure is shown in Table B.3.

Table B.3 Applications of various units of exposure.

Units of exposure	Applications
Photometric	Traditional sensitometry, derivation of film speeds.
Radiometric	Determination of sensitivities of photographic systems, including those sensitive to invisible radiation. (Such figures should be accompanied by spectral data on the exposure.) Commonly used for non-silver photographic processes.
Quantum	Fundamental mechanistic studies on radiation-sensitive systems. Comparisons of system efficiencies.

15 *Relations between photometric, radiometric and Quantum units.* If we have the following units of exposure it is often useful to be able to relate them:

Photometric M lux s ($= lumen\,s\,m^{-2}$)
Radiometric E $J\,m^{-2}$
Quantum q quanta m^{-2}

Radiometric units are related to photometric units by the equation

$$M\,lux\,s = K_m \int E'_\lambda\,V_\lambda\,d\lambda\;lumen\,s\,m^{-2}$$

where K_m is the maximum luminous efficiency ($= 6.8 \times 10^2\,lumen\,s\,J^{-1}$), E'_λ is the spectral irradiance at wavelength λm in units $J\,m^{-2}\,m^{-1}$, and

and V_λ is the visual (photopic) luminosity function for the standard observer; it is dimensionless and $0 \leqslant V_\lambda \leqslant 1.0$.

Care must be taken to standardize units in calculation. Thus

$$M \,(\text{lux s}) = M \,(\text{lumen s m}^{-2})$$

$$= K_m \,(\text{lumen s J}^{-1}) \int E'_\lambda (\text{J m}^{-2}\,\text{m}^{-1})\ V_\lambda \text{d}\lambda \,(\text{m})$$

relates the exposure in lux s to exposure in J m^{-2} (a radiometric unit).

The relation between photometric and radiometric units of exposure with the units illustrated above is simplified to

$$M = 6.8 \times 10^2 \int E'_\lambda \ V_\lambda \text{d}\lambda \tag{1}$$

To relate radiometric and quantum exposure units we make use of the relation:

$$q = \frac{1}{hc} \int E'_\lambda \lambda \text{d}\lambda$$

where h (Planck's constant) $= 6.626 \times 10^{-34}$ J s, and c (the velocity of light) $= 3.0 \times 10^8$ m s^{-1}. Once again care must be taken in standardizing units. Thus

$$q \,(\text{quanta m}^{-2})$$

$$= \frac{1}{h} \,(\text{J}^{-1}\text{s}^{-1}) \,\frac{1}{c} \,(\text{m}^{-1}\text{s}) \int E'_\lambda (\text{J m}^{-2}\,\text{m}^{-1})$$

$$\times \lambda \,(\text{m}) \ \text{d}\lambda \,(\text{m})$$

The relation between radiometric and quantum units of exposure with the units shown is

$$q = 5.03 \times 10^{24} \int E'_\lambda \lambda \ \text{d}\lambda \tag{2}$$

If monochromatic radiation is used, this expression reduces to

$$q = 5.03 \times 10^{24} E_\lambda \lambda \tag{3}$$

The relation between photometric and quantum units of exposure is

$$q = 7.4 \times 10^{21}\ M\ \frac{\int E'_\lambda \lambda \ \text{d}\lambda}{\int E'_\lambda V_\lambda \ \text{d}\lambda} \tag{4}$$

where q is in quanta m^{-2}, M is in lux s and λ is in m.

If the instrument is calibrated and then an optical element of spectral transmittance F_λ is placed in the beam the equations shown above have to be modified:

(1) $\qquad M = 6.8 \times 10^2 \int E'_\lambda F_\lambda V_\lambda \ \text{d}\lambda \tag{5}$

(2) $\qquad q = 5.03 \times 10^{24} \int E'_\lambda F_\lambda \lambda \ \text{d}\lambda \tag{6}$

(3) $\qquad q = 5.03 \times 10^{24} E_\lambda F_\lambda \lambda \tag{7}$

(4) $\qquad q = 7.4 \times 10^{21} M\ \frac{\int E'_\lambda F_\lambda \lambda \ \text{d}\lambda}{\int E'_\lambda \ V_\lambda \ \text{d}\lambda} \tag{8}$

In any conversion of photometric units, care has to be taken that the difference between the V_λ function and the spectral sensitivity distribution of any sensitive element does not lead to the kind of nonsense described in paragraph 14.

Appendix C

Tone reproduction and subjective aims in photographic printing

1 Tone reproduction can be classified as being either objective or subjective. Objective tone reproduction in printing refers, in general, to the relationship between the log luminance differences presented by the various tones of the scene photographed, and the density differences of the corresponding tones in the print. It therefore involves comparative measurements of the two. The objective aspect of tone reproduction is considered in paragraphs 5.25 to 5.27 and in Chapter 7, and the subjective aspect is introduced in paragraphs 6.53 and 7.33.

The subjective aspect of tone reproduction is concerned with a similar relationship, but a comparison is attempted between the sensations and perceptions produced by viewing the various tones in the scene and those produced by viewing a reproduction of the same tones in the print. Subjective tone reproduction is thus particularly related to the response of the human eye and the complex interpretations of images by the brain. These effects of visual sensation cannot be expressed in objective terms as a measurement or a curve on a graph, and in any case it is seldom that subject and print can be directly compared. Thus for pictorial photography in particular, the quality of results can only be judged subjectively, by viewing the print. Because of this, and with regard to the general subjective tone reproduction aims in printing, and assessment can be obtained by submitting a variety of known prints, having different tonal characteristics, for consideration by a group of competent observers, and by averaging their evaluations of print quality in terms of the prints they prefer. Thus the known objective characteristics of subjectively chosen excellent prints can be related to objective measurements made in producing the photographs. By this means, the subjective judgement of observers may be used both by manufacturers to modify the tone reproduction characteristics of their materials, and

by the photographer to make related considerations, particularly at the printing stage.

2 *Subjectively preferred tone reproduction as a function of subject luminance range.* When considering the subject of preferred tone reproduction, we should bear in mind that the tones of grey in a print from dark to light rarely match the tones and colours of the scene, but because we have become used to seeing such reproductions they are quite acceptable and considered to be satisfactory visual representations of original scenes (see also paragraph 5.25). Such is the response of our eyes and experienced brain that we accept a two-dimensional black-and-white photograph as presenting a satisfactory portrayal of a three-dimensional coloured object.

Extensive studies have been carried out into the objectively measured tone reproduction that turns out to be subjectively preferred. In a particular thorough investigation, the research workers Jones and Nelson examined the relation between the negative density ranges of 170 negatives of outdoor scenes and the useful log exposure ranges of the photographic papers that were subjectively found to give the best prints. A panel of observers was convened and the members required to consider prints made at a variety of printing exposure levels and on a range of paper grades. These were viewed under standard lighting conditions and the observers asked to select the prints they preferred. Altogether several thousand prints were made for this experimental programme and a number of interesting and useful results emerged.

In general it was found that the density range of the negative dictated the choice of a paper grade with a similar log exposure range, in order to get optimum results in printing. However this was only applicable when the variations of negative density range were due to differences in the camera exposure, development of the negative or the type of film used. It was found also that the scene itself influenced the preferred pictorial tone reproduction, and that its effect sometimes tended to go against the idea that we should always aim to record most subject tones and occupy the full tonal range of the paper. This idea was undoubtedly true for average scenes, which gave average negatives at normal levels of exposure and development, and which might all be successfully printed on a normal grade of paper. It was not, however, necessarily the case for other than average subjects. For example, a subject with a long luminance range, which would yield a normally exposed and developed negative with a long density range, was found to give the best subjectively preferred print when the log exposure range of the paper was insufficient to record all the subject tones. In other words, either highlight or shadow detail, or both, would be degraded and might be lost in the preferred print of a subject of long luminance range. Subjects of short luminance range, on the other hand, yielded best prints in which all the subject tones were recorded well within the capabilities of the printing paper; highlights were thus recorded darker and shadows lighter than might have been expected. The same criteria can of course be applied to colour photographs, where for the majority of pictorial presentations a moderate difference in tone and colour between subject and reproduction is usually quite acceptable.

Consideration of mass-produced colour photographs for the amateur market suggests that a single grade of colour printing paper and the normally developed colour negative form a combination that is usually successful, despite the variety of subject luminance ranges that must have been photographed. It is also true that, for the mass market, correctly exposed colour reversal film is usually successful in achieving a pleasing record of a huge variety of subjects. Both these observations support the conclusions of the subjective studies of tone reproduction, and caution the photographic printer that objective considerations may not always be the best guide, especially if the print is to be used for subjective effect.

We must however bear in mind that these conclusions refer only to subjective tone reproduction. When all the visible detail and texture in a subject is required and has been recorded in the negative, the subject tones must all be printed so that they are contained by the accepted log exposure range of the printing paper. The full tonal range and texture of the subject will then be well presented in the print.

3 *Preferred tone reproduction of pictorial scenes.* The work of Jones and Nelson established the preferred tone reproduction curve of the average sunlit outdoor scene (with a subject luminance range of 160:1. Curve P in Figure C.1 represents a similar tone reproduction curve, and we can see that it shows a middle-tone contrast higher than that of an objectively ideal gradient of 1.0 (shown by the dashed line at an angle of 45°). As we would expect, tones become compressed at the ends of the curve, although this is not necessarily subjectively offensive. Experiments with illuminated positive transparencies (curve T) have shown, however, that less compression of shadow detail would be preferred. In other words, if the printing paper D_{max} were higher, the tone reproduction would be subjectively improved. The differences are shown in Figure C.1. Since these tests were carried out, manufacturers have indeed been able to increase the D_{max} and improve other relevant characteristics of photographic printing paper. These improvements have not of course changed the principles of preferred tone reproduction, and subjective considerations in printing are fully applicable, particularly for pictorial photography.

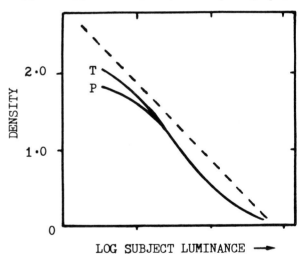

Fig. C.1 Tone reproduction characteristics of the preferred print of an outdoor scene are shown as curve P. The curve T shows the characteristic preferred using a suitably illuminated positive transparency which enabled a higher D_{max} to be obtained. The dashed reference line shows a hypothetical reproduction at a uniform gradient of unity.

During the tests carried out to examine the conditions for preferred tone reproduction it was found that, whereas there was a large spread of points on the paper characteristic curves corresponding to the printed lightest tone, this was much

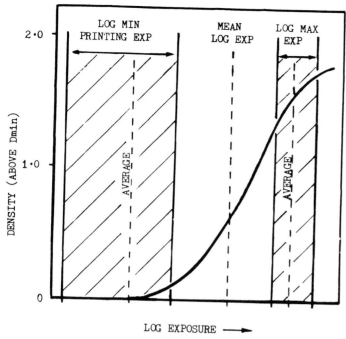

Fig. C.2 A representative summary of the printing of more than forty negatives of outdoor scenes, which yielded first-choice preferred prints on paper with the characteristic shown by the curve. The prints were judged for subjective quality by a group of competent observers. The ranges of maximum and minimum densities as printed show that the shadow tones were all exposed to show as gradients on the paper characteristic curve much greater than zero (averaging 1.0 or so), indicating a satisfactory reproduction of shadow detail. On the other hand, highlight details were frequently exposed to give a zero gradient on the curve, indicating a complete loss of highlight detail. The average printing of the maximum negative densities lay at the extreme toe of the paper characteristic curves, while that of the minimum negative densities was well below D_{max}.

less true for the darkest tone. The positions of this spread of highlights and shadows of outdoor scenes are shown as shaded bands in Figure C.2. The characteristic curve represents the response of forty or so prints made from selected negatives on the same grade of paper. It was found that the deep shadow detail usually lay close to the point on the curve at which a line drawn from very near the extreme toe touched the shoulder, or at a lower exposure position depending on the negative density range. Therefore it was unusual for a preferred reproduction to possess shadow areas devoid of detail. On the other hand, some fifty per cent of the extreme highlights were printed at a position on the paper characteristic curve at a lower exposure than those at the bottom of the curve where the gradient was zero. Any extreme highlight detail present in the negative was thus lost under these conditions.

4 *Conclusions on subjective tone reproduction in printing.*
For pictorial photography we can deduce that, although shadow detail and contrast in the print should be maintained for a satisfactory visual result, the reproduction of highlight detail and contrast is found to be less important than we might think. The latter may be because with scenes having a long luminance range, such as outdoor scenes with bright highlights (for example white clouds or small specular reflections), the detail and contrast (luminance differences) in the highlights, which may be recorded on the negative, are in fact not perceived at all by the human observer viewing the subject. Thus while a print may not reproduce the complete range of luminance differences present in the original scene, and in the negative, it may still be judged to be a preferred print having excellent quality. We must however remember that whenever it is important to record in the photograph the lightest important highlight and the darkest important shadow, these must be recorded in the negative and printed so that they are contained within the log exposure range of the printing paper.

Appendix D

Integral and analytical densities and the sensitometry of colour exposures, colour masking and inter-image effects

1 The sensitometry and measurement of densities in colour photographic materials is complicated by the fact that the yellow and in particular the magenta and cyan dyes produced in the image layers are not ideal for photography. They tend to overlap each other in their effect so that each dye, although it has a major subtracting or absorbing result in approximately one-third of the visible spectrum, also absorbs a small but often significant amount of light in other parts of the spectrum (see Chapter 11). This effect, which may be described as 'secondary absorption', causes deterioration in the colour quality of the photograph. In most colour negative and reversal materials these unwanted effects are mitigated, and colour quality thus improved, by the use of either colour-masking or inter-image effects (see also paragraphs 11.9 and 11.10). However, before we consider the sensitometry of these in more detail, we need to know something about the different ways of measuring the colour densities of exposed and processed colour materials.

There are two major classifications and methods of determining and measuring colour density, and the use of one or the other depends upon what information is required.

(a) Integral densities measure the combined densities of all three dye image layers together. Integral densitometry is thus used to measure the effect or performance of the whole colour material.
(b) Analytical densities measure the densities of an individual dye image layer alone. Analytical densitometry is thus used to measure the composition or amount of dye in each image layer.

2 *Integral densities.* Integral densities are those we considered throughout Chapter 11; they are used, for example, when testing and comparing colour materials, in process quality control, and when assessing colour films before printing. For integral density determination, the material may be exposed in a sensitometer to (for example) standard photographic daylight through a neutral-density wedge to produce a 'neutral or grey-wedge exposure'. After processing, the results may be measured on a colour densitometer through red, green and blue filters, to indicate the combined visual or printing effect of all three image layers together.

3 *Analytical densities.* Analytical densities are used mainly by colour material manufacturers and by research workers, whenever it is necessary to consider colour images with regard to the individual amounts of dye in each layer without incorporating the overlapping absorptions of the other dyes present. An analytical density is directly proportional to the concentration of the dye measured and has no contribution from other absorbers.

Such densities are usually computed from integral density values using simultaneous equations established by the examination of single dye concentration series. These are obtained by exposing the test material to (for example) standard photographic daylight filtered to suit the individual sensitivity of each emulsion layer. This can be done by using a very sharp-cutting colour filter in the sensitometer (see Figure 11.3), thus giving an exposure to coloured light instead of neutral, white light. The coloured light then passes through a neutral-density wedge to produce a 'colour wedge exposure'. After processing, integral densities measured from such samples are used to assess the proportional contribution of each dye to each of the three integral densities. Equations are then set up that enable any set of three integral densities to be transformed to analytical densities.

An alternative procedure is to use a calibrated

analytical colour densitometer. A typical instrument would use calibrated (cyan, magenta and yellow) colour wedges containing the same dyes as those used in the test material, instead of the red, green and blue filters used for measuring integral densities. The sample to be measured would be placed on the densitometer in one of two identical light beams and the calibrated colour wedges inserted into the other beam and adjusted until the two colours matched. By this means, the cyan, magenta and yellow analytical densities of individual dye layers of the colour material could be measured directly. However, because of difficulties in these procedures, analytical densities are most often found more easily after exposure to white light and by using a computer to convert the measured integral densities to analytical values. It is emphasized that analytical densities are more difficult to obtain than integral densities and are seldom required by the photographer, the processor or the user of the material. They are, however, of particular value to the manufacturer of colour materials.

4   *The sensitometry of colour wedge exposures.* The general method used for finding the sensitometric characteristics of a colour material is by exposure to white light through a neutral grey step wedge, colour processing the exposed sensitometric strip and measuring the results on a colour densitometer. Integral density values are found by taking three readings in turn of each step of the strip through narrow-cut red, green and blue filters (see paragraph 11.24). Three separate characteristic curves are then plotted on the same graph for viewing and interpretation. This general integral density method measures the combined effect of the three dye image layers. For example, if the density of the yellow dye layer (to blue light) is being measured, the measurement is in addition affected by the secondary absorptions of the other dye layers, and particularly those of the magenta dye layer, which also absorb a small but significant amount of blue light. Integral density measurements are therefore suitable for use when comparing colour materials, for process control, and when assessing colour films before printing, because the combined effect of the dye images is measured and this simulates the way in which the material will respond in practice. However, with regard to the quality of colour reproduction, there is often a need to consider the effect of one individual dye image without the overlapping effect of the other layers. This can be done by exposing the test material to

coloured light instead of white light. The sensitometry of this 'colour (or non-neutral) exposure' generally consists of exposure of the material to red, green or blue (and in some cases yellow) light through a primary-coloured filter, measurement on a colour densitometer through its red, green and blue filters, and plotting the results as colour characteristic curves on the same graph for viewing and interpretation. So in the first case we have what can be called 'neutral wedge exposure' and in the second case 'colour wedge exposure'.

Colour wedge exposures can give us information not available from the customary neutral wedge exposures, and particularly information concerned with the quality of colour reproduction. For example, this method of colour sensitometry can be used to reveal and quantify the imperfections of the image dyes. This can be important sensitometric information in the design of colour photographic systems for scientific purposes, and can reveal the causes of unsatisfactory results or unusual visual effects in conventional applications.

5   *The reproduction of red in a colour reversal film.* Probably the most interesting case of colour quality deficiency that can be shown by using colour wedge exposures is the reproduction of red by colour photography. The result of a red sensitometric exposure of a colour reversal film is shown in Figure D.1 and is an excellent example for analysis. We would expect that the response of the red-sensitive emulsion would show as a normal characteristic curve and those of the blue- and green-sensitive emulsions as horizontal lines at D_{max} (indicating no response to red light), as shown in the smaller diagram of Figure D.1. However, in an actual situation the characteristic curves usually display three regions, as shown in the larger diagram of Figure D.1. The first or low-exposure region shows the effect of exposure on the red-sensitive emulsion alone, as a steep fall in red density to a plateau, accompanied by a less contrasty drop in the blue and green densities. The latter corresponds to the reduction in secondary blue and green absorptions of the cyan dye as it decreases in concentration. Over this low-exposure region the appearance of the sensitometric strip changes from black through a series of increasingly lighter steps, gradually colouring to the most saturated red that the dyes can produce. The mid-exposure region may be a long or short log exposure range, depending on the film and the range of wavelengths comprising the red exposure. In this region the response of the film is such that

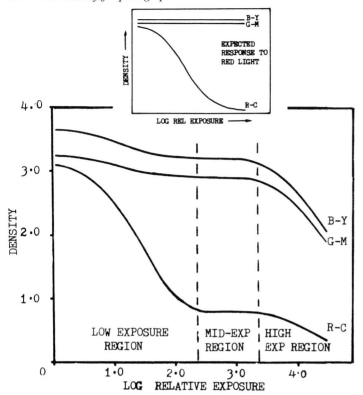

Fig. D.1 Characteristic curves of a colour reversal film showing the effect of sensitometric exposure to red light. B, G and R refer to the original sensitivities of the emulsion layers, and Y, M and C to the dyes in the layers after processing. The small diagram shows the expected response and the larger diagram the actual response. Three exposure regions (low, medium and high) are clearly visible. The low and high regions show a fairly typical response to red-light exposure, but the mid exposure region is characterized by a plateau in all three characteristic curves, indicating that in this region the tones of a red-coloured subject will not be satisfactorily reproduced. Notice that the log exposure range shown is greater than 4.0 (10 000 to 1).

there is no change in any density and therefore no step differences are visible in the sensitometric strip. At the higher exposure levels (because the filter used to produce the red exposure is not perfect) the inevitable (small) blue and green content of the red exposing light takes effect and the blue and green densities decrease steeply. There is also a corresponding drop in the red density, owing to the reduction in secondary red absorption of the yellow and magenta image dyes. This high-exposure region shows on the sensitometric strip as a change from saturated red through a series of progressively lighter steps.

In a photograph of a vivid red subject possessing form and texture, both should be revealed by changes of lightness when viewed. However, any part of the subject image that lies in the mid-exposure region described above may in fact be devoid of apparent form and texture, and will lack contrast and thus appear very 'flat'. In the context of objective photographic recording, this sensitometric data could indicate a very serious loss of information. Sensitometry could even suggest the need for a change of film, recording system or conditions, so that the desired results could be obtained. If the subject to be recorded was geographically remote, and therefore costly to get to, or if it was part of an expensive experiment, or an elaborate set in a studio, such preliminary sensitometry could save a lot of time, money, and personal prestige.

The recording of red by a colour reversal film has been discussed in this example because exposure to red light most clearly shows the three regions of sensitometric interest and also the extensive mid-exposure plateau shown in Figure D.1. However, it is not unusual to find a similar plateau effect with exposure to yellow light. In most other cases the log exposure separation of the three curves is not sufficient to give this effect, although pronounced colour changes may be found from end to end of such sensitometric strips, and therefore from one exposure level to another.

6 *The function and sensitometry of integral colour masking.* The sensitometry of exposure to coloured light can be used to explain the effects of the automatic integral colour masking of colour negative materials that occurs during processing. As we know, such masking is present because the absorption properties of the dyes used in colour materials are not ideal for photography. The yellow dye layer is fairly satisfactory and needs no correction, but the magenta and cyan layers absorb some light of colours that they should ideally transmit. Because of this effect, which may be called 'secondary absorption', almost all colour negative emulsions contain couplers (colour-formers) which are themselves coloured. The coloured couplers that are not used up during development produce a pale orange-coloured, low-contrast, positive mask. This integral mask counteracts the colour-absorption deficiencies of the magenta and cyan dye images, so that when the negative is printed satisfactory colour quality can be obtained. The different colour sensitivities of emulsion layers in the colour printing paper are designed to respond correctly to the effects of the pale orange masking in the negative.

The sensitometric consequences of integral colour masking are shown in Figure D.2, representing the characteristic curves of a colour negative film following sensitometric colour exposure to red light. Diagram A illustrates the effects in an unmasked negative, B the effects in a masked negative. In each case (because there has been a red sensitometric exposure) we see the red density giving a fairly typical negative characteristic curve, representing an increasing amount of cyan image dye as log exposure increases. When the negative is measured on a colour densitometer or when it is printed, because the cyan dye is imperfect it absorbs a small amount of blue and green light as well as red light. Therefore as the cyan dye concentration increases, not only the red density but also the blue and green densities increase as shown in diagram A. This is an unwanted effect, since the cyan dye is intended only to restrict the red content of exposure during printing and not the blue and green contents.

In order to mask (and thus correct) the effect of the unwanted blue and green absorptions of the cyan image, the cyan-forming couplers incorporated into the film emulsion, can themselves be made with colour absorptions substantially similar to the unwanted absorptions of the image dye. In the cyan-forming layer the couplers will therefore be reddish and absorb blue and green light. These

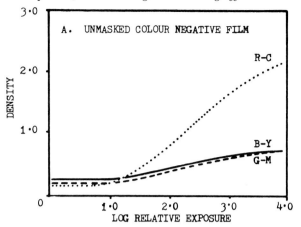

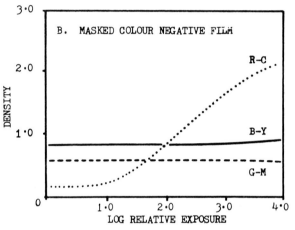

Fig. D.2 An example of the sensitometry of integral colour masking. R, B and G refer to the original sensitivities of the emulsion layers, and C, Y and M to the dyes in the layers after processing. Diagram A shows characteristic curves representing the effect of sensitometric colour exposure to red light of an unmasked colour negative film, and the unwanted effect of blue and green absorptions by the imperfect dye in the resultant cyan image. Diagram B shows a similar red density characteristic curve, but with the unwanted effects of blue and green absorptions corrected by a pale reddish-coloured (Y + M) positive mask, formed during development by the unused colour-couplers left in the emulsion layer after the negative image has been produced. A similar situation exists in the green-sensitive magenta-forming layer, where a pale-yellow positive mask is formed. The combined integral masks thus give the familiar pale-orange appearance of a masked colour negative.

couplers are also made so that their colour is dissipated when dye formation takes place during development. Thus the reddish-coloured couplers that are left in the emulsion, after the colour negative image has been produced, form a low-contrast positive mask in the image layer, and this compensates for the unwanted blue and green absorptions of the cyan image. In this way the sensitometric effect shown in diagram B is achieved. The blue and green densities remain very nearly constant over the usual log exposure range of the film, and the printing effect is thus very similar to that of an ideal cyan image with no unwanted absorptions. A similar masking method is used to correct the unwanted (mainly blue) absorptions of the magenta dye, by making the colour-couplers in that layer yellowish. The combined effect of the masking couplers is seen in the high blue and green D_{min} values shown in diagram B, representing the pale orange appearance characteristic of masked colour films.

The pale orange appearance of an integral colour mask means of course that this masking method is unsuitable for reproductions, such as colour transparencies, that are to be viewed directly. Therefore, to minimize the effects of dye deficiencies in colour reversal films, inter-image effects are used. These have a similar correcting function to that of integral colour masking. Inter-image effects can also be used in colour negative materials to supplement the effect of the mask, and because of this the amount of mask coloration required in the film can be reduced.

7 *The function and sensitometry of inter-image effects.* The sensitometry of exposure to coloured light can be used to explain the function of the designed inter-image effects which occur during the processing of colour materials (see also paragraphs 2.103 and 11.10). Such effects are, in part, used to correct the unwanted effects of dye deficiencies, and are necessary because the absorption properties of the dyes used in colour materials are not ideal for photography. The yellow dye layer is reasonably satisfactory, but the magenta and cyan layers

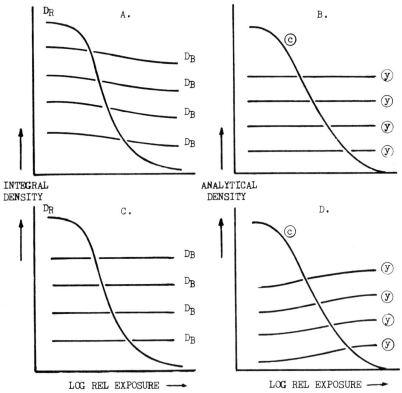

Fig. D.3 Representative diagrams illustrating the sensitometric response of colour reversal films to inter-image effects. The red-sensitive emulsion layers have received a sensitometric exposure to red light; the blue-sensitive layers are considered as having received a series of four different uniform exposures to blue light; the green-sensitive layers have been totally exposed and thus produce no magenta dye. Diagrams A and B represent an unsatisfactory condition where no inter-image effects have been used: A is the result of this, and shows increases in blue density (D_B) as the red density (D_R) increases, owing to the secondary blue absorptions of its cyan dye; B shows the actual cyan (c) and yellow (y) dye concentrations (analytical densities) involved. Diagrams C and D represent a satisfactory condition as a result of the colour corrections achieved by inter-image effects enhanced by using DIR couplers. C shows no increases in blue density as red density increases, and D shows the dye concentrations (analytical densities) required to obtain this.

absorb some light of colours that they should ideally transmit, and these 'secondary absorptions' cause degradation in the colour quality of photographs. Correction of this degradation cannot be made by using the integral colour masking used in negative materials because the coloration of the mask makes it unsuitable for colour reversal materials, which are viewed directly. Fortunately, however, the problem does not arise with inter-image effects, and they can be used to correct or to mitigate the unwanted results of secondary absorptions in reversal materials.

The correcting function of inter-image effects is controlled and encouraged by development-inhibitor-releasing (DIR) couplers, which are incorporated into the film emulsion during manufacture. They operate with the developer and the by-products of development by controlled diffusion between adjacent image layers so that the amount of image dye produced in one layer is beneficially affected by the amount of development in the adjacent layer (explained in more detail later). By this means, the effects of dye deficiencies are lessened and results of a satisfactory colour quality suitable for direct viewing are obtained.

In order to understand how inter-image effects (as encouraged by DIR couplers) improve colour reproduction, we can best consider their sensitometric effect in colour reversal materials by studying the representative diagrams in Figure D.3.

The red-sensitive layer in each diagram has received a sensitometric exposure to red light, and its response is shown as a typical characteristic curve. The blue-sensitive layer is considered as having received four different, but uniform exposures to blue light which correspond to the four levels of blue density shown in diagram C. (If this were done in practice, four pieces of film would of course be exposed.) The green-sensitive layer has previously been totally exposed and has thus produced no magenta dye, so there is no magenta image to consider. Now, if the cyan dye produced in the red-sensitive layer were ideal in its effect and possessed no secondary blue absorptions, diagram C would represent the satisfactory response we would expect to see. If, on the other hand, we consider the effect of the (imperfect) cyan dye actually used in colour reversal film, we find that,

because of its secondary blue absorptions, the blue density increases as the red density increases, as shown in diagram A.

Diagrams A and B represent an unsatisfactory condition where no inter-image effects have been used. A shows that blue density (D_B) increases as red density (D_R) increases, owing to the uncorrected secondary blue absorptions of the imperfect cyan dye. The blue density thus varies in proportion to the cyan dye concentration, and because of this the result of a red exposure controls not just red light but also some blue light. The secondary absorptions of the cyan dye thus cause a degradation of colour reproduction when such a transparency is viewed. Diagram B represents the actual dye concentrations (c for cyan and y for yellow) that are present in the image layers of A, and these are found by converting the integral densities of A to analytical densities (see paragraphs 1 to 3). We can see in diagram B that, when no inter-image effects operate, the yellow dye concentration remains constant while that of the cyan dye changes.

Diagrams C and D represent a satisfactory condition where inter-image effects, enhanced by DIR couplers, have been used. D represents the dye concentrations involved (analytical densities) and shows a reduction in yellow as cyan increases. This is because the formation of cyan dye is accompanied by the diffusion of a mobile developer inhibitor into the yellow-forming layer, and this inter-image effect reduces the amount of yellow dye in inverse proportion to the cyan dye concentration. This reduction in yellow as cyan increases gives rise to the integral densities shown in diagram C where, overall, the cyan dye appears ideal in that no variation of blue density accompanies the large change in red density. Similar-acting inter-image effects are used to correct the effect of additional unwanted secondary absorptions and also those in other dye layers.

It can be seen that the compensating yellow dye curves in diagram D are similar in their effect to the integral masking used in colour negative films (see paragraph 6). Inter-image effects enhanced by the use of DIR couplers are in fact used to augment the colour masking in colour negative films, and thus allow the amount of mask coloration to be reduced.

Appendix E

Electronic terms and methods used in photographic evaluation

1 Photography, like all sciences, has a terminology of its own, most of it obtained historically. The photographic meaning of words such as exposure, speed, developer, contrast, gamma, etc. are understood by photographers, but may have a different meaning or be misunderstood by, say, an electronics engineer. Therefore, now that photography is being increasingly allied to and compared with other reproduction and communication systems, such as television, it is logical that the terminology and methods used for evaluating such systems should, as far as possible, be alike.

2 *Photographic terms and their electronic analogues.* Some of the established techniques, terminology and measurements used in telecommunications are now used also for evaluating the production of photographic imagery. Both systems involve the communication of information and it is therefore convenient to assess them in a similar manner. Many of the terms used in telecommunications and electronics can be applied also to photography. Exposure is similar to the input signal received by an electronic circuit, while development is similar to amplification. Image quality is fidelity, and granularity becomes noise. The ratio of the image contrast to the granularity is the signal-to-noise ratio, and loss of contrast is similar to attenuation. Some examples of photographic terms and their close analogies in electronic terminology are as follows:

Photographic	Electronic
Emulsion speed	Sensitivity
Exposure	Input signal
Developer	Amplifier
Characteristic curve	Transfer characteristic
Image quality	Fidelity
Granularity	Noise
Modulation transfer function	Frequency response
Spatial frequency	Temporal frequency

3 *Spatial frequency and temporal frequency.* It is feasible to analyse the behaviour of a photographic material or a photographic reproduction process in much the same way as that used for measuring frequency response in electronics. For instance, we can use the established techniques and terminology used in electronics, when producing modulation transfer function curves for a photographic process (see Chapter 12). However, in deriving the MTF we are concerned with measuring the change in modulation that occurs as a function of the 'spatial frequency' (variation in the spacing between successive cycles), whereas in electronics measurement is made of the change in modulation that occurs as a function of the 'temporal frequency' (variation in the time between successive cycles). Therefore, for the analysis of a photographic process, distance is substituted for time, and the frequency is expressed in cycles per millimetre instead of hertz (cycles per second).

Appendix F

Answers to self-assessment questions

Question		Answer or location
2.37		$T = 0.8, 0.059; 1/T = 3.23, 50;$
		$D = 0.16, 0.95, 1.52, 1.89$
2.58	(a)	Para. 2.6 and Fig. 2.1
	(b)	1000 to 1
	(c)	Para. 2.7 and 2.8
	(d)	Para. 2.5
	(e)	Para. 2.5
	(f)	Para. 2.34; $D = 1.4$ (1.3980)
	(g)	Para. 2.41
	(h)	Para. 2.42
	(i)	Para. 2.51
	(j)	Para. 2.46
	(k)	Para. 2.52
	(l)	Para. 2.53
	(m)	Para. 2.55 and Fig. 2.12
2.78	(a)	Between A and S1
	(b)	Between S1 and below D
	(c)	Highlights above D
	(d)	All on density A
	(e)	Approx. $D = 0.12$
	(f)	Para. 2.53
	(g)	Para. 2.54
	(h)	Para. 2.55
	(i)	Approx. $D = 2.52$
	(j)	3.3
	(k)	2000 to 1
	(l)	1 second
	(m)	$D = 1.4$
	(n)	Para. 2.62 (b) to (f) and 2.69
2.90	(a)	Para. 2.81
	(b)	Para. 2.81 and 2.85
	(c)	Para. 2.80 (b)
	(d)	Para. 2.80 (c)
	(e)	Para. 2.81
	(f)	Para. 2.87
	(g)	On straight line and to gamma 1.0
	(h)	Para. 2.86 and 2.88
	(i)	Fig. 2.22
	(j)	Fig. 2.19
	(k)	Para. 2.82
	(l)	Para. 2.89

Question		Answer or location
2.124	(a)	Para. 2.93 and Fig. 2.17
	(b)	Para. 2.94
	(c)	Para. 2.85, 95 and 96
	(d)	Para. 2.101 to 104
	(e)	Para. 2.113
	(f)	Para. 2.114 to 118
	(g)	Para. 2.113
	(h)	Film A; 10 times
	(i)	Para. 2.117
	(j)	Para. 2.88
	(k)	$\frac{1}{60}$ second
3.27	(a)	Para. 3.3 (a) and Fig. 3.3
	(b)	Para. 3.3 (c) and Fig. 3.3
	(c)	Para. 3.4
	(d)	Para. 3.4
	(e)	Para. 3.6
	(f)	Para. 3.4
	(g)	One stop up or down
	(h)	Para. 3.5 (b)
	(i)	Para. 3.5 and Fig. 3.3
	(j)	Para. 3.5 and Fig. 3.3
	(k)	Para. 3.11
	(l)	Para. 3.11
	(m)	Para. 3.13
	(n)	Para. 3.15
	(o)	Para. 3.17
	(p)	Para. 3.18
	(q)	Fig. 3.11
	(r)	Para. 3.26
4.19	(a)	Para. 4.3
	(b)	Two stops more
	(c)	Para. 4.6
	(d)	Para. 4.6
	(e)	Para. 4.6
	(f)	Para. 4.7
	(g)	Para. 4.6
	(h)	Para. 4.10
	(i)	$\bar{G} = 0.66$
5.9	(a)	Para. 5.5
	(b)	Para. 5.4 and 5.5 (a)
	(c)	Para. 5.5 (d)

Question		Answer or location	Question		Answer or location
5.9	(d)	Left; Para. 2.112		(m)	Para. 7.23; $\gamma = 1.25$ by correct exposure
	(e)	Para. 5.3		(n)	1.56; para. 7.23 and/or 5.24
	(f)	Para. 5.6		(o)	1.31, Para. 7.25; 0.71, para. 7.23
	(g)	Para. 2.46	7.42	(a)	Para. 7.36
	(h)	Para. 5.8		(b)	Para. 5.12
5.21	(a)	Between 2 and 4 minutes		(c)	Para. 7.37
	(b)	Para. 5.10		(d)	Para. 7.38
	(c)	Para. 5.10	8.11	(a)	Para. 8.1
	(d)	Para. 5.11 (c)		(b)	Para. 8.2
	(e)	Para. 5.11 (d)		(c)	Para. 8.2 and Table 8.1
	(f)	Para. 5.11 (b)		(d)	Exposure duration of $^1/_{10}$ second
	(g)	Para. 5.12		(e)	Exposure + 2 stops and less dev (less dev = loss of speed)
	(h)	No; para. 5.12		(f)	$\bar{G} = 0.7$
	(i)	Para. 5.12		(g)	Reduced speed, lower gradient
	(j)	Para. 5.8	9.17	(a)	Para. 9.2 and Fig. 9.1
	(k)	Para. 5.12		(b)	Para. 9.6 and Fig. 2.7
	(l)	Para. 5.14		(c)	Para. 9.8
	(m)	Para. 5.18 and 5.19		(d)	Fig. 9.4
	(n)	Para. 5.20		(e)	Para. 9.12
5.39	(a)	$\bar{G} = 1.2/1.4 = 0.86$ Para. 5.23 and Fig. 5.10		(f)	Para. 9.15
	(b)	Para. 5.26	10.9	(a)	Para. 10.1 and 10.2
	(c)	Para. 5.29 and 5.33		(b)	Fig. 10.1
	(d)	$\gamma = 0.43$; para. 5.34		(c)	Para. 10.6 and 10.7
6.55	(a)	Para. 6.2		(d)	Para. 10.8, 11.81 and 11.82
	(b)	Para. 6.3 and 6.39	11.84	(a)	Para. 1.19
	(c)	Para. 6.5		(b)	Para. 1.22 and 1.23
	(d)	Para. 6.6		(c)	Para. 11.2
	(e)	Para. 6.7 and 6.9		(d)	Para. 11.7 and 11.8
	(f)	Para. 6.8		(e)	Para. 11.9 and 11.53
	(g)	Para. 6.17		(f)	Para. 11.11
	(h)	Para. 2.120, 2.121, 6.18 and 6.20		(g)	Para. 11.3
	(i)	Para. 6.24 and 6.30		(h)	Para. 11.15 to 11.18
	(j)	Para. 6.34 and 6.37 (c)		(i)	Para. 11.15, 11.17; Fig. 11.3
	(k)	Para. 6.34 and 6.37 (a)		(j)	Para. 11.19
	(l)	Para. 6.37		(k)	Para. 11.24
	(m)	Para. 6.42		(l)	Fig. 11.4
	(n)	Para. 6.44 and 6.47		(m)	Para. 11.47 and 11.53
7.35	(a)	Fig. 7.1 caption		(n)	Fig. 11.9
	(b)	$\bar{G} = 0.88$		(o)	Fig. 11.11
	(c)	Para. 7.3 (c)		(p)	Para. 11.48
	(d)	Move positive curve upwards in quadrant 2; para, 7.4 (g)		(q)	Fig. 11.5, para. 11.48 and 11.54
	(e)	Para. 7.3 (f)		(r)	Para. 8.2, 11.31 and 11.119
	(f)	Para. 7.3 (f) and 7.4 (b)		(s)	Para. 11.41 and 11.42
	(g)	Print toe gradient; para. 7.4 (c) and (d)		(t)	Para. 11.47 and 11.100
	(h)	Increase neg exp; para. 7.4 (g)		(u)	Para. 11.66 and Fig. 11.15
	(i)	1.68: para. 7.4 (f)		(v)	Para. 11.49
	(j)	Av. gradient 1.2; para. 7.4 (e)		(w)	Para. 11.49
	(k)	Para. 7.4 (a)		(x)	Para. 11.66
	(l)	Para. 7.6, 7.8 and 7.13		(y)	Para. 11.23
				(z)	Para. 11.67 to 11.70

Appendix G

Further reading

Applied Photographic Theory, P. Kowaliski (J. Wiley and Sons).

Applied Photography, C. R. Arnold, P. J. Rolls and J. C. J. Stewart (Focal Press).

Advanced Photography, M. J. Langford (Focal Press).

Basic Photo Science, H. J. Walls and G. G. Attridge (Focal Press).

Basic Sensitometry, L. Lobel and M. Dubois (Focal Press

Colour Photography in Practice, D. A. Spencer, L. A. Mannheim and Viscount Hanworth (Focal Press).

Exposure Control in Enlarging, G. L. Wakefield (Fountain Press, Argus Books Ltd).

Focal Encyclopedia of Photography (Focal Press).

Fundamentals of Photographic Theory, T. H. James and G. C. Higgins (Fountain Press, Argus Books Ltd).

General Sensitometry, Y. N. Gorokhovskii and T. M. Levenberg (Focal Press).

Introduction to Photographic Theory, B. H. Carroll and G. C. Higgins (J. Wiley and Sons).

Kodak Handbooks for the Professional Photographer (Kodak Ltd).

Manual of Photography, R. E. Jacobson (Focal Press).

Photographic Considerations for Aerospace. G. C. Brock *et al.* (Itek Corporation, Lexington, USA).

Photographic Sensitometry, H. N. Todd and R. P. Zakia (Morgan and Morgan, New York, through Fountain Press, Argus Books Ltd).

Physical Aspects of Aerial Photography, G. C. Brock (Dover Publications, New York).

Practical Sensitometry, G. L. Wakefield (Fountain Press, Argus Books Ltd).

Principles of Colour Sensitometry, edited by R. T. Ryan (Society of Motion Picture and Television Engineers, Scarsdale, New York).

The Reproduction of Colour, R. W. G. Hunt (Fountain Press, Argus Books Ltd).

Sensitometry in Practice, K. Hornsby (Henry Greenwood & Co. Ltd).

SPSE Handbook of Photographic Science and Engineering, edited by W. Thomas (J. Wiley and Sons).

Theory of the Photographic Process, edited by C. E. K. Mees and T. H. James (Macmillan, New York).

Photographic material manufacturers' technical books, leaflets and data sheets: with regard to photographic emulsions, these usually include characteristic curves and spectral sensitivity curves. They may also contain graphs showing the resolution characteristics of particular photographic materials.

International and national standards relevant to sensitometry and photography: many ISO, ASA, BSI and DIN photographic standards are for all practical purposes identical, and the literature issued by the various organizations explains in detail all the factors involved in the particular standard. International Standards Organization (ISO) literature can be obtained directly from the national standards body of most countries.

Index